The Miracle of Healing Hands

The Complete Guide to Ancient Yogic Healing and Massage Techniques

Waheguru S. Khalsa, D.C.
as taught by Yogi Bhajan, Ph.D.

Rishi Knot Publishers
Beverly Hills, California

Published by Rishi Knot Publishers, 264 S. La Cienega Blvd., Beverly Hills, CA 90211
Telephone (310) 274-8291.

Library of Congress Cataloging in Publication Data
Khalsa, Waheguru Singh, 1948-
The miracle of healing hands: the complete guide to ancient yogic healing and massage techniques
Waheguru S. Khalsa, D.C.
Includes bibliographical references and index.
ISBN 0-9658497-4-0

Design by Barbara Kimbrough
Cover design by Victoria Coulter
Photos by Nancy Santullo
Illustrations by Lauren Kilgore

This book is intended to be an educational guide. It is essential that any reader who has any reason to suspect serious illness seek appropriate medical advice and care promptly. This book is not to be used as a diagnostic tool or as a substitute for qualified medical care.

This book contains many references to actual cases the author has encountered over the years. However, names and other identifying characteristics have been omitted or changed in order to protect their privacy.

Over the ages many people have received benefits from these techniques. This is no guarantee you will have the same results. This author hopes many people will benefit from the wisdom and knowledge contained in the pages of this book.

Kundalini Research Institute

"This Seal of Approval is granted only to those products which have been approved through the K.R.I. review process for accuracy and integrity of those portions which embody the technology of Kundalini Yoga and 3HO Lifestyle as taught by Yogi Bhajan."

Acknowledgements

Many people have been generous with their time and information as I've written and produced this book.

Pranpati Singh (John Ricker) provided writing and editorial advice to this project and made the index. He truly was a "hammer and chisel." Thanks to Tej K. Khalsa for transcribing all the lectures, Josh Townshend, for guiding the talent search that located the models, and M.K. St. George, Sibel Ergener, and Will Potter for modelling the treatment sequences. Elizabeth Lancaster, my dear sister, made incisive editorial comments and writing suggestions. Guru Jiwan K. Khalsa made edits in the treatment steps. Special thanks to my wife Hari Kirn K. Khalsa for her applause and cheering from the sidelines the entire time.

Thanks also go to Deva Powell, Leena Hannonen, Bobbi Lane, Santokh S. Khalsa, D.C., Guru Sahay S. Khalsa, D.C., Nirvair S. Khalsa, Shakti Parwha Kaur Khalsa, Ek Ong Kar K. Khalsa, Guru Atma K. Khalsa, and all of my colleagues in the Khalsa Chiropractic Association.

Table Of Contents

CHAPTER 4

Quicktouch Treatments

CHAPTER 5

Treatments and Meditations for Emotional Balance

Foreword

Miracle is a powerful word, a concept laden with hope, promise, and change. This volume delivers all three. Each chapter guides you a step at a time along the path of the healer. If you are a beginner, it gives you a foundation and sure footage to travel the path. If you are more advanced, it reminds you of timeless truths and attitudes which are healing in themselves.

Each technique taps the potential of healing and the drive towards wholeness that is woven into the nerves and tissues of our body/mind. The changes that occur often seem far more profound than the elegant simplicity of the technique that triggered the change. It seems miraculous. What is the source of all that healing and power?

Yogi Bhajan is a master teacher and healer. He would see the sudden sparkle in our eyes as we filled with amazement at the changes we could bring using his techniques. But he knew that our effectiveness depended on staying receptive. We must not become limited by our own expanded sense of ego. So, he would remind us repeatedly: "Where there is mystery there is no mastery, and where there is mastery there is no mystery. The only miracle is that by God's grace you put your ego aside and let God have a chance. Then there is no limit to your intuition, intelligence, and healing presence."

He would teach us by demonstration. He would teach by giving us a challenge or problem to solve, then correcting our actions as we went ahead using instinct and intuition. He would teach with stories and wonderful metaphors that hold within them the key concepts needed to understand the real heart of healing. He would teach us any way he could to transform us from enthusiastic helpers into expert healers.

During one late-night session he explained the source of that healing power. He gave us an insight into the aura of the miraculous that comes with proficiency in these techniques. He said there were three sources that we can draw on. We are designed that way in our very structure as Human Beings. One source is the Known; the tangible open senses; the rapport between skin, muscle, and nerve. To tap this fully he gave us exercises that increased the sensitivity of the hands (p. 7) and refined our perception (p. 21).

The second source is the Knowable Unknown. This is the intelligence of the mind and imagination under the discipline of neutrality and inner stillness. When you can align your mind to your actions and synchronize the flow of thoughts, both conscious and unconscious, to heal, you affect unseen dimensions of your client. Your aura and mental field of energy create immediate impact, even before the tangible treatments from the Known. To tap this fully he gave us treatments that included communication and interaction with the client as the body is stimulated (p. 124) and meditations for both client and practitioner (p. 130). In a departure from many traditional approaches, the client is an active part of the process. When you use this source as well as the Known you are a healer.

The third source is the Unknowable. This is the realm of spirit. This is the intuition that guides your action and mind from your totality. It is certain, sure, and spontaneous. It is a connection that develops a prayerful mind and keeps you linked to a sense of vastness and possibility. It is not so much doing any one thing as it is an act of Dwelling in your Being. Your very presence acts. You notice things that may have escaped the focus of the mind, that pass on the periphery of normal awareness. It brings you solutions when there was only conflict. This is the healing energy of Guru Ram Das[1] and all the saints. It is the power of blessing and Being. To tap this Yogi Bhajan gave us practices to develop our intuition and put aside our limitations, healing music to open the heart, and treatments that use the golden chain of healers—a linkage to a legacy and lineage of miraculous healers. Using all these levels you open the Miracle of Healing Hands and the power of the healing technology of kundalini yoga.

This is the great gift that Dr. Waheguru Singh Khalsa has given us with this book. It is a labor of love that shows his meticulous attention to detail, thoroughness, and respect for the integrity of the technology shared by Yogi Bhajan. The book is easy to read and clear to follow. This book gets my highest and most enthusiastic recommendation. It is now on my required reading list for all students and professionals who want to deepen their experience and understanding of healing.

Gurucharan Singh Khalsa, Ph.D.

Introduction

THIS IS A BOOK FOR PEOPLE WHO WANT TO LEARN HOW TO USE TOUCH TO HELP CLIENTS, FRIENDS, AND FAMILY TO RELAX.

Licensed professionals including massage therapists, physical therapists, body workers, medical doctors, and chiropractors will all find this book useful. It is also for those who do not realize their "touch" potential but want to discover and expand it. Unlike some other undeveloped natural gifts, it's never too late to begin hands-on healing. Natural gifts are often ignored but that is not a reason to continue starving them.

There are no muscle names to look up, no body landmarks to learn, and no jargon in this book. As a potential healer you do not have to know the meaning of such terms as *quadratus lumborum*, transverse process, or cervical spine strain to be effective and alleviate pains.

Using the hands to massage is not a skill that some people are born with, like a gift for art or perfect pitch. Hands-on healing is just that: placing hands on the body with intent to heal. Or at the risk of oversimplifying, if you can put a shirt on a hangar, if you can pack a suitcase, and if you care about people, you can heal with confidence and joy.

Treating, caring for, and managing health problems has been my career for 20 years. In writing this book one goal was to help people with an interest in hands-on bodywork become more comfortable with touching other people.

This book grew out of a series of meetings about healing with my teacher, Yogi Bhajan, from 1982 through 1995. Before I tell you about those meetings I want to give you a picture of one facet of Yogi Bhajan's teaching personality. The facet that sometimes pokes and provokes a student. I remember house-sitting for him. It was the first time I had met him in person. He was going out to the movies, and his secretary had called me asking if I wanted to take care of his house for the evening. The duties were simple: no guests were expected so let no one in, and answer the phone.

The woman had told me, "See if you can stay awake until we return. Most people who come here in the evenings fall sound asleep." I like challenges so I said, "I'll come over."

When I arrived at the house I met Yogi Bhajan's sister who was in Los Angeles visiting from Europe. She was being charming and complimentary as we spoke with each other in the living room. In her enthusiastic way she remarked how handsome and pleasant I was as Yogi Bhajan and the members of his household walked across the room in silence to leave for the movies. He paused as his sister finished with, "Isn't he just beautiful?"

Then as he continued toward the door, he glanced over to me and with a low growl said, "You're so dirty … you need some polishing."

And so my first meeting with him ended and I stayed awake the rest of the evening wondering what his comment meant.

The meetings that helped sprout this book were sponsored by the Khalsa Chiropractic Association. Most of those present were members of a national organization of Khalsa doctors that still meet once a year with Yogi Bhajan. Healers, massage therapists, medical doctors, and the general public also attended.

We had arduous and profound experiences in our long afternoon sessions with Yogi Bhajan, and some evenings he gave challenging homework. The kind of teaching assignment where the students learn at a deep, from the heart place. One meeting in Millis, Massachusetts ended around 6 p.m. Then Yogi Bhajan announced that everyone was to practice the treatment of the day. But some were hungry, so a doctor in the front of the room asked about dinner. Yogi Bhajan said, "No dinner." Then we all asked, "How about Yogi tea?" He said, "Stay in the room till you finish and no Yogi tea."

The assignment was for each of us to perform the treatment on every other person in the room. "Well, that's no big deal, there are only eighteen of us here," someone said. “The treatment is short; we can go through it fairly fast,” another voice piped in. “Short!” shouted the doctor, “It looks like the treatment is more than twenty minutes long.”

Then the mathematicians calculated, while stomachs growled and blood-sugar levels plummeted. Soon everyone realized that we would be up all night. So we got organized. After writing the treatment steps on a blackboard and marking the times, we chose partners. We worked on into the evening, treating each other while a designated timekeeper let us know when to switch treatment steps. We had discovered the way to get the assignment done, but it still took us until 4 a.m.—just as people were filing into the room for morning *sadhana*[3].

There were many topics discussed in our meetings with Yogi Bhajan: the nature of the soul in man, the ethics of practice, the need for the healing practitioner to rejuvenate, the necessity for high moral calibre, and the use of intuition for diagnosis and treatment. All the topics were laced with healing insights, whether women’s health, foods to eat for better health, or herbs to use for energy and digestive strength.

At each meeting there were new physical treatments as well as a variety of body-mind techniques to learn. Massages using oil, treatments with clothes on, and meditating in tandem with the patient were some of the techniques presented by Yogi Bhajan.

What I learned about healing the body, mind, and soul, I put into practice with my patients. I have used all these techniques on my patients and have found them to be valuable. These treatments have brought me closer to the center-court position that superior healers have held through the centuries: treat the cause of disease not just the symptom that brings the patient.

In my mind many of the treatments were easy enough to do that my patients could even do them at home with loved ones.

One night at Yogi Bhajan's house I let it slip that I wanted to write a book about these treatments. When I went home that night I had misgivings: why had I spoken so boldly about writing, never having written before? I went to sleep that night filled with both excitement and fear, sensing a long and rugged journey. Six years later, here is the result.

What you have here is a sampling that I consider to be many of the best hands-on healing techniques from Yogi Bhajan. I hope you will find as many good results with the people you touch and as much value here as I have.

Waheguru S. Khalsa, D.C.
June 1997

How to Use This Book

There are several ways of using this book. If you are new to bodywork and hands-on healing, read through Chapter 1 to gain an understanding of the laws of healing. Then read Chapter 2 on the power of touch and practice of healing. If you have experience with massage, bodywork, or chiropractic, review Chapters 1 and 2, then move on to Chapter 3.

In Chapter 3, you will learn how to develop your strength to heal and boost your client's ability to relax with stress-release treatments. You will also learn a variety of ways to use your hands: in a foot massage, in a cranial massage, in a body-drumming (percussion) treatment, and in a treatment for release of tension and stress.

For short techniques turn to Chapter 4, Quicktouch Treatments. There are 17 fast, easy-to-do hands-on therapies. Most take 3 minutes or less to complete; the longest Quicktouch treatment is 8 minutes. Quicktouch Treatments have few steps, and they get results. Chiropractors can use these treatments to augment spinal adjustments.

In Chapter 5, you will discover that touch has a powerful effect on the mood and metabolism of a client. The two cranial treatments include Cranial Adjustment for Reaching the Heavens, to change your client's state of mind.

See Chapter 6 for treatments that help strengthen the body and immune system. For example, the Seventh Rib Massage is a simple, focused massage on the seventh rib. This treatment has cleared sinus congestion, opened the chest, and reduced middle back pain.

An introduction to hydrotherapy (Chapter 7) gives advice on using water for health, strength, and improving the immune system. One of Yogi Bhajan's favorite recommendations for vitality and strength is taking a cold shower every day. The Narayan Treatment is a refreshing massage using a blend of fragrant oils; then cool towels are used to cover and massage the body.

Bibliographic information and additional references are in the Chapter Notes.

General Caution for All Treatments

1. There are specific conditions under which pressure with the hands or massage with the hands should never be undertaken. Do not work on:

   - anyone with serious conditions that could be worsened by either pressure or stretching.
   - anyone whose bones are brittle from calcium loss (osteoporosis).
   - anyone who has cancer. Consult with the person's physician before you proceed with any massage.
   - anyone who is bedridden.

   Especially in the case of the bedridden, there is danger of a blood clot breaking loose from a blood vessel or the heart (thrombosis). When that happens the lungs, arms, legs, and kidneys may be damaged.

2. Do not work in the navel and abdominal area during pregnancy or a woman's menses.

3. Do not work in the navel and abdominal area of young children, older debilitated individuals, or people who have abdominal pain associated with tumors, masses, or chronic digestive problems.

4. Do not massage surgical scars and adjacent tissues unless there is no pain. It should be at least 8 weeks after surgery, and there should be no complications. Be cautious around abdominal surgical scars no matter how much time has elapsed since the surgery.

5. Use care in the groin area due to the presence of large numbers of nerves and blood vessels.

6. If the person is recuperating from an illness and is especially weak or exhausted, work very gently.

7. If you see swelling or puffiness in the muscles be careful. You can increase inflammation in an area by pushing too deeply for too long. Rubbing and pressure can aggravate tissues that are already swollen. Do not proceed if the muscles are injured, inflamed, swollen (as in a sprained ankle), or red in color.

Reference Diagrams

There are several diagrams in the text that help explain anatomy, bone structure, and the hand positions used in hands-on healing.

Hand positions. There are four special hand positions or *mudras* used in this text.

1. **Collar mudra** is performed by bending the fingertips to the palms to contact the client with the thumb and knuckles (Fig. H-01).

2. **Jacket mudra** is made by curling the fingertips to the palm. Then pressure is applied to the client with the thumb and adjacent knuckle of the index finger (Fig. H-02).

3. **Knife-edge mudra** is applied with the edge of the hand on the little-finger side. It is applied as a karate chop to the client's body with percussive movements (Fig. H-03).

4. In **cone mudra**, place the fingertips and thumb together to contact the client with the pad of the thumb and the fingertips (Fig. H-04).

Vertebrae. See Chapter 6, Fig. 6-01, on page 134.

Feet and Reflexology. See Charts 1, 2, and 3 on pages 37 and 38.

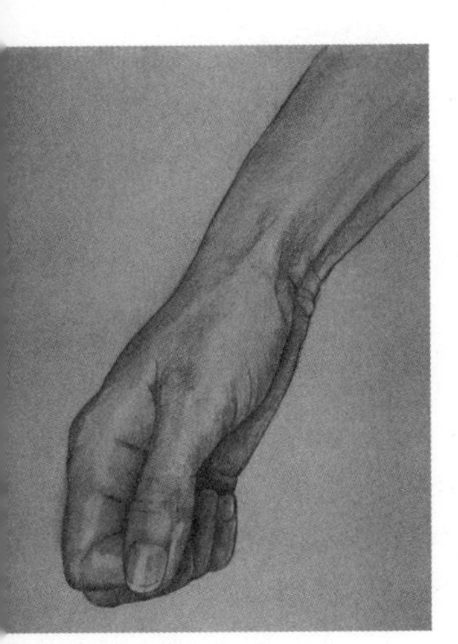

Fig H-01

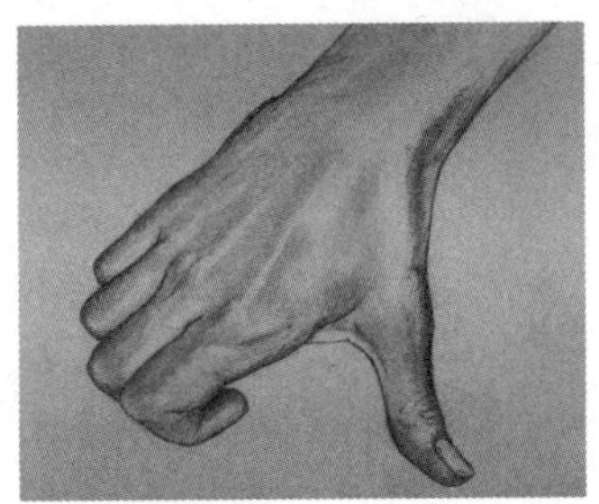

Fig H-02

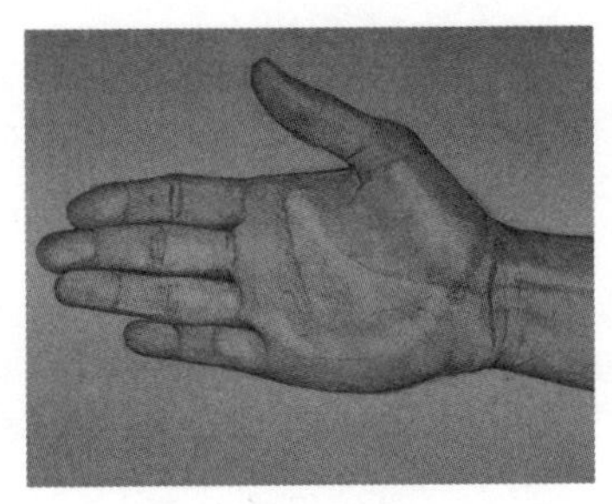

Fig H-03

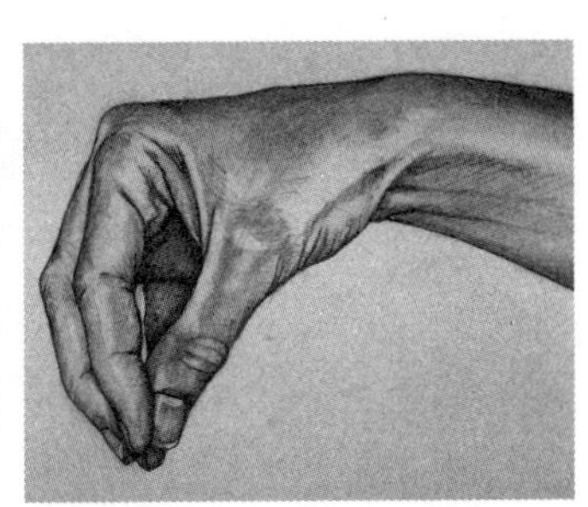

Fig H-04

Treatments

The language used in the treatment sections usually refers to the person you are treating as a "client" or "patient." However, in the material for beginners, "partner" is often used. References to the gender of the client in the treatments are in accordance with the illustrations.

Boldfaced terms within the text are defined in the Glossary.

All the Khalsa Chiropractic Association meetings in which Yogi Bhajan demonstrated the healing techniques in this book were videotaped.
These videotapes are available from Golden Temple Enterprises,
Box 13 Shady Lane, Espanola NM 87532. Telephone 505-753-0423.

The Profession of the Hands-On Healer

"Whenever your intuition and your impulses interact and intuition takes over, something great happens—you become objective, you are successful, you are saintly. The moment your impulses take over your intuition, you are debauched, you are destructive, you are demoralized. Not only you'll destroy yourself, but you'll destroy everything you touch. There is nothing in success and failure. If the intuition takes over your impulse, success is absolutely guaranteed. If impulse takes over intuition, destruction is in your corner."

—Yogi Bhajan[1]

The Laws of Healing

There are laws of healing that are unwritten and untaught. I know that medical schools, chiropractic colleges, and massage schools do not teach these laws, although they are alive in the practitioners who are healers. These laws are expressions of human nature at its highest, and you do yourself a great favor by understanding them.

First Law of Healing. "Expand Intuition" is the First Law of Healing. Increase your confidence about the intuition you already have, and learn to unite yourself with your client. Sometimes this means developing your ability to enter an altered state of mind. An altered state is one in which any of the senses are different: seeing more acutely, hearing with different ears, feeling more with the body or the hands. For example, I find myself open and transparent, when I am treating patients. This means that I can shine light through myself to the person that I treat. I hold an image in my mind that I am like a large window, with glass panels letting light through to the person receiving treatment.

Without expanding your intuition, how will you know the best way to help? How will you know the root cause of the client's aches and pains? You won't. You will only guess. Guessing goes on all the time. We do it with ourselves when we go to the drug store to relieve a headache: "I must have a "Tylenol" deficiency, or is it an "Excedrin P.M." deficiency because it's 4:30 in the afternoon?" Guessing may work well, and when it doesn't, we go in another direction.

How do you expand your sense of intuition? One way is to learn to increase your power of concentration. Your ability to concentrate your mental force has brought you everything in life. Sometimes that is a lot of grief, struggle, and suffering. Other times it is goals achieved; it is responsibilities executed with grace; it is the capacity to give outside of your work life.

I recommend a yoga exercise to increase the ability to concentrate the mind. It is an easy exercise to begin, yet not so easy to complete. It can show you some beautiful vistas if you stay with it long enough. This exercise develops strength in the nerve pathways between brain and eyes, the link we have with the external that creates the view, the panorama, the vision. If you do this exercise you may be surprised at what happens; you may be fascinated by what you see.

Tratakam Exercise

(7 minutes)

"THE FOCUSED MIND CAN PIERCE THROUGH STONE."

—JAPANESE ADAGE

Tratakam is the practice of keeping the eyes open. It is for the development of subtle seeing, for helping you remove preconceived notions about the appearance of everything in the visual field. It is for multiplying your ability to concentrate and for expanding your ability to bring mental force to your work. In yoga there is a term, *eka grata*, meaning one-pointed mind. This exercise helps create that focused mind.

This exercise can be done at any time of day. Do it in a room that is pleasant to you, where there will not be any interruptions. Night makes a fascinating time to do *tratakam* because of the contrast between the flame and the darkness.

1. Place a lit candle on top of a table at eye level. If it is a windy day close the windows so that the candle flame is steady.

2. Sit in a chair 6 to 9 feet away with your spine straight, hands resting on your thighs.

3. Stare at the candle flame with your eyes open, to cultivate a new pathway to your visual cortex. Keep the eyes open no matter how much they want to blink, water, or twitch. Concentrate on the core of the flame around the blue portion. Stay there. You will see the surrounding layers of the flame–sometimes in flux, sometimes at rest. The colors will change, overlap, and shift.

4. Practice every day. I know a yoga student who does this 3 days a week, 11 minutes each time. Increase the time of practice gradually over 3 or 4 weeks to 31 minutes.

Comment

The goal is to develop your ability to see at a subtle level and to strengthen your concentration. Your eyes will want to close; they will fill with tears; and you may feel a strong need to blink. Please control that urge. Perhaps you will squint instead of blink. Pass beyond the automatic urges of your body to develop your seeing ability.

When concentration is perfected the object reveals its essence to you. You will be able to see all perfections and imperfections at the same time. And you will be able to talk about what you see. The *tratakam* exercise expands the ability to see an object—the candle flame—in its essence. You can carry over this refinement of sight day-to-day with friends and companions who you touch. This will help you develop insight, in-depth seeing, and perhaps the ability to see the human aura.

The inability to concentrate is one of the enemies of self-improvement and excellence that has been known since the beginning of time. The others include: doubt, mental laziness, sickness and disease, lack of enthusiasm, and clinging to sense gratification. Persistence helps overcome all these obstacles.

This particular meditation is a remedy. The more you cultivate the ability to concentrate your mind, the easier it is to practice the exercise. As Patanjali, the Indian sage who lived before Christ's time, stated: "Those forms of concentration which result in extraordinary perceptions encourage perseverance of mind[2]." So when you have a profound experience in this *tratakam* it can inspire you to explore more of the same.

There are many variations in the experience of *tratakam*. The key is persistence in cultivating the ability to concentrate on the flame for a long time. The mind delivers many distractions, yet the man or woman who excels in *tratakam* passes through the distractions to obtain a one-pointed mind.

Everything that receives your attention grows. So concentrate on your intuition and it will grow. Pay attention to your own style of sensitivity in order to help it expand. Consider yourself to be an accurate "gut reactor" and succeed as an intuitive person, as a person with the ability to know the unknown. Cultivate your ability to listen to the subtle voice within that has the answers. Whatever sense channel works the best for you is where to put your attention.

The truth is that we all are intuitive. We may not assert it each moment, yet we are intuitive. When intuition mixes with confusion, we make poor decisions. I remember the times I operated on gut feelings, but never recognized it as intuition. I received messages from the "air," sometimes acting on them and succeeding. For example, I have recalled a person that I had not seen for a long time, and a day and a half later that person called on the phone asking for some advice.

See yourself as the person your imagination pictures, who perceives what is happening to the individual. When you look at your partner and see the physical posture—go for immediate understanding. Go with your first impression. Perhaps you see things about this person (for example, droopy shoulders) that just triggers the knowing. Remember it doesn't take years of time and study to do this; it takes one moment. It takes you one moment to remember what your kitchen looks like. It takes maybe 2 or 3 seconds to form the image clearly. And it takes a total of 9 seconds to fill in the details in order to describe the image to a friend. Well, it takes the same amount of time to be able to see and diagnose a new client.

It doesn't matter how this gift develops in you. It matters only that you expand on your sixth sense and trust in it.

Second Law of Healing. "Touch People With Love and Deep Caring" is the Second Law of Healing. Both are essential if the healing endeavor is to succeed. Not the love of a woman for her husband, not the sexual desire that lovers have, but the love of family members: the deep caring that a woman feels for her sister, her brother, her parents, or her children.

Find a way to connect with each individual you touch. Treat that person like you would your dearest family member. First light up your inner self with love, then beam it on the person you are going to touch. Extend yourself. This may take you into a zone of behavior where you are not comfortable. Good. Transporting yourself outside your comfort zone is positive.

I know that this means acting. Some behavior can only be achieved by performing, by sticking to the script of the moment. So don't stand at a distance being a theater or movie critic, be an actor. Then act that way again and again and again. Pretty soon all this rehearsal pays off, and as actors know, we become the part. We become the behavior; we are the behavior that we were only practicing. It is no longer an act; we aren't feigning. We are feeling love and compassion.

There are additional things you can do to help yourself along the path of excellence. Cultivate noble thoughts; entertain inspirational ideas, because you do become what your mind dwells upon[3]. Say this affirmation to yourself,

"I am effective because I have presence of mind, presence of body, and presence of soul." Develop this habit of talking to yourself in a positive manner. Repeat the affirmation over and over to yourself silently, with enthusiasm. Repetition is the key to success in many areas of life: practicing sports, playing music, driving a car, etc. There is a tape series by Shad Helmstetter, *Winning from Within*, which gives many practical affirmations[4,5]. The program comes with affirmation flash cards. You can practice as you commute. Or you can prepare your mind before seeing clients.

Exercise for Touch Sensitivity

(approximately 2 minutes)

HERE IS AN EXERCISE TO DO TO AWAKEN YOUR TOUCH SENSITIVITY, TO ENHANCE THE KNOWING OF YOUR HANDS, AND TO HELP YOU DEVELOP YOUR INTUITIVE TALENTS.

The tips of the fingers are packed with more nerve endings than any other skin region of the body. In a surprising study medical doctors performed autopsies on a group of deceased blind people. The physicians found that the nerve endings in the fingertips had been transformed. They were no longer yellow-white in color like the nerve endings outside the spinal cord. They had turned a gray color much like the color of brain tissue. The examining doctors surmised that these blind people had turned their hands into miniature brains, through using the fingertips to read braille and by using them as supplementary eyes[6].

Through the fingertips you can know the depths of the person's body in front of you. Palpation can be used to know more about the health of an individual than any other solitary diagnostic tool.

1. Your partner is lying face down. Touch lightly on different areas of the back, moving around in a random way with the aim of understanding what is right, what is wrong, and what you need to concentrate on in your treatment (Fig. 1-01). Touch the upper back, the shoulder blade area and the neck, moving around from place to place. Time: about 1 minute.

2. Rub your hands together until there is heat generated. Then with your hands apart 2 feet (Fig. 1-02), place

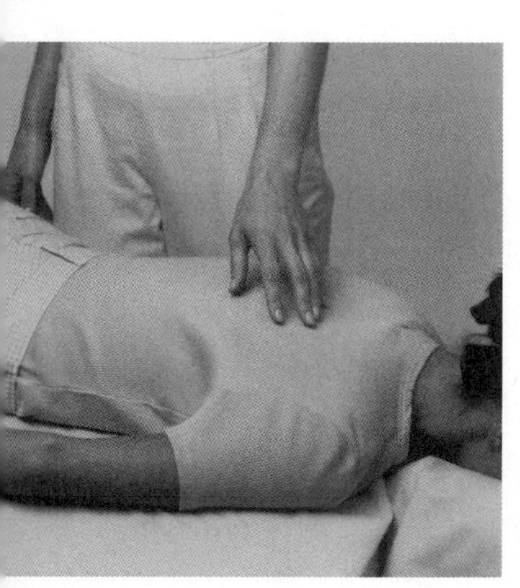

Fig 1-01

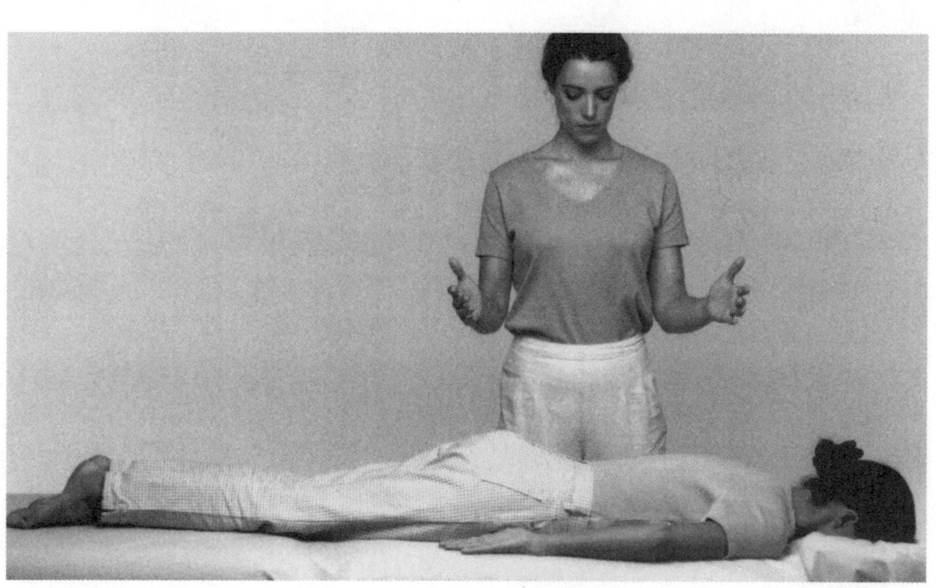

Fig 1-02

your palms down 1 foot above the spine (Fig. 1-03). Now bring the palms together near your chest so that they are touching (Fig. 1-04). Then sweep them apart 3 to 4 feet, then back together again. Go back and forth like this 6 times or more. Time: about 1 minute.

As an alternative, instead of bringing the palms together, keep the palms down and just cross the wrists 6 times or more.

Be aware of what you see. You may see subtle levels of your partner, you may see colors, or indentations in the electromagnetic field. The idea in this exercise is to be a diagnostic presence receiving the readout that is being transmitted from your partner. Concentrate so that you join your partner's reality. Feel what there is to feel with your hands as you do the sweep. Imagine your hands radiating and receiving like a Geiger counter, looking for problem areas that need help. Let your brain and body and hands compute the feelings, thought forms, visuals, and sounds that you receive.

3. Now go to work on the first part that needs your healing touch.

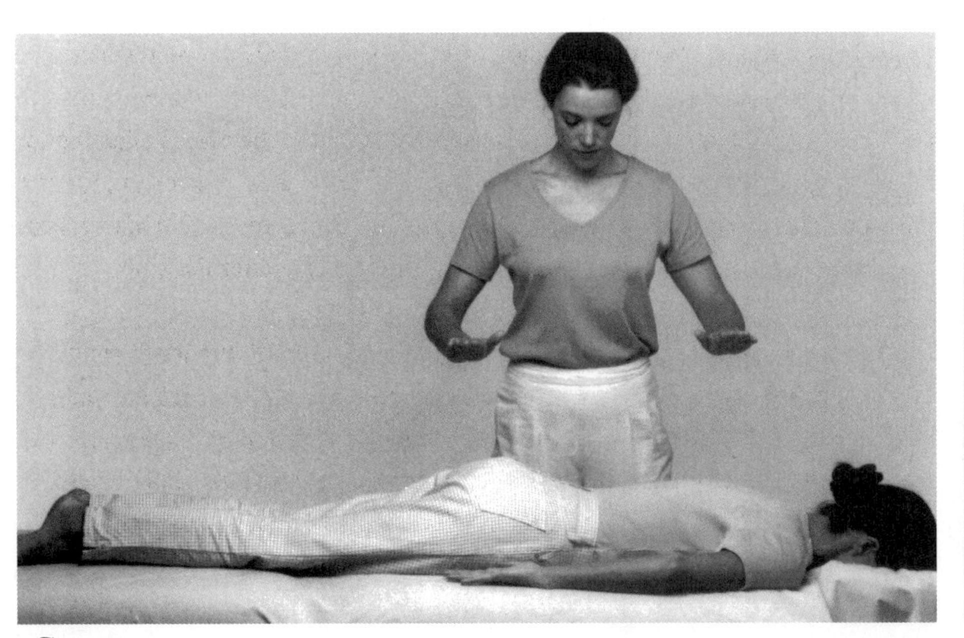

Fig 1-03

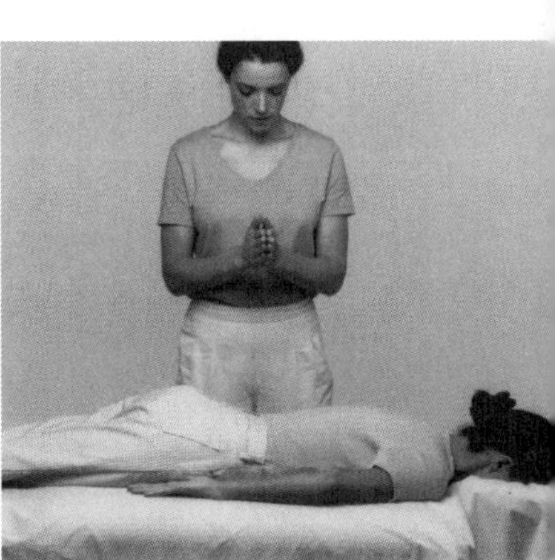

Fig 1-04

Third Law of Healing. "Having a Strong Intent to Heal" the person you touch is the Third Law. An article in The Chiropractic Report[7] discussed placebos and their role in treating disease, pain, fevers, etc. The one thing that placebos prove beyond a doubt is that the person providing the therapy is a powerful therapeutic agent. It is the human being surrounded by the mystique of a profession who has the strongest influence[8]. Testing with placebos shows that confidence and a focused intent to heal are at the core of the successful practitioner.

Deciding to accept and then treat a patient is a large responsibility. Inherent are risks of failing in the attempt to cure or relieve pain. Nevertheless, you must exact courageous behavior with the intent to heal.

You will need to develop strong "muscles" of intent. When you have a focused intent to heal people, they know it. They feel it rolling off you; they read it in your face; they take it in from the heat of your hands; they hear it in the sound of your voice; and they see it in your eyes. And all these subtle influences have an impact.

Some may not like it. You may have a client who likes personal pain and your sympathy more than your intention to help him heal. Some ailing humans are attached to the attention they get for their suffering. It replaces love. For such people your strength and giving can kindle their desire for health. So a man or woman with strong intent has a healing presence.

Great expectations. In my experience, high expectations always help when going into a treatment. The human body changes and is influenced by them. I envelop the patient that I am treating with my expectation by communicating in a way that the person can understand. I have discovered that what I want for my patients can be more powerful than what they want for themselves. I also expect that the person's vitality and love of life will be increased after the visit.

My starting point is serving the person before me. The most important truth that we have to deal with initially is the symptom that has motivated the person to seek care. It is also helpful to remind clients that a change of body gears—feeling better, getting relief from pain, cultivating a new attitude about health, and seeing the "light at the end of the tunnel" in a chronic problem—all take time to register: an hour, a half day, or longer.

It is human nature to want someone strong and confident to handle the conditions that cause suffering. For example, a chronic neckache that had bothered a woman for 4 months caused her to consult her physician. The prescription that the physician gave her didn't do anything for the pain. Then she heard about you from a friend, and she sits with you, describing her problem. It's obvious to you that her problem is big; it's been around for too long; it's rough; and you feel there are lots of gnarly emotions around it. It even seems to you like she has an untamed rottweiler that she wants you to take care of for her. It's scary. It gives you butterflies in your stomach. You think, "Why didn't the doctor help this lady? What can I do?"

Holding fast to the idea that your intent is to heal, you proceed to massage this woman. If you find lots of tension, lots of sore spots, painful points in her neck and shoulder muscles, you can recommend follow-up visits. And so it will go with a few of your clients. Most of us have our share of unresolved muscle tension, impaired deep circulation, and daily stress all accumulating to create symptoms, and they need follow-up visits.

Let the spirit of expectation take you where it will. When your purpose is to serve your clients, then you shall be taken on a voyage. You become a detective searching yourself for the answers to their problems. So, do something that augments the massage treatments. Give additional advice to clients: suggest changes in diet, give exercises, teach a meditation, suggest cold foot baths, and involve the client in doing something at home that will improve health.

The power of projected positive thought. According to Yogi Bhajan: "It's the quality of the healer, not the quantity of the man. It is trust, it is faith, and it is honesty in his own prayer. Work with the purity of prayer to heal. [The] license [that your state gave you] is a permission, not a guarantee. If you fail to heal people, you'll be as useless as anything else[9]."

You can project for the person as you do the treatment. I do this much of the time. Offer a long, silent prayer. Be as complex or as simple as you want to be, using visual images to enhance positive goals that you announce in silence for the person you are treating. Visualize the person succeeding in personal life. Of course, the more you know about the people you treat the more specific you can make your mental pictures.

Even project simply, something short, on your client's behalf. When you repeat simple statements such as, "Let Your will be done in this person's life," or "May the best outcome manifest now," you create a powerful magnetic field. The nature of the projection or prayer can be detailed and goal-directed or it can be non-specific and brief. Both work—all projection and prayer works. Use projected positive thoughts and prayer to increase results with the people that you treat. Scientific research demonstrates the power of projection or prayer. Overlooking this powerful tool in your practice is like refusing to use your hands to do the physical treatment that the client expects from you[10,11].

Your word is your value as a human being. When your words are virtuous and have the strength of infinity in them, then you are a great human. If you do not value your words, you do not value yourself. Choose words that represent the soul in action. Choose words of grace and beauty. Choose words that have the power of the infinite in them. Concentrate when you say, "God bless you. May you be restored to health." Or mentally say, "With thy grace be healthy, God's mercy upon you." Make your projection one of thanks to the creative force. Nothing stops an attitude of gratitude.

Much of the time in treatment is silent. Communicate through the power of your silence. During treatment, your mentally projected thoughts make a difference. Even if prayer only works two times out of ten, those two people need the miracle of your projection or prayer. I urge you to explore this invisible mode of enhancing your healing touch.

Self-restraint. Self-restraint is mandatory. The demands of the healing profession include a need to exercise strict self-discipline and high moral character. Once, after leading a class in kundalini yoga, a beautiful black-haired woman asked me over to her house. She was very insistent. I said no. I appreciated the compliment, the ego boost, and I still remember her intense charm, the physical magnetism, and the sexual promise. It was an unexpected moment, and I predict that you will have your share of surprises too. Be ready.

Practice a transforming discipline. If you feel that you have what it takes to do healing work with people, there are a few more things that you can do to help yourself develop. Practice a transforming discipline—kundalini yoga[12], tai chi, or another martial art, zen meditation—whatever helps you focus mental energy and tap your inner well of vitality.

Choose a discipline that helps you cultivate many sides of your self. For example, the practice of yoga includes eight facets, which combined together help expand human potential:

- the practice of the physical postures
- breathing exercises
- concentration exercises
- meditation practice
- character development through moral and ethical codes of behavior: called the do's as well as the don'ts
- absorption in deep meditation, and
- controlling the sense organs (gathering towards oneself).

The Power of Touch–the Healer's Practice

"Your power lies in the hands, and the hands of a clean man, an honest man are holy hands. There is a soul and the antennae of the soul is in the touch of your hands. Actually, you have to be super honest and a saintly person to heal people. You can't be a flirt, and fool around with the clients you see. This is totally ridiculous. It is not for you. For you the body is a very beautiful temple of God and you are to touch it in extreme reverence and worship. It doesn't matter whose body it is.

"You have to understand, you are not a man, not a woman, you are a healer! A healer is above a saint! You are not healing through the power of medicine, you are the healing."

—Yogi Bhajan[1]

There is great and untapped power in touch. We know that babies who lack physical contact fail to thrive. Without contact a child wastes away, does not grow to full height, and can die before early adolescence. Adults deprived of contact may survive but at what physical and emotional cost? Surviving and thriving are not synonymous.

Seemingly, the human body already has all it needs—a continuous source of strength from inside, a charge of life with each inhale, new red blood cells each day, and the ability to digest and assimilate. The body can exchange old bone cells for new ones, and slough yesterday's skin as new cells generate instant by instant. However, the body needs to rest and recoup. It needs wise hands to guide it further.

Yet there is a gap in our experience of touch. In childhood, when frightened or frustrated we were picked up, stroked, talked to, and caressed. In adult years, when we get wound-up and frazzled we may turn to alcohol, recreational drugs, or prescription drugs such as Prozac. Where's the touch? What happened to the therapeutic touch, the loving touch, the tender touch? Where's the healing touch, the touch that cares?

Touch is so primal that we take it for granted just like breathing. And when we are forced to think about touch, we mumble something like, "Oh, it feels o.k... But there's much much more to touch than it feels o.k. We need to touch and b touched like we need food, water, and shelter. Touch is so powerful and necessary that researchers like Saul Schanberg, MD and Ashley Montagu have spent much of their lives studying it. Dr. Schanberg says: "Think about touch. Often we regard it as an amorphous, non-specific kind of thing. But it isn't. I can make you roll over with laughter when I tickle you, or I can put you to sleep with touch[2]."

The human touch is the touch of comfort, the touch of love, the touch that relaxes and reassures. It is the caress of kindness, the touch that brings effects in a flash. The healer's touch is all these and more. No wonder it is a supreme compliment to say of someone that she has "healing hands."

I remember thinking many times during chiropractic studies that there were no courses to teach me or my fellow students how to be successful healers. There was no bedside manner course. I guess the colleges felt we did not need to learn it, since we were doctors in the making. We would gather care and concern by osmosis. To me healing went beyond blood pressure and heart rate; beyond orthopedic and neurological examinations; and beyond x-rays, ultrasound pictures, and magnetic resonance imaging. Rather, the art of healing is hands-on, for those who are committed to knowing, serving, and communicating with the patient.

The healer also creates a greater healing capacity through intuition and an ability to sense the human aura. The healer learns to listen to the voice of the client, to look at the face and the skin color, and to notice any fragrance, for clues about improving the client's health. The healer learns to use the hands as heat-generating tools, and to perceive the colors that radiate from the hands as healing assistants. And the healer learns to tap **pranic energy** and to manipulate the interacting electromagnetic fields surrounding both client and healer. Being a healer is an adventure, and it's at your fingertips.

Uplift and inspire. As a hands-on healer you have the opportunity to inspire the people you touch and to improve both physical and mental health, for the two are inextricable. For example, you can safely assume that over half the people you see have a form of stress overload that is interfering with their happiness and well-being. This is an unspoken opening for you.

One form of overload is depression (Chapter 5), a serious mental illness that can become life threatening. About one-third of your clients will suffer from depression. However, I feel that fatigue and low motivation are the only part of depression that they will discuss with you. Usually you will talk about the physical body: the shoulder tension, neck stiffness, leg cramps, low back pain, and headaches. These are the primary complaints that motivate people to seek hands-on therapy.

However, you can inspire, uplift, and motivate your clients. Your ability to help them relax and rejuvenate is always enhanced by the words, stories, and metaphors that you use. You can tell a funny story or ask the client to make you laugh with a joke. Advocate a change in attitude. Inspire your clients to drop their suffering, anxiety, and fatigue. Nurture them into giving up the limiting emotions of their lives. And suggest that they leave their mental stress in the room, just as you do when you leave work.

Find out the power of your spoken words. They become the primary reason for your growing clientele. When you leave the room near the end of the treatment you can say such things as: "You are free of emotional trauma, your brain is synchronized and those issues you brought with you are resolving even as we speak."

Your clients have enough neurosis and depression, so reverse the order. They have unresolved conflicts and a list of volatile problems. Yet they have come to you to solve only one—to unwind and have an experience that is akin to meditation. It is your job to go further and help them solve more than what they came for. Give your clients the hope to overcome and the means to persist. Converse in sweet, smooth, uplifting language—the language of a higher sphere. Touch on realms of grace, goodness, and dignity. Make major changes in their world by using language that opens them to wider horizons and infinite possibilities. Your clients may be skeptical and even cynical about this. It doesn't matter. Surprise and empower them with your inspiration.

In one of my treatment rooms there was a sign done in calligraphy: "We expect miracles." I expected miracles and still do. And I want the patients that come to me to confirm my expectations. They do want you to say it though, with confidence and faith. They love to hear, "I expect to help you with this neck pain you have. Please give the treatment 24 hours to start the changes in your body." And they love reassurance that the soreness that they feel will begin to go away in half a day. Never mind that it may take 3 days to feel better. People in pain want their minds set at ease.

I believe that human health potential is reached when there is touch therapy. Everyone has the potential to be great—in strength of mind, strength of body, and strength of soul—and the potential can be attained through the touch of someone who cares. The body needs restoring through the warm hands and love of the bodyworker.

Energy. Be extremely energetic. You will need a deep well of inner vitality. Touching people takes strength. Serving, inspiring, and understanding them takes extraordinary patience as well. After 9 years of working closely with massage therapists, I have often heard them say something like this: "I feel so drained when I'm finished massaging. They really needed everything that I had. And you know what? They took even more. How am I going to get my energy back?"

Everyone will have a different way. For me, one way is: "meditate on the sun at sunrise." The way to do this without injuring the eyes is to find a place where you can sit, with an unobstructed view of the sun, before it rises. As it appears over the horizon keep your eyes open and focus on that small section of light. Keep your spine straight. Continue to look at the sun for as long as it takes to rise one or two diameters above the horizon. This meditation is only to be done during the first 15 minutes that the sun travels above the far horizon. Remember that looking directly into the sun when it is high in the sky can burn the retina, damaging the eyes. If you have a 12,000 foot mountain 1 mile to the east of you blocking the initial rising, go to the place where you can see the sun as it peeks above the earth's curvature.

You can develop the strength and natural reserves necessary to massage people for hours if need be. You will have to develop character muscles—patience, compassion, and love for the person that you touch. I love my patients like a father loves a son, a brother, a sister, or a daughter. Inner strength comes from serving the inner purpose: uplift, elevate by taking away pain, and heal by laying on hands.

Preparing the Healing Hands

Using hands is an everyday affair. For example, for breakfast the number and combinations of hand motions is endless: open the refrigerator door, look for the orange juice, reach and hold the carton, and put it on the counter top. You get the milk out also. Then pull the English muffins out, flip up the butter door, and pick up the quarter-pound stick. And the orchestra of motions led by the hands continues. Then you feed yourself with fork and spoon never missing your mouth: amazing.

It's the same thing with touching a partner who needs to relax. You use your hands to do that. And it's not that much different from the long long list of hand movements you make each day.

Here are five suggestions for preparing your hands: give yourself permission to touch, keep your hands clean, make your hands warm, take care of the skin of your hands, and be prepared.

Permission to touch. It's okay to touch your partner. Have confidence. Cast your doubts aside and be comfortable about your power. You've nothing to fear but fear itself—doubts creep up, unbidden from the buried parts of ourselves. Gordon Inkeles says it well: "The familiar resistance to physical contact, so common in the United States, merely reinforces old puritanical fears that the body is dirty and animalistic[3]." Most of us have taboos, hesitations, and those creepy-crawly feelings about touching someone else.

Still, by far the most important realization is that you can overcome your own misgivings. It is much less important to know why doubts besiege us than to proceed with confidence. Like the first attempt to drive a stick-shift car: with all the new movements there are fears and tribulations. You may grind the gears or pop the clutch, stalling the car.

Clean hands. Keep your hands clean. Always wash your hands before you start a treatment. If you are between massages or expect to touch someone else—wash them again, it's essential hygiene. Also be sure your fingernails are clean and clipped.

Warm hands. Make sure your hands are warm. When I first started practice my hands were cold. After I was in practice for a number of months my hands warmed up, and I was grateful for the opportunity to concentrate on other people's problems. Somehow I equated being in practice and making changes in my attitude and personality with having warm hands in the morning. There are still days when my hands are cold. That's when action is necessary to start the blood flowing through the fingers. Here are a few steps that can help you warm your hands.

First, if you need to warm your hands quickly, run hot water over both hands and wrists. Massage your hands together as if you were lathering with soap for one full minute under water as hot as you can bear. Dry your hands with vigor, using a terry cloth towel. The next step: swing the arms up over your head, then down towards the floor past the hips. Your arms move straight out in front of your body, all the way up over your head. The emphasis is on the downswing. Concentrate on your fingers getting a full supply of warm blood on the downswing. Make this a movement with grace, and relax as you do it. Now you are ready to go, with warm hands.

Here are other ways to warm your hands:

- Carry a hand warmer in each hand. Do this as long as it takes to get your hands warm.
- Wear mittens until your fingers are hot.
- Sip a hot cup of tea, holding the cup in your hands for 5 minutes. Then sit on your hands in a soft chair or sofa for 5 more minutes.
- Use a hot water bottle as a source of heat. Wrap it in a towel, put the bottle in your lap, and hold it with your hands.
- Take biofeedback training. It can improve your ability to change the temperature of your hands through conscious control of the ability to relax.

Care for the skin of your hands. The skin surface is saturated with nerve endings making it highly sensitive. Everyone you treat feels your touch through the texture of their skin. They also feel the myriad other unspoken messages: how much you enjoy what you are doing, how much you like them, how much you care for them, and how much confidence you have. All these messages are being transmitted through your skin and hands. Keep that in mind as you touch your partner.

Hands that are ready have soft, smooth skin. Using skin moisturizers is important in massage because the hands are exposed to soap and water when treatments are finished. Washing dries the hands even though vegetable oil is used during massage. Please keep your hands soft, your skin healthy. The message of soft hands is a strong one.

Once I was massaged by a woman with rough, scaly skin on her hands from the base of the palms to the fingertips. The experience reminded me of a fishing trip with my grandfather, when he showed me how to clean the freshwater fish that he landed. Fascinated, I rubbed my hand on the sides of the fish against the grain, the scales popping up against my fingers all the way along the body—a strange sensation. The stroke of the masseuse's hands produced a similar abrasive sensation that I can still recall years later. Tiny flaps of skin curling away from her palms made an irritating, sandpaper-scraping sound, despite the fact that she used massage lotion. I felt like a piece of furniture going through its last sanding. During that unforgettable massage, I imagined a loofah rub at a spa where the attendant scrubs the top layer of skin cells off the body with a loofah sponge as big as a loaf of bread. And I imagined myself getting new shiny skin when I was in that massage as a strategy to make myself laugh, because I wanted to leave.

So take care of your hands, pamper them. If you have dry, peeling palms, take care of them so your clients won't wonder what's happening. Help your clients enjoy the service you offer. Massage oil is important for the feet, hands, groin, sternum, chest, and abdominal muscles. Use a small portion of oil, just the right amount to help your hands slide smoothly on the skin. Use more oil if the person's skin is dry, or if there is much hair.

Be prepared. Make sure that you and your hands are ready. The Boy Scout motto, "Be prepared," is an exemplary mental attitude to adopt before beginning any treatment. As a former Boy Scout myself I recited the Scouts' oath at every meeting and earned merit badges in the areas that interested me. When my troop went camping, whatever I needed for the trip I packed before leaving, with some help from mom. To help us accomplish the task we had a checklist. It's still good advice, so make a checklist.

How do you prepare yourself to do a treatment? How do you get ready to touch someone you have just met? What do you do if the apprehension in your voice gives you away or if your hands are still cold and shaky, even after you wash them in hot water? You just have to start, knowing that you have prepared yourself as best you can. Take a deep breath and dig in. In the end, my advice is: feel the fear and do it anyway.

Exercise: First Impressions

(a few minutes)

THIS EXERCISE CAN HELP SHARPEN YOUR SIXTH SENSE DURING THE FIRST MOMENTS OF MEETING A CLIENT. INTUITION CAN BE USED ANY TIME. IT IS ALWAYS PRESENT, YET WE FORGET TO USE IT IN OUR DAY-TO-DAY ACTIVITIES WITH CLIENTS. WE ALL DEPEND ON AN EXCHANGE OF INFORMATION THAT IS VERBAL. WE EXCHANGE NAMES; WE SHAKE HANDS; WE TALK ABOUT WHO THE REFERRAL SOURCE HAPPENS TO BE, AND THEN DISCUSS HEALTH PROBLEMS. FIRST IMPRESSIONS CAN DISAPPEAR AND BE FORGOTTEN AS THE MEETING CONTINUES.

This exercise helps center the body at the navel and fosters feeling from the guts concerning the state of the client. Here are the steps:

1. Concentrate on your gut feelings. Do this just before you are about to meet.

2. Push your stomach muscles out, making them tight for a moment.

3. Pull the muscles of the entire abdomen back towards the spine as you shake the client's hand.

4. Now that you are in the first impression, what do you feel? What do you see? What do you hear? What are you smelling?

This exercise helps me curb any fear or anxiety I have about the first meeting. And it also promotes being anchored in the moment of first impression.

Exercise: Bring Energy to Your Hands

(about 3 minutes)

"NEVER TOUCH A CLIENT UNTIL YOU ARE READY. PREPARE YOURSELF—REVITALIZE YOURSELF BETWEEN PATIENTS SO THAT YOU ARE READY FOR ANY NEGATIVITY.

"THIS IS PREPARING YOURSELF TO HEAL. NEVER TOUCH THE PERSON YOU ARE TREATING UNTIL YOU ARE RIGHT. WASH YOUR HANDS. ALWAYS AND EVER THE HANDS ARE THE TOOLS THAT YOU HAVE FOR YOUR WORK. THEY ARE INFINITELY VALUABLE. SOME HAVE INSURED THEIR HANDS FOR 500,000 DOLLARS EACH."

—YOGI BHAJAN[4]

1. Place the hands together, thumbs and fingertips touching, in front of the chest (Fig. 2-01). With a small circular motion push the fingers together (Fig. 2-02), then extend in a rhythm back and forth, back and forth. Like the joke that asks, "What do you call this?" Answer: "It's a spider doing push ups on a mirror." Do that movement for 1 minute.

2. Place your palms facing each other with the left one palm-up. Then squeeze them together (Fig. 2-03). Then change to the right hand on top and squeeze again. Go back and forth for 1 minute.

3. Place your fingertips and thumbs touching as in Step 1. Compress with heavy pressure once for 5 seconds. Clasp the hands as in Step 2, once each way with your maximum pressure. Place your fingers over your eyes, applying pressure for 15 seconds. Then be ready to go.

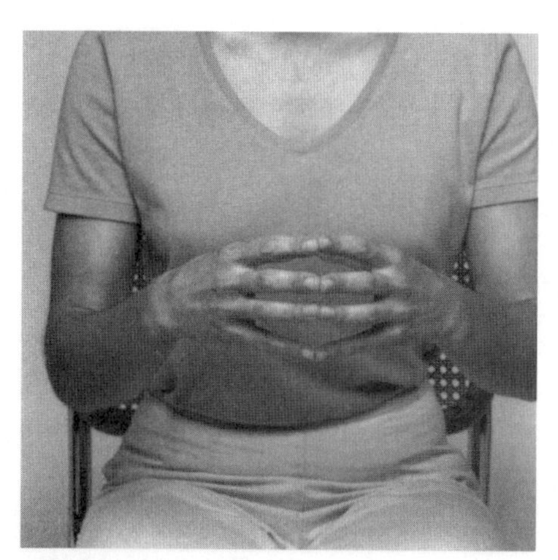

Fig 2-01

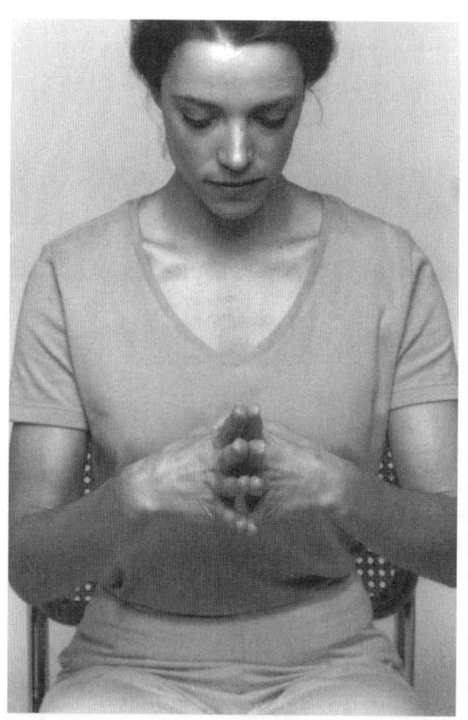

Fig 2-02

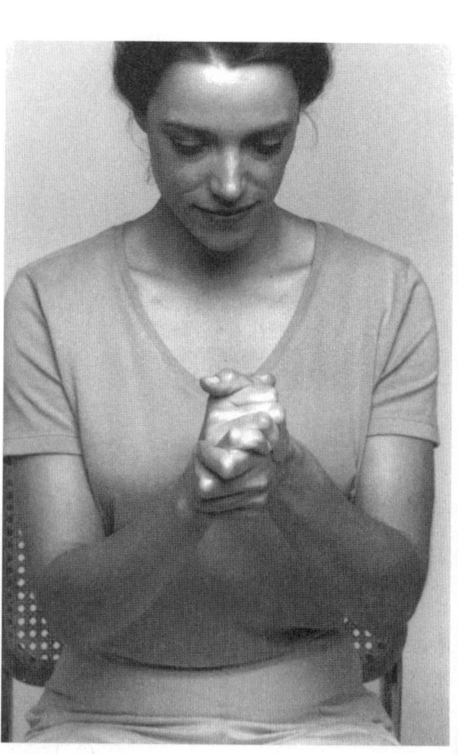

Fig 2-03

Treating Clients

Once you are ready, it's time to do the business of hands-on healing. So enter the room with your client, placing your hands and body in position to serve the client's health.

Before treatment. Before starting, sit and talk to the people that you are treating. Become familiar with their present complaints and past history by asking a few questions. Ask the client: "What's bothering you?" (or: "Where's the problem?") "How long have you had the problem?" "How severe is the pain?" "Are you being treated by a doctor for it?" "Do you have cancer or another serious disease?" As you talk with the client take notes about the conversation.

If you are working with someone of the opposite sex or someone underage, it may be helpful to have another adult in the room while you are performing a treatment. If the treatment involves sensitive areas, discuss the treatment with the client well in advance.

Learning to use the hands. Physical treatment is simple because the mechanics of hands-on healing are simple. Once you choose a technique to do, go one step at a time, concentrate on your hands, feel what the hands are doing and what they tell you about the person you are treating. You can learn from your hands. Your hands will move to new locations as if they have a mind of their own. Your hands are part of the sensory equipment that makes you intuitive.

If you feel anxious about touching a person you have just met, you can use your mind to help you relax by treating that person like a brother, a daughter, an uncle, or a cousin. In other words, imagine treating a person who will tolerate your mistakes. As you imagine that, remember that everything you are doing feels good to the person you are touching.

Healing hands deliver a message. Approach the person you are going to touch in a calm manner, with purity and kindness. When your intention is to be kind, the person will know that through your touch. The true definition of hands-on healing is giving a message to the person that the tension, pain, and stress are only temporary. Hands-on curative healing is:

- giving a message of relief to the other person.
- communicating the message that there is hope, even in the midst of hopelessness.
- giving reassurance that the person can relax, let go, and return to a healthier state.
- quiet listening.
- restoring the person and yourself through your own faith, confidence, and belief in hands-on therapy.
- relaying your kindness and compassion.
- reminding the person that he or she can excel, be great, and succeed in life.
- sharing some of your strengths.
- holding a person's hand, walking down the road together.

All touch heals, all human contact from hands to body is for healing when that is the intention, even when there is dislike from either side. I give my clients a report of findings after their first visit. We go over my recommendations; the clients see the x-rays; they find out more information about chiropractic; they ask questions; and then they start care if they are ready. I often ask myself, how long will it be before the client responds in a positive, pain-relieving manner. Will the client stay with the treatment long enough to get the results wanted? Clients respond at different rates. Some heal quickly; others heal slowly.

I have treated people who did not like me. And once I sat with a fellow who stopped me in my first sentence. He said, "I don't like you; I don't believe you can help me. Give me my x-rays. I'll have my doctor call you about what he sees. Are you really a doctor?" Then he stood up and left.

Nor do I like everyone I treat. It's not ideal, but it's human—I treat the person because they made an appointment with me, regardless of the initial chemistry.

So maybe the first question is: can I go into a profession in which I use my hands and make lots of money? Sure you can for a while. But from my years of experience, people know how you feel about them and their well-being through your touch. As with most body language, there's no lying with hands. You cannot hide what you feel as you touch a friend, family member, or stranger.

Sending your prana. Another way to direct and preserve your energy is to mentally penetrate the points that you press, passing energy from your fingertips to the interior of the person's body. Use your subtle abilities to visualize colors extending from the fingertips. Here are some examples for you to try:

- Green is the color of the plant kingdom, the sustaining color of the earth. Visualizing green is helpful for inflamed muscle tissue, for cooling the heart, and for releasing anger.
- Visualize a gold color to warm a region and unblock the **channels**. Gold brings seed energy to all the **chakras**. The color of this precious metal is endearing to all body channels, just as it is in jewelry.
- Visualizing red brings heat, stimulates circulation, and helps rid an area of stagnant energy and blood.
- An orange visualization radiates from the fingers and thumbs to help relax the tissues being treated.

Treatment time and mastery. In my profession an average of 5 to 10 minutes is spent with a patient. There are many chiropractors who spend an average of 2 minutes with each patient and obtain good results. (See Chapter IV for techniques that last from 1 to 8 minutes.) I urge you to be ready for good results. Have an eager desire to help and a belief that what you do is valuable. That self-confidence is important for beginners to develop. Staying with a short time sequence when one is suggested is admirable. Yet, when you are new to bodywork it can interfere with becoming familiar and confident with your hands. Can you stay flexible in the learning process? I believe that part of intuition is staying flexible. Stay with a stroke as long as you feel that it is necessary, even when that is longer than the time given in the step that you are practicing.

It is best for you to get familiar with the hand strokes, to learn to give to your client, and to develop your confidence. There is no need to put a timer on yourself for each step. So, when you start with this book, approximate the times listed in the treatment steps. Also be aware of the extra time needed when you are learning these treatments—whether it is looking to the book, forming the hand strokes, talking with your client, deciding whether to use massage lotion or vegetable oil, turning the CD player on, or lighting a candle.

Preserving your energy and stamina. To help yourself stay relaxed and powerful during any treatment, use only the muscles you need to do the massage. Keep as much of your body in a state of relaxation as you can. Conserve and consolidate the outflow to your client, even though maximum force may be necessary.

Once Yogi Bhajan discussed that there is a favorable side in treating clients. The way you find out is to stand on the side of the client that suits you the most. Do the stroke called for as you observe and feel what is happening. Then change sides and repeat the stroke. Which side is the best for you and the client? You decide. On one side you are sharpest, most effective, and have the strongest impact on the client.

Go to your strongest side when you treat a client, even new ones. Don't allow a different time or a different location change the side where you are most powerful.

If you use a massage table, keep both feet on the ground, and bend your knees a little. Curl then uncurl your toes as if grabbing the floor, even if you wear shoes. This helps you stay in contact with the earth and consolidates body energy.

During treatment, roll your shoulders forward as you press down into each **pressure point** or perform the stroke. A natural tendency is to hike the shoulders up around the ears while applying pressure.

If you use the floor, use as much of your body weight as you can. For example, when you lean over the client to press into the upper back points on the level of T-4 keep your arms almost straight, leaning down with as much body weight as you can muster. The idea is to use the leverage of your body weight, not just the muscle power of the arms.

Pain threshold. Work with your client's ability to tolerate pain while remembering that the techniques are for healing and rejuvenating. To help clients achieve rejuvenation in some treatments, you must put them through a rigorous, sometimes painful experience. And although each person tolerates pain differently, there are parts of these treatments that can be painful for anyone. In addition, when you are working with clients much larger than you are, they may experience no discomfort at all.

If you press a point that is already sore and the client jumps, do you go deeper? That calls for judgement. Ask yourself: "Do I go deeper on the sensitive area or stay light and tolerable?" You do have to meld with the threshold of your client. That way you know by your touch, by the client's body language (flinching, making funny faces, moaning, crying out) how you are doing with that person. Be aware also that clients can falsify reactions.

Your client's emotional state. "In structural bodywork the practitioner also enters his client's unconscious—though this is not the particular aim of the work—this time through the body[5]." Most of the people you will treat have a negative mental or emotional component to the muscle tensions that they bring to your table. Do bodyworkers absorb negativity from the persons they touch? I think so, but how aware are we of that exchange? Since there is no separation between the mind and body, your massage moments with clients are an interaction of your magnetic field with theirs. When the inner negativity of clients is dominant, or when shadow forces are potently affecting them, you may develop symptoms. I have felt ill just touching a patient on the back during an examination. At that moment I felt something jump from the patient to myself, like an electromagnetic charge that made me feel sick for about a day. It does not happen often. However, you do have to be prepared mentally and spiritually for whatever transpires during a session. Even though you may not know the details or the depth of client conflicts, you will improve their lives in these situations by taking on some of their negativity.

However, I never set out to treat a client's emotional problem. I enter the treatment room ready to treat the physical body. It is always a physical touch procedure.

When it is appropriate to counsel a person about emotional stress, I do it. There are times when the client only wants to talk and is satisfied with undivided attention and conversation. When it is evident that my patient needs more than brief counseling, I refer them to a psychotherapist or psychiatrist.

There are other times when clients do not want to talk about their problems. Someone who was talkative last week clams up this week. It may happen to you one day as you do bodywork. The client may be tired from long hours of work or be grouchy and uncommunicative for no apparent reason. The client has come to see you, and all that is wanted is to lie down and to be touched in total silence.

If that is the case, the treatment can be cathartic. When you are done, ask what is bothering the client … then just listen; often that is all that is needed. Use your intuition to decide whether to finish by inspiring them.

Nevertheless, the interaction between the client and practitioner always includes the deeper causes of symptoms. Even when there is no conscious communication between patient and practitioner at the cause level—the symptom is still being worked on, manipulated, changed, transformed, and healed in some way. I believe information can be transferred subconsciously. So in my imagination I see the patient improved: healed, whole, energized, prosperous, whatever seems in tune with the person at that moment. The way that I do this is silent. I project this new image over the person that I am treating. And when you know that image is true, you can bring miracles into the lives of your clients.

Learning long treatments. Learn the longer treatments one step at a time. If you are new to bodywork have fun with this, because it is fun. Go slowly—read the explanation; look at the illustrations; put your hands on your partner and go. And remember: there is nothing "wrong" on the receiving side of massage; it all feels good. Keep in mind what you feel like when a massage therapist puts warm hands on your tight muscles. All parts of the massage feel good. The hands-on touching is reassuring; being the focus of attention is pleasing; taking time to relax in a safe place away from stress is calming. For these reasons, there is no such thing as a mistake when putting hands on a client who is tense.

To begin, consider memorizing the Surrender the Stress Treatment (Chapter 3). Repeat it, doing the movements over and over until you are familiar with the way the treatment works, and how it fits on the persons you treat. Then, consider memorizing the Massage for Security and Connectedness with Earth (Chapter 5). Perform the movements until you are familiar with the way the treatment works and confident about how to do the strokes. Bodywork practiced by a person who knows the treatment by heart is smooth and hypnotic. You as a bodyworker will farm the private landscape of the client. You will use your hands like shovel and hoe, digging the ground of surface tissues. You will be like the shining sun radiating warmth. For clients receiving treatment there is nothing like it. Bodywork from someone who has mastered the individual steps of a treatment can transport clients. Where the clients go in their imagination is private, like a vacation to exotic places filled with new sights, sounds, and unexpected turns in the road.

After treatment. By the end of a longer treatment, every part of your client's body feels restored and energized, loved and pampered. A client may feel sleepy, as if in a hypnotic trance. A client may enter a physical, deeply restful awakened state, where the mind is not obsessing on problems. Anxiety has disappeared; the mind is at ease.

Your client will feel the difference during the massage and for hours afterwards, and sometimes for days later. There are many feelings that your clients will have during these healing treatments. They may feel warm everywhere, because blood and ***prana*** circulate better through the body and because you have caused tight muscles to relax.

I know that I can never remember what strokes were performed on me after a massage is over, because time is suspended during the massage. Clock time dies and subjective time takes over. The loss of clock time makes me say, "An hour is over? Wait, you can't stop now. Just a little more."

Additional treatments. Here are two ways that you can make suggestions for additional treatments. If the person has a chronic problem (pain or symptoms for more than 3 weeks) recommend a number of massages equal to the number of weeks they have suffered. When it is 3 to 6 weeks recommend three to six massages. If it's been much longer, recommend massage for 10 percent of the time they have had symptoms.

Another way to recommend additional treatments is to use your intuition when you discuss more massage. And remember, everyone you touch is going to like what they receive. How eager they are to return depends on whether you charge for your services (and how much); how motivated they are to feel better; how much time they have for treatment; and whether they like you.

SOVEREIGN HANDS

The hands are priceless.
They are the living healing.
They are the moving medicine.
The touch of a king in times gone by took away scrofula[6].
Moral sensitivity in hands that touch is depth healing.
Touch is the characteristic of a healer.
Without touch there is no effect.
Touch is the beginning of every miracle.
And the end of every pain.
The hand is the vehicle of prana.
The wand of health and healing unseen.
There is no effect without a touch.
Penetrating every barrier, all surfaces,
Blending all tissues in her sacred presence.

Stress Release Treatments

Stress, the number one cause of disease in the 1990s, is connected with life-threatening diseases like alcoholism, cancer, diabetes, stroke, asthma, heart disease, and high blood pressure. There is no doubt that prolonged stress produces fatigue in the immune system, also called lowered resistance. When resistance is low we are susceptible to viral or bacterial invasion; then the flu or a cold is just around the corner.

Stress is a household word because each person in every house has to deal with it in order to remain a household. The pace of life is so fast and the changes are coming at us from so many directions that it is difficult to adapt and adjust. Television informs us of the violence in our communities and across the world. We see earthquakes, floods, riots, and other crises that we cannot solve. The planes we fly in and the cars we drive take us more miles in one month than our great-grandparents traveled in one lifetime[1].

There is a bombardment of information in newspapers, magazines, online services, television commercials, and direct mail solicitations that gives every adult a low-level attention deficit disorder (ADD). A child with ADD used to be called hyperactive. Today, most adults have a level of ADD that makes relaxation nearly impossible. The nervous system becomes overloaded with too much information and the high pace of life. There is not enough time to absorb one change before two more demand attention. So, stress becomes chronic. It piles up. Anxiety becomes a way of life.

What do you do about stress? Use the treatments in this chapter to help your clients and friends experience relaxation—a sense of ease, a floating sensation, an altered state of mind. These treatments also yield quiet moments of enjoying the sensual experience of soft muscles and smooth skin.

On Foot Reflexology

Foot reflexologists, sometimes called simply "reflexologists," are foot massage specialists. They know the foot like a hair stylist knows hair. They only massage the feet. According to reflexologists the body is divided into 10 zones of equal proportion: five on the right side and five on the left. These zones start at the toes, extending to the top of the head and then down the arms to the fingers. There is a flow of energy through each zone, linking all the areas of the body situated in the same zone[2,3]. The rule of thumb in reflexology is that the zone where an organ (or the symptom) is located dictates the zone on the foot to be massaged. Therefore, if a person has nausea, a reflexologist may start on the left foot in the stomach reflex area, then move to the corresponding area in the right foot (see Chart 1, page 37).

There was a chiropractor in Minnesota who only treated the feet. He lived in a small farming community and decided that his focus was the feet. That's all he did. He got so busy that he put up a large circus tent in his backyard to serve as his waiting room. He dug a big round trench in his yard 5 1/2 feet deep and 12 feet across. Around the trench he placed chairs for his patients. They sat with their feet propped on the edge of the trench.

The doctor stood at the bottom of the trench, giving him easy access to his patients' feet. He adjusted their foot and ankle bones and charged a dollar per foot—some people only wanted one foot worked on. He saw 300 to 400 people per day. His patients sought treatment for a whole range of complaints: ankle sprains, bunions, arthritis, knee problems, low back pain, constipation, headaches, neck pain, and poor circulation. The year was 1938.

Foot Treatment

(approximately 4 minutes)

THIS IS A SHORT, SWEET, EASY WAY TO HELP THE FEET RELAX. DO THE TREATMENT WITH YOUR CLIENT'S SHOES AND SOCKS OFF. RUN A WASHCLOTH UNDER HOT WATER, WRING IT OUT, AND SCRUB EACH FOOT. DRY THE CLIENT'S FEET WITH A HAND TOWEL, AND APPLY A SMALL AMOUNT OF MASSAGE LOTION TO THE ENTIRE FOOT.

1. Have your client lie face down. Place your thumbs underneath the ankle bones and the index fingers across the Achilles tendons. Press down on both tendons at the same time as your thumbs press the ankles for 15 seconds. Then, still pressing the tendon down toward the floor, slide an inch away from the heel toward the calf muscle for 15 more seconds (Fig. 3-01). If you are working on someone much larger than yourself, use both thumbs together on one tendon (Fig. 3-02).

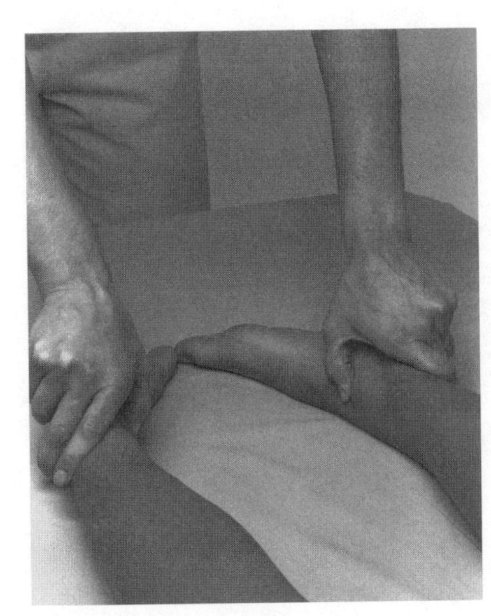

Fig 3-01

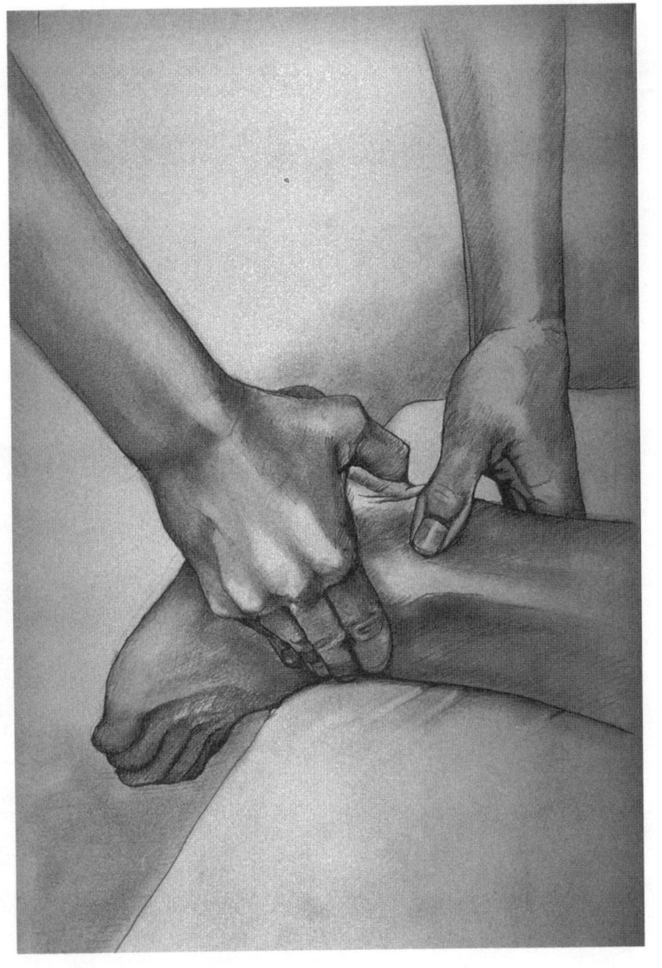

Fig 3-02

2. Your client is still face down. Hold each foot by wrapping your fingers around the front of the ankle, thumbs across the Achilles tendon (Fig. 3-03). Squeeze firmly on both tendons for 15 seconds. If you have a client who is bigger than you, squeeze one tendon at a time with both hands.

3. The client is face up. Your index finger presses on the top of the foot (between the large joint of the big toe and the same joint of the client's second toe). At the same time and on the bottom of the foot, your thumb squeezes toward the finger (Fig. 3-04). Massage the foot with firm pressure, sliding your finger one way as your thumb moves the other, back and forth for 30 seconds.

4. Hold the top of the left foot with both hands, wrapping your right thumb around the arch and your left thumb around the opposite side of the foot. Next, squeeze the foot as if you are milking the tissues (Fig. 3-05). Start close to the ankle and move

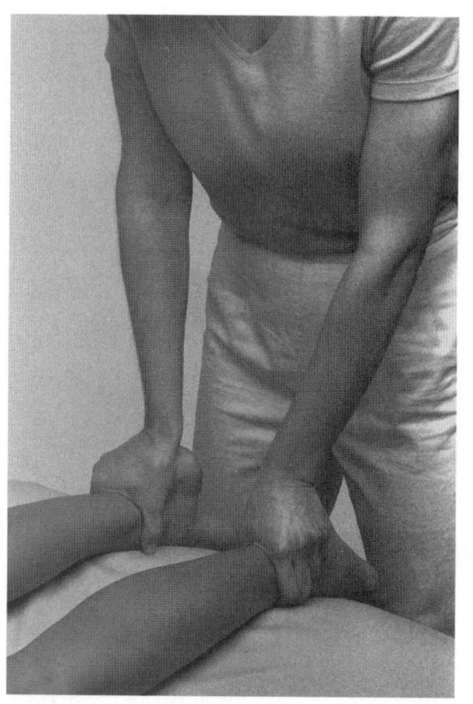

Fig 3-03

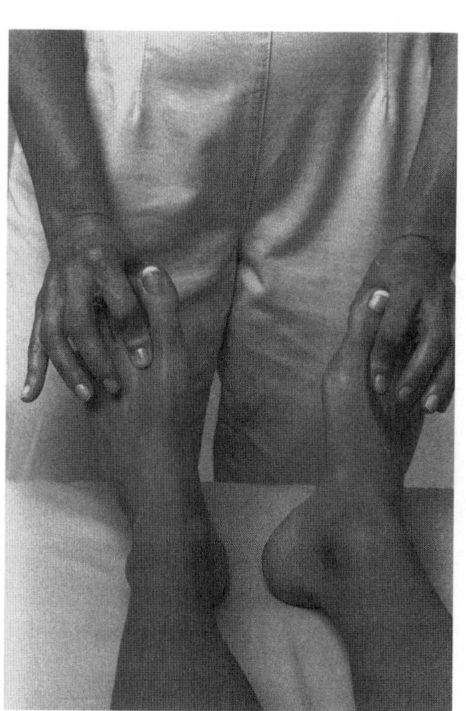

Fig 3-04

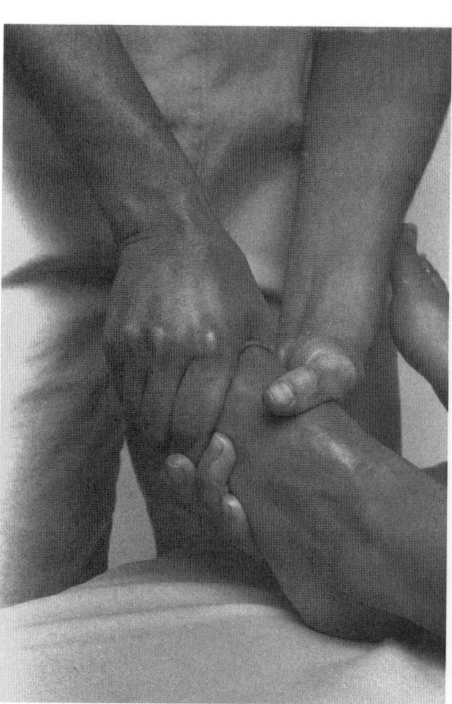

Fig 3-05

down to the toes. Massage for 15 seconds on each foot. The chart on page 38 shows the areas influenced.

5. Massage the bottom of the foot with the knuckles of one hand, stroking from the heel along the arch all the way to the toes (Fig. 3-06). Take 30 seconds on each foot. The charts on pages 37 and 38 show the regions of the body affected.

6. Hold the large toes with your thumbs on the outside, fingers on the inside, between the large and second toes. Now squeeze and roll the large toe between your thumb and fingers for 15 seconds (Fig. 3-07). Lift both feet off the table as you do this.

7. Lift the heel of the left foot off the table with your left hand; your right hand curls around the top of the foot, bending it down to the floor. Stretch the front third of the foot forward and down toward the floor (Fig. 3-08). Take 10 seconds on each foot.

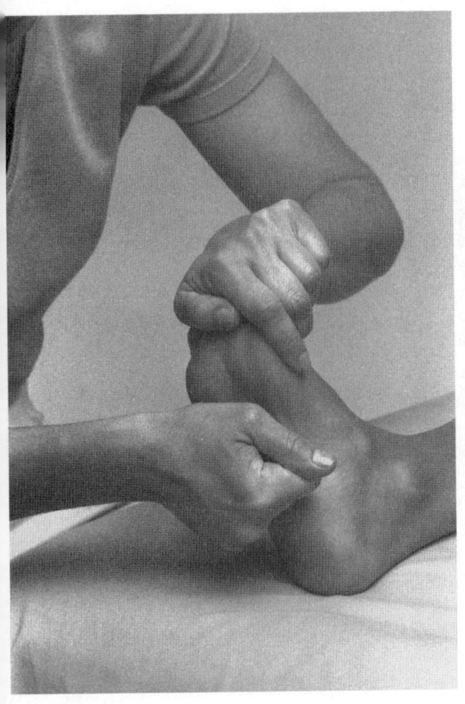

Fig 3-06

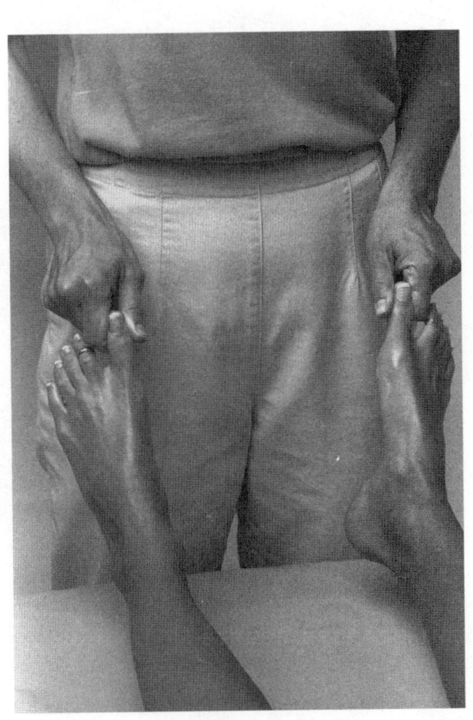

Fig 3-07

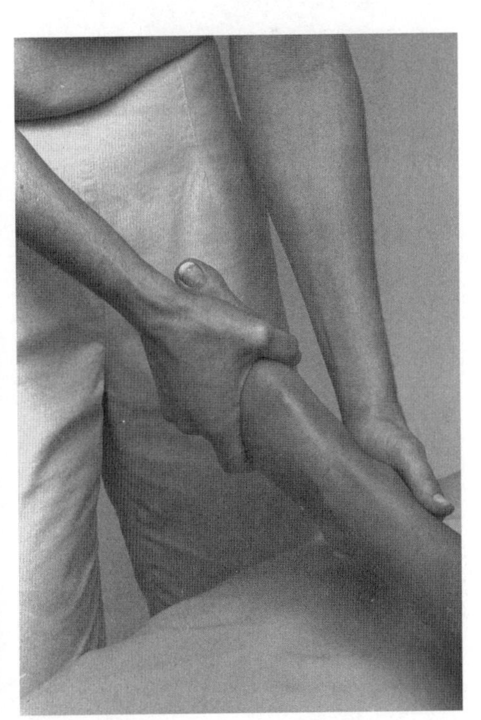

Fig 3-08

Place the ankle in traction by grasping the foot in both hands (fingers on top of the foot overlapping each other; thumbs cross each other underneath), and bend the foot straight back toward the shin (Fig. 3-09). This movement stretches the Achilles tendon. Point the toes to the ceiling as you do this (no tilt, no twist, no turn-in, no turn-out). Take the "slack" out of the foot (without twisting the ankle) by pulling slowly on the foot as you hold the foot bent back. The foot may move an inch. If you are sliding the person along the table, you are pulling too much. Once the "slack" is out, give a gentle tug, pulling the foot toward you. Take about 15 seconds to do both feet.

8. The client is face down. Wrap your hands around the ankles—thumbs contact the Achilles tendon, fingers cross over the front ankle (Fig. 3-10). Then squeeze the ankles and tendons with strong force 15 times in a period of about 20 seconds.

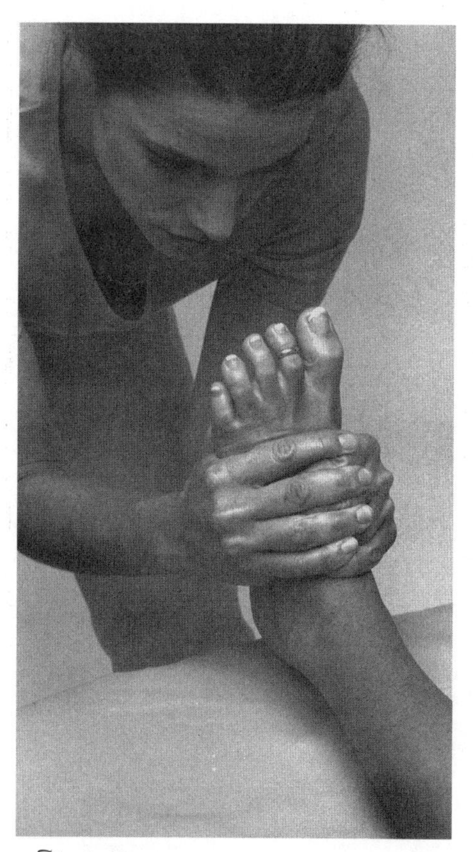

Fig 3-09

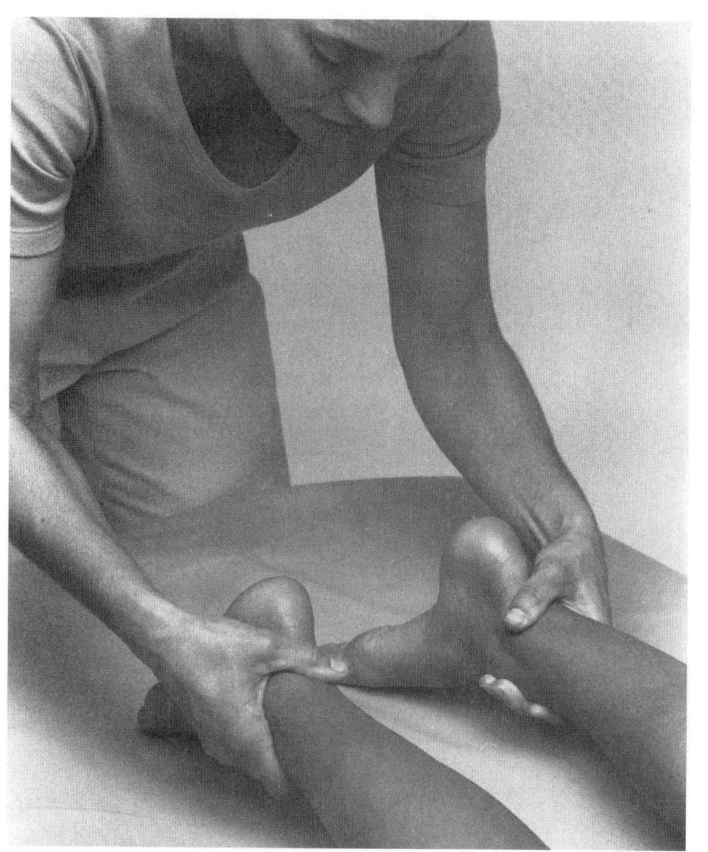

Fig 3-10

Foot Reflexology

Chart 1

Bottom View

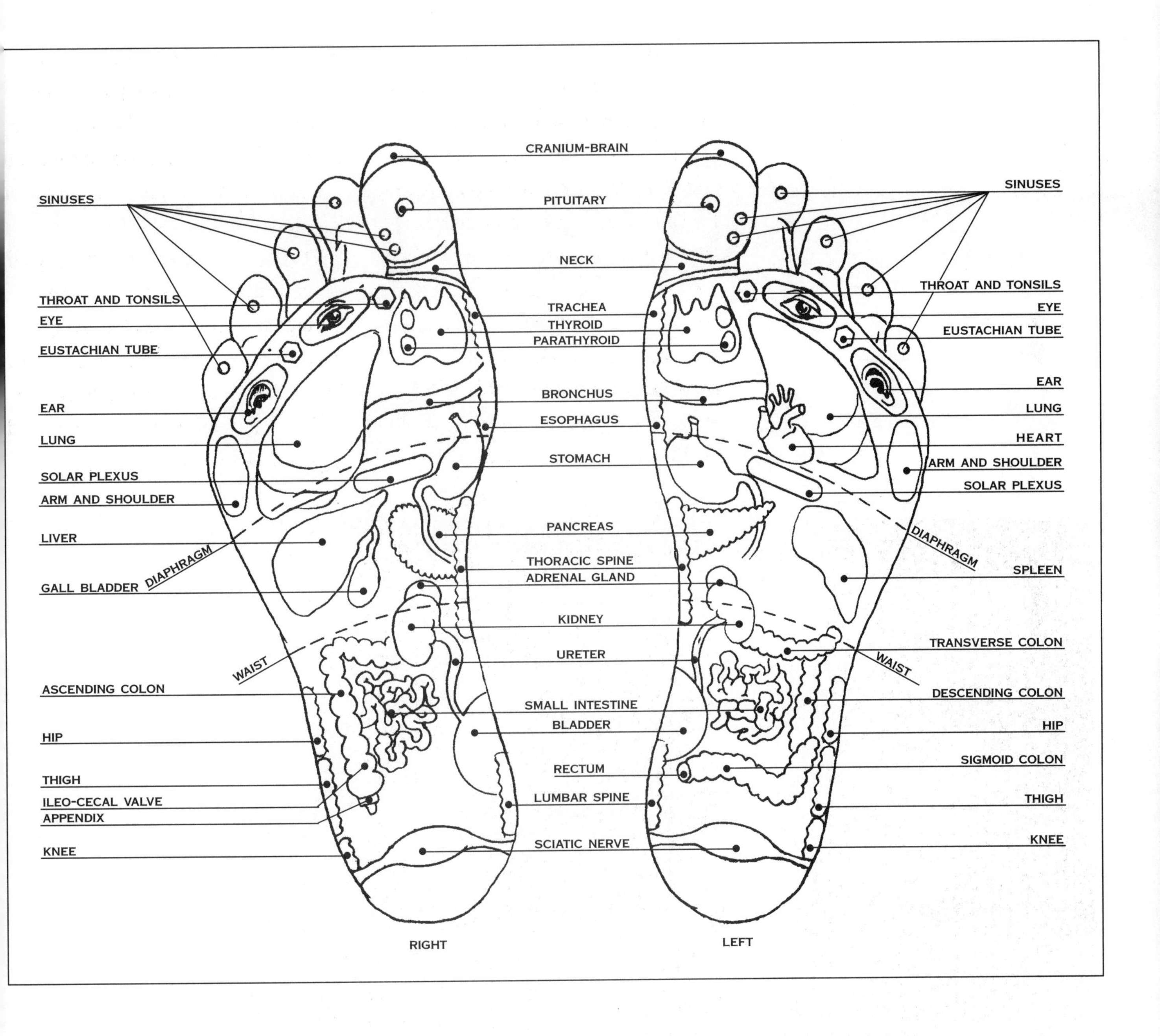

Foot Reflexology

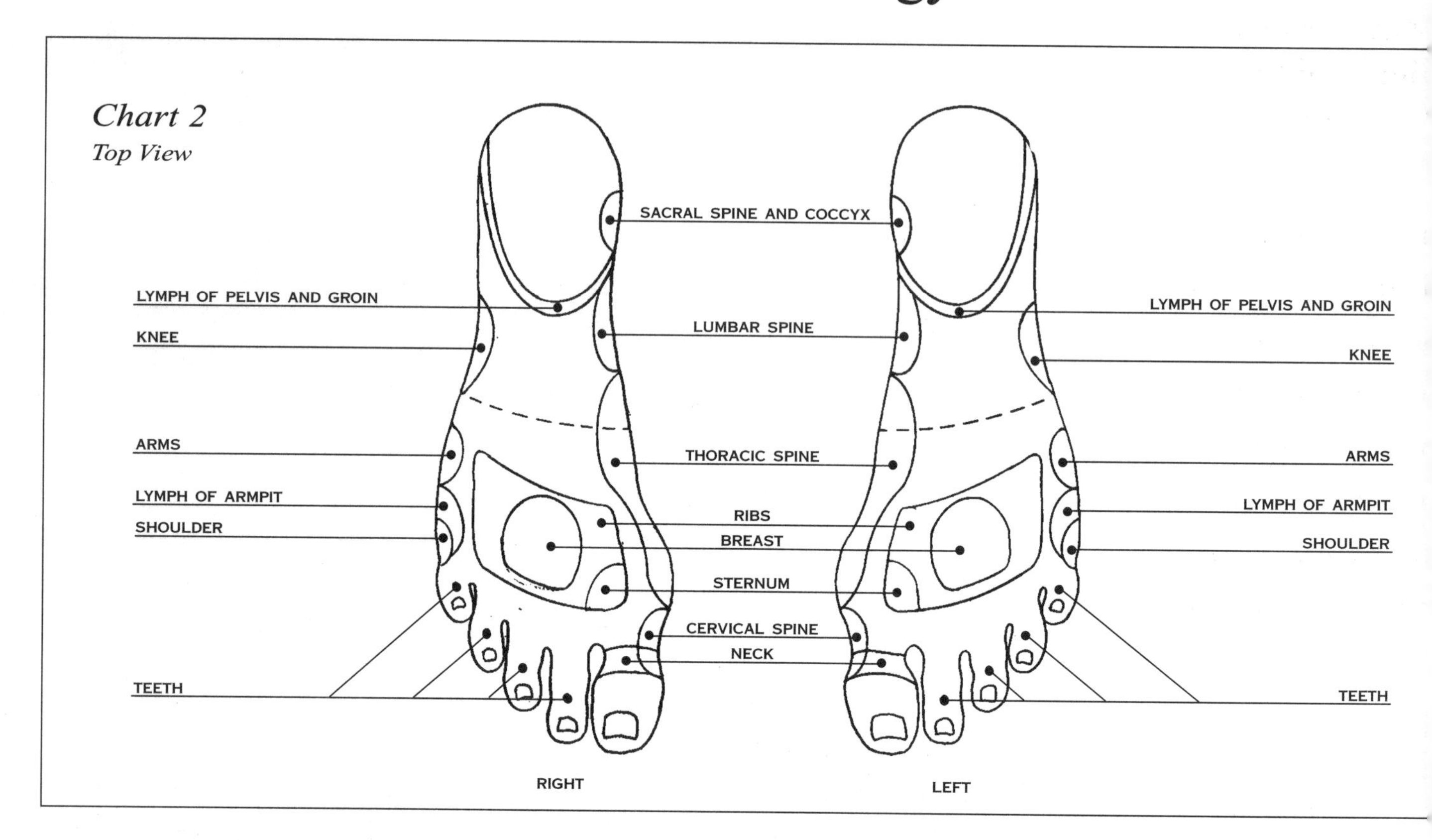

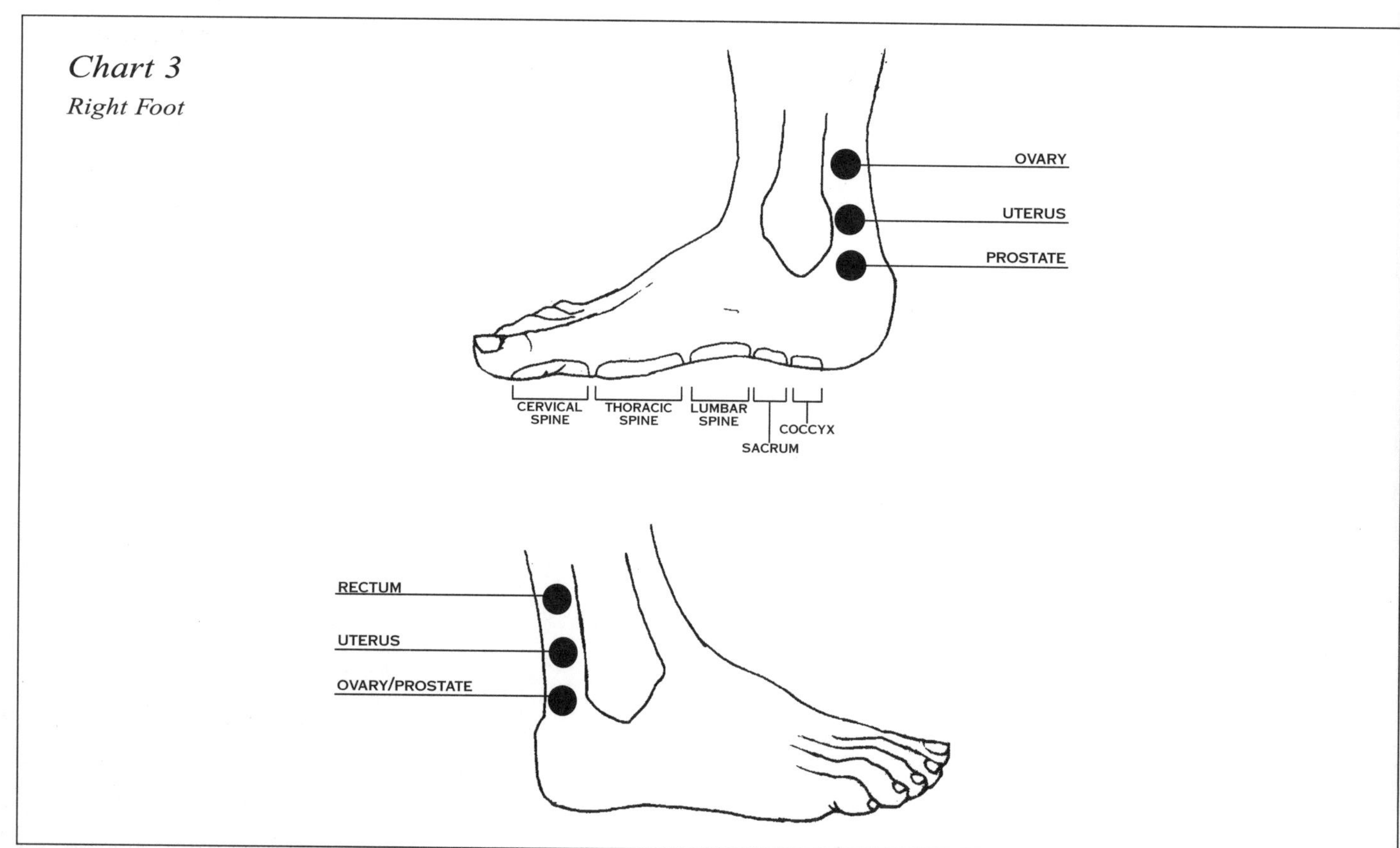

Body Area Drumming–Thighs, Buttocks, or Chest

(11 minutes)

HE THREE LARGEST MUSCLE GROUPS N THE BODY ARE THE FRONT THIGHS, HE BUTTOCKS, AND THE LOWER BACK USCLES. THEY ARE ALSO THE TRONGEST MUSCLES THAT WE HAVE. HEY OFFER PADDING TO THE BODY ND CAN TOLERATE THE RHYTHMIC ERCUSSION OF THIS TREATMENT.

Choose one of the muscle groups and proceed with this treatment for 11 minutes. Depending on the client's needs and your stamina, you may then proceed to another.

There is a principle here that is important to understand. When the body is stimulated in one region for 11 minutes, the entire nervous system comes into play. Any lymphatic congestion in the region is released. Blood flow is increased. Also, your client's focus stays in the stimulated area causing a relaxation not possible with only a few minutes of massage. This stimulation can help make the region stronger and more resilient to stress.

The constant rhythm tends to bring on an altered state close to a hypnotic trance. You can play drum music to help you establish a rhythm[4]. There is much pleasure in having the body tapped like this. The body is a drum—hollow on the inside, with skin covering the outside. Play it as if it's an instrument, having fun, watching your client disappear into another state of mind. The effects on my clients have lasted for more than 72 hours.

Stimulating the Buttocks

THERE ARE TEN MUSCLES IN THE BUTTOCKS REGION. THE GLUTEUS MAXIMUS BUNDLE IS THE BIGGEST ONE, LYING CLOSE TO THE SURFACE. THEY ARE CONNECTED WITH THE POWER TO MAINTAIN THE TRUNK IN THE ERECT POSITION AND THEY LEND STABILITY TO THE OUTSIDE KNEE JOINT.

The client lies on his stomach. Stand to one side of the table.

1. Make fists of both hands and alternately hit the buttocks muscles. You are hitting on his left buttock with your left fist; the right fist strikes the right buttock (Fig. 3-11). Stay off the bony areas; hit only on the muscles.

2. In 11 minutes you can cover the entire muscle, using different angles of punching. Use both fists on one side if you feel you can do a better job this way. And make sure you give equal time to each side.

Use strong force and concentrate on hitting the muscles. Help your client to relax as you do this, in order to enjoy all the benefits.

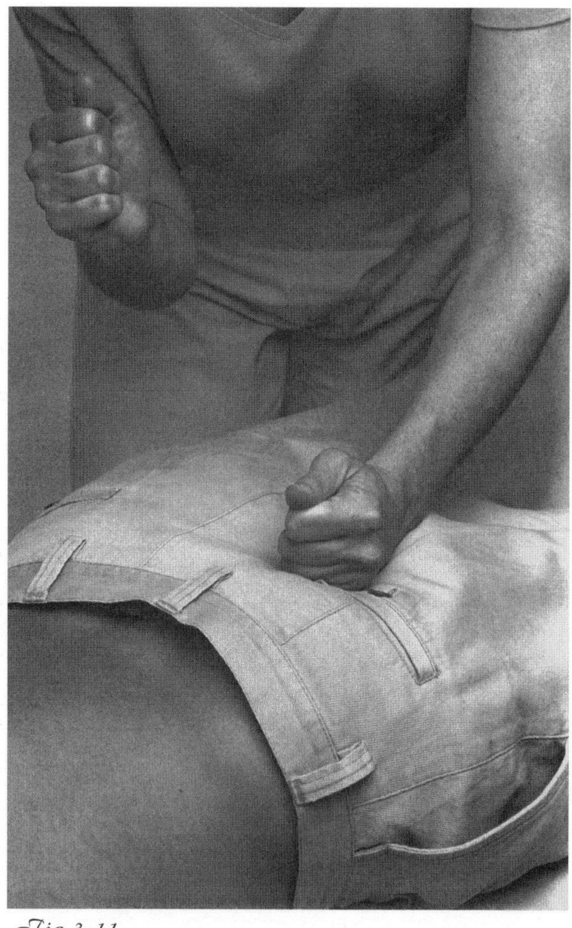

Fig 3-11

timulating the Front 'high Muscles

HE THIGH MUSCLES ARE A SOURCE OF TRENGTH, STAMINA, AND SUPPORT FOR HE ENTIRE BODY. THE FRONT THIGH USCLES ARE THE ACTION MUSCLES OF ORWARD MOVEMENT. SYMBOLICALLY, HEY ARE ALSO THE MUSCLES THAT LLOW PEOPLE TO STAND UP FOR THEM-ELVES AND WALK FORWARD INTO THEIR ESPONSIBILITIES OF LIFE.

The client is on his back. Stand to one side of the table. The best way to stimulate this large body of muscle is to percuss one side at a time (Fig. 3-12). The three muscle divisions that make up the front thigh cover the entire leg from groin to knee.

1. Begin this drumming movement at the upper thigh near the groin, then move down the leg to the knee.

2. Start again at the groin, finding a rhythm you can stay with for the entire time. You can include some of the inner thigh and some of the outer edge of the thigh muscles.

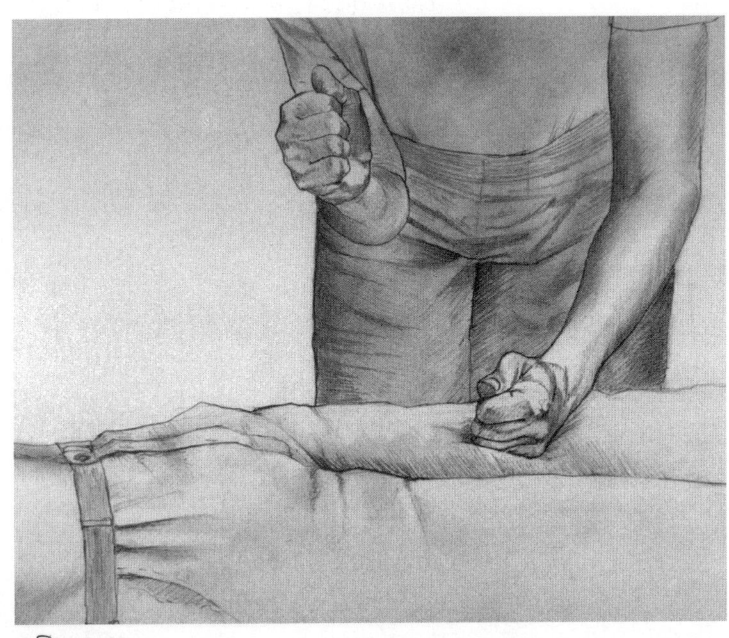

Fig 3-12

Stimulating the Chest

PERCUSSING THE CHEST CAN PUT YOUR CLIENT INTO A RELAXED STATE. FOR MOST OF THE CHEST, CHANGE YOUR HANDS TO THE KNIFE-EDGE MUDRA, WITH FINGERS APART.

1. Percuss the chest with alternating hands, fingers open as the side of the little finger hits the chest muscles or sternum (Fig. 3-13). You will feel and hear your fingers snapping together with each stroke.

2. Switch to fingertip percussion on soft, sensitive areas on men or women, especially near the breasts. This stroke is done by using a loose wrist, palm-down. Lift the wrist off your client, bending your hand back, then swing your hand down tapping the chest with your fingertips. This stroke can be done with wrist movements only. Use forearm movement along with the wrist if it is easier for you to create a rhythm.

In most men you can do the entire chest, including the sternum, with your fists (Fig. 3-14). Use a soft percussing movement with the fists. Tell your female clients that you will be touching the breasts with gentle movements. Percuss the entire chest, being soft with the breasts. If you or your woman client is not comfortable with the breasts being percussed you can have a third person present to help the client feel more secure. Or do what you can of the entire chest going around the breasts.

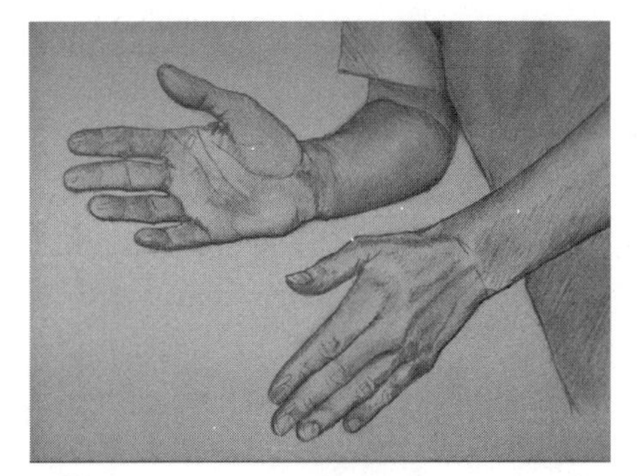

Fig 3-13

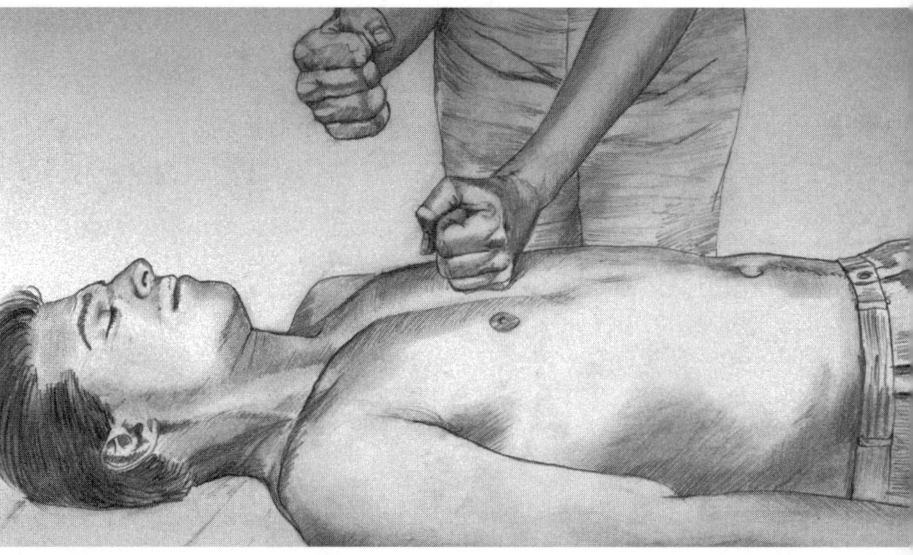

Fig 3-14

Three Identities Treatment: Navel, Calf, and Achilles Tendon

(approximately 7 1/2 minutes)

WHEN MASTERED, THE THREE IDENTITIES TREATMENT CAN HELP HEAL MANY PROBLEMS THAT PLAGUE THE HEALTH OF YOUR CLIENTS.

This treatment stimulates the reserve energy of the body, and it is also calming. It is good for runners, athletes, and those who stand on their feet for long hours during the day, and it also helps anyone who needs rejuvenation.

The three identities are:

1. Navel: the original socket, the first connector with mom, the source, the center of the body, the center of gravity.
2. Calf muscle: for pushing forward in life and as a storage tank of primal energy. Yogi Bhajan calls the calf muscle the "purse" of life energy.
3. Achilles tendon: connector to the heel, source of agility and movement.

Navel area

Work on the navel area brings awareness to the central axis of the body and the navel—site of the umbilical cord, the original connecting stem. The navel is also the approximate location of the third **chakra**, and the source region for anger, raw emotions, and power drives. Treating this area helps you overcome: anxiety, nervousness, excessive worry, and obsessive thinking. The client will relax and become stronger from the navel down to the feet.

Calf Muscles

Massaging the calf muscles helps anyone who stands for hours and needs to establish better circulation. A person might complain of aching calves at the end of the day; there may be foot cramps, tired feet, or lower back aches. The calves are postural muscles—important for standing up, running, jumping, and moving the feet quickly. Massage in the middle of the calf muscle invigorates the blood, relaxes lower leg muscles and tendons, and relieves lower back stiffness and sciatic nerve pain.

Achilles Tendon

The mythological Achilles, hero of the Iliad, was a great warrior who was killed by an arrow that struck his only vulnerable spot—his heel. The heel and connected muscles are associated with movement and agility in the body. Pushing off the ground to step forward is the primary motion controlled from the heel.

The heel is overlooked in most therapies. You can help create energy in the client by massaging the heel. Massaging this area helps forward movement, energizes the entire leg, and strengthens the lower back. Squeezing the soft tissue underneath the Achilles tendon (between the ankle bone and the tendon) quells pain anywhere in the body and activates the sex glands. The inch and a half of soft tissue from the heel bone up the leg can be sharp and full of pain. Massaging this soft tissue helps relax and relieve pain in the shoulders, neck, and base of the skull. It even relieves headaches at the base of the skull.

Procedure

1. This first step starts the relaxation response by working in the entire abdominal region. Have the client practice **long deep breathing** for a few minutes. Then, with the exhale, press to the side of the navel with the fingertips of both hands at the 3 o'clock position (Figs. 3-15, 3-16). Press down slowly, going as deeply as you can, according to the pain tolerance of the client, for about 2 seconds. Move to the 4 o'clock position and press straight down again with the fingertips of both hands. Again, go as deeply as you can.

a. Watch for reactions when you find tight spots or lumps. The reactive areas are the ones to spend a little time treating. Press down to the point of discomfort, moving the fingers to one side of reactive areas. (Stay off the tight spots.) Hold your position for 2 seconds then release.

b. Then repeat 10 more times: once at 5 o'clock, 6, 7, and following all the way around to 2 o'clock.

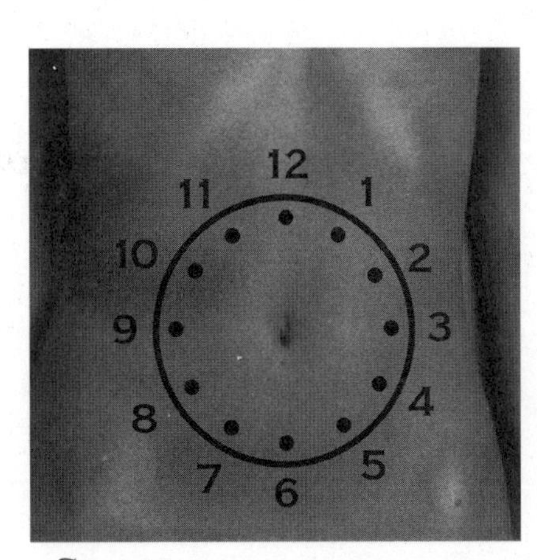

Fig 3-15

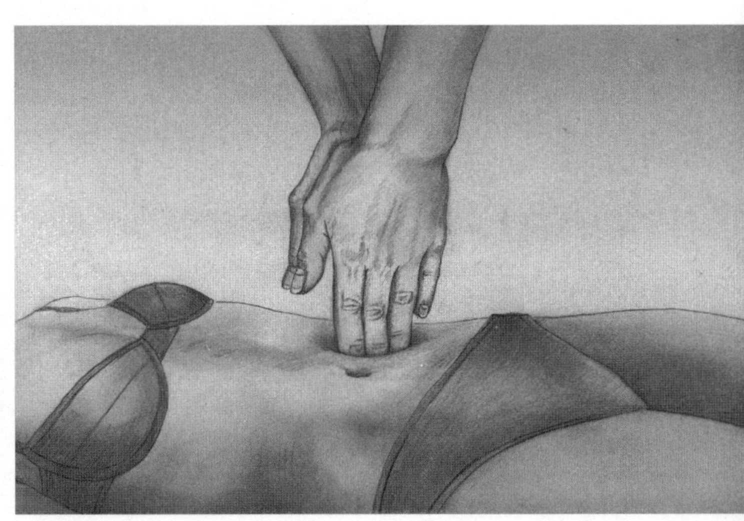
Fig 3-16

c. Then move 3 inches above the navel, pushing down in the center of the abdomen for 2 seconds. Total time: 1 1/2 minutes.

I have noticed that many patients have a tight knot, an uncomfortable lump, or an area of pain in the abdomen. When those spots of tension are pressed, they will relax—sometimes right away. In follow-up visits, with this same

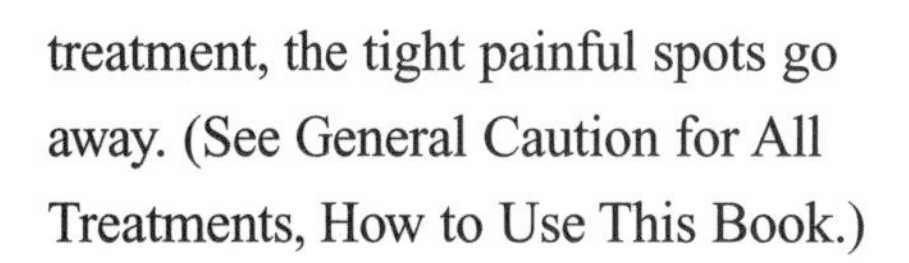
treatment, the tight painful spots go away. (See General Caution for All Treatments, How to Use This Book.)

2. With your client face down, hold the lower legs with both hands. Place your fingers underneath the shins and your thumbs in the middle of the calf muscles (Fig. 3-17). Press down with both thumbs on 5 different points along the center line of the muscle, moving up toward the knee, and then 5 more points along the inside edge. Do both legs at once. Total time: 1 minute.

3. Place some massage lotion along the tendon and soft tissues underneath it. Using both hands, place the thumbs on one side under the Achilles tendon, your index fingers on the other side. Squeezing your fingers and thumbs together, slide from the heel bone along the tendon up the leg 4 inches (Fig. 3-18). Stroke back down to the heel bone. Do 3 minutes on each side.

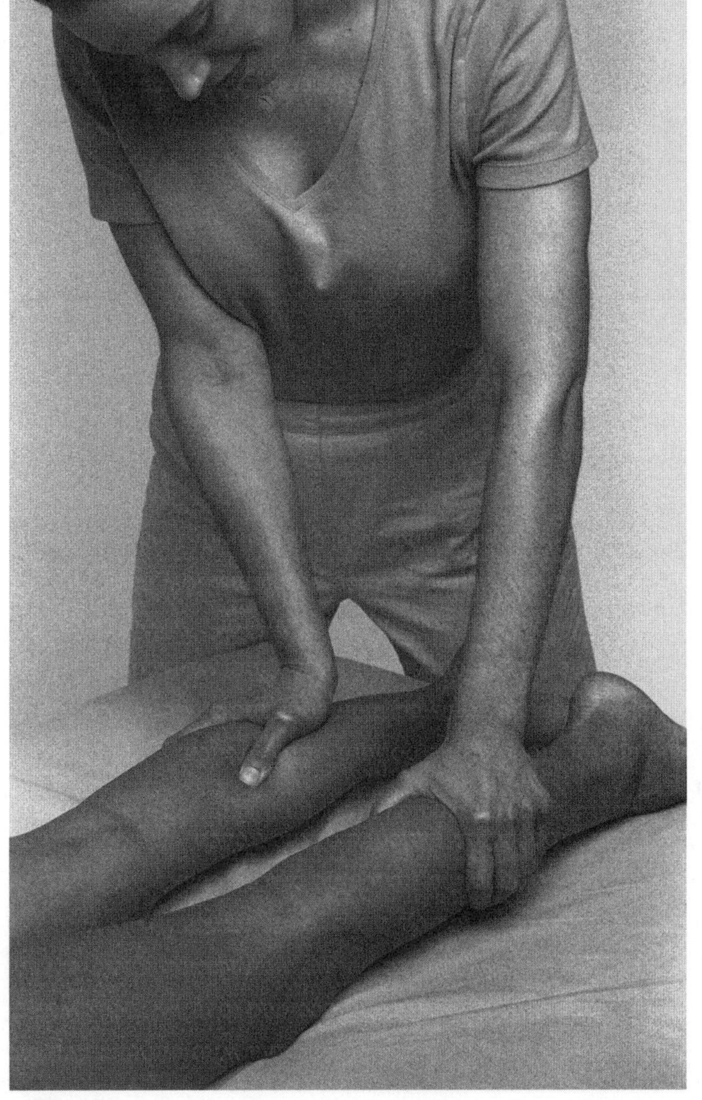

Fig 3-17

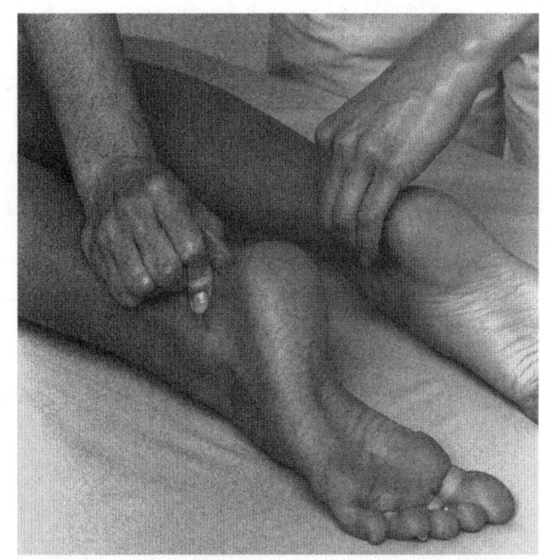

Fig 3-18

Nada Brahma: Listening to the Unstruck Melody

(approximately 16 minutes)

"IF YOU WILL MEDITATE ON THE PRIMAL SOUND YOU WILL SEE THE UNSEEN, YOU WILL HEAR THE UNHEARD, AND YOU WILL FEEL THE UNFEELABLE."

—YOGI BHAJAN[5]

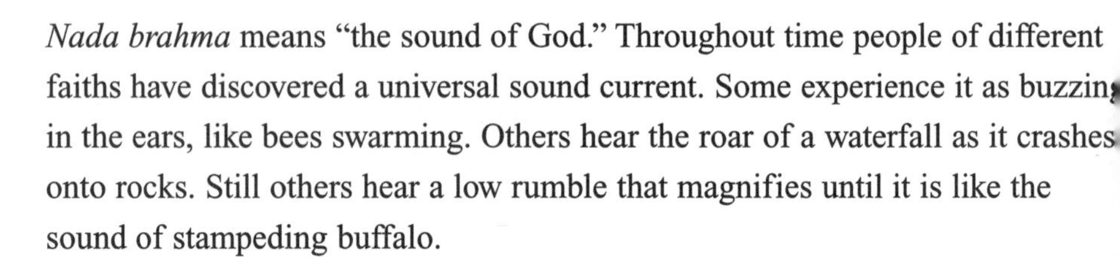

Nada brahma means "the sound of God." Throughout time people of different faiths have discovered a universal sound current. Some experience it as buzzing in the ears, like bees swarming. Others hear the roar of a waterfall as it crashes onto rocks. Still others hear a low rumble that magnifies until it is like the sound of stampeding buffalo.

Those following that sound find that it leads to realms of perception that are beyond the visible world. Those who meditate on the inner sound discover that the boundaries of the human body do not interfere with happiness. Happiness is meditating on the music of your unstruck instrument. "This sound is the source of all manifestations.... The knower of the mystery of sound knows the mystery of the whole universe[6]."

1. Have your client lie on the back, face up. Sit close to the head.

a. Place your index fingers over the small fold of tissue near the ear canal and press in firmly. This will close the ear canal. Your thumbs press down on the forehead above the eyebrows with great pressure for 1 minute (Fig. 3-19).

b. Then bend the middle fingers so the large knuckle presses the side of the head, keeping the ear canal closed for 30 seconds more.

c. Have your client listen to the internal "sound" that exists when the ear canal is closed. There are two tones to distinguish—a lower, rumbling, roaring sound, and a much higher buzzing sound like a swarm of bees. Ask your client to concentrate on the higher pitched sound. This sound is present all the time, needs no instrument to elicit it, and is part of the cosmic sound current called God's name. Yogis for eons have called this the "unstruck melody."

d. [Do it yourself now. Close your ears off with each forefinger and listen to the sound that has the highest pitch. There are more than two frequencies: choose one of them and concentrate on it for 2 minutes. Enjoy

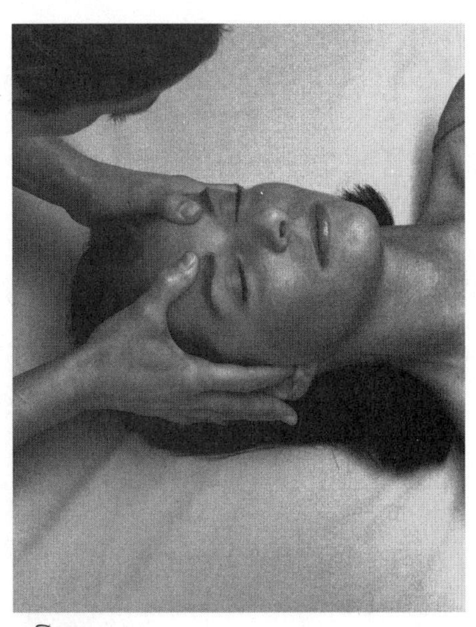

Fig 3-19

the sound. When you can concentrate longer, follow the sound and find the joy it brings. Be curious. You may find surprises there.]

Step 1 concentrates energy and blood flow in the head area. You can also open new pathways to the interior regions of the client. Suggestion: Extend the time of the first step so your client can hear and experience more.

2. Your thumbs still touch the forehead above the eyes, as in Step 1 (refer to Fig. 3-19). Drag the skin toward the hairline, so the eyebrows slide up higher, with your forefingers still covering the ear openings, for 1 minute.

3. Leaving your thumbs above the eyebrows, rotate your hands so that the knuckles of the index fingers press below the cheekbone close to the nose for 30 seconds (Fig. 3-20).

4. Stand to the left side of your client. Place your right thumb at the third eye point (in the middle of the forehead above the nose) and the left thumb on the middle of the chin (Fig. 3-21). Press down slowly and firmly for 1 minute. The client's mouth may open.

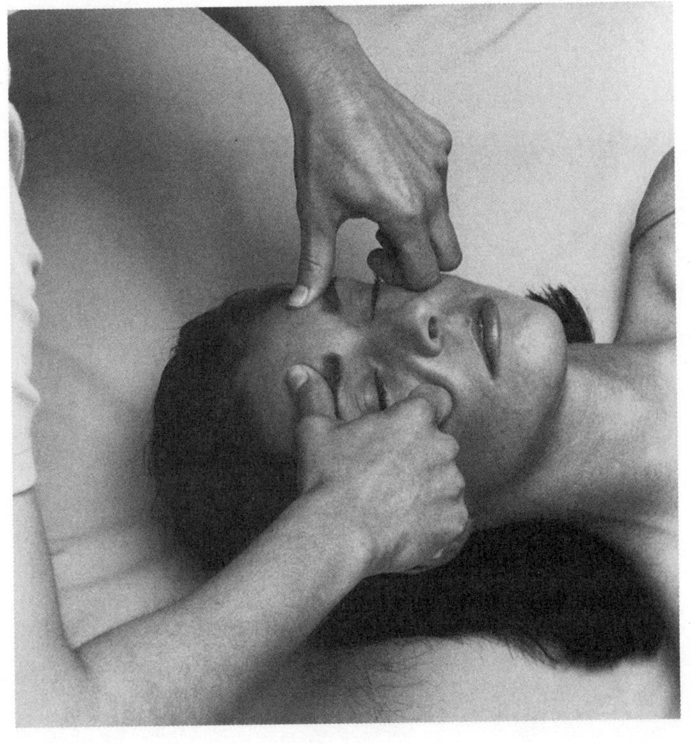

Fig 3-20

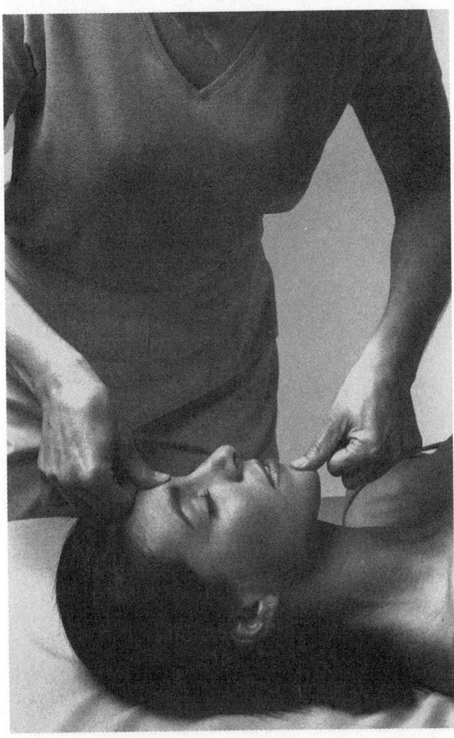

Fig 3-21

5. Sit at the head of the client. Curl your fingers underneath the base of the skull, cradling the rest of the head with the heels of your palms (Fig. 3-22). Then pull the neck toward your body for 1 minute.

6. Shift your fingers a little lower into the neck; the thumbs are above the ears (Fig. 3-23). Push the fingers into the neck rotating the head backwards and pull toward your body for 1 minute. This tractioning movement makes the neck longer. Lift the head up a few inches as you do this for 15 seconds.

7. Place the heel of your hands on the forehead, while curling your fingers underneath the cheekbones, and pull up (Fig. 3-24). Keeping your palms on the forehead, squeeze your fingers towards the heel of your hands for 1 minute.

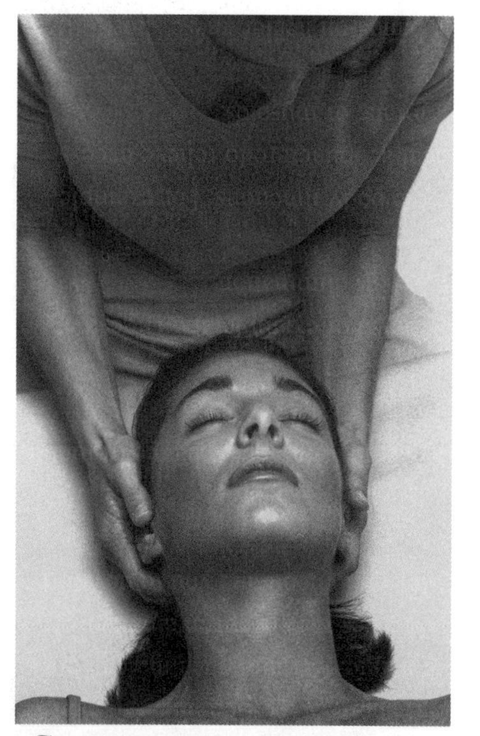

Fig 3-22

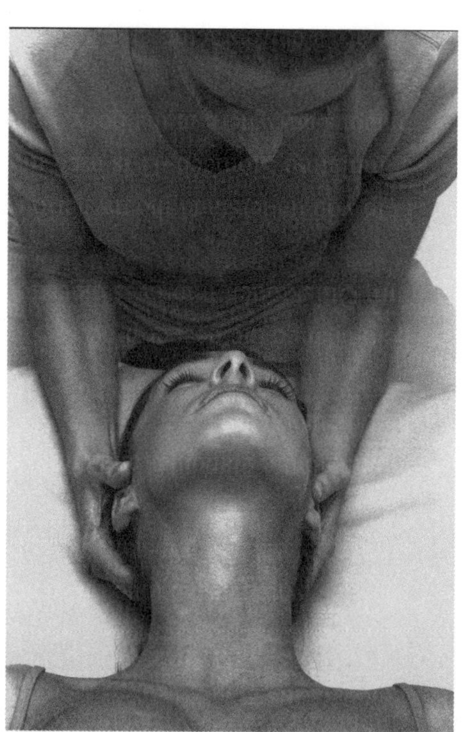

Fig 3-23

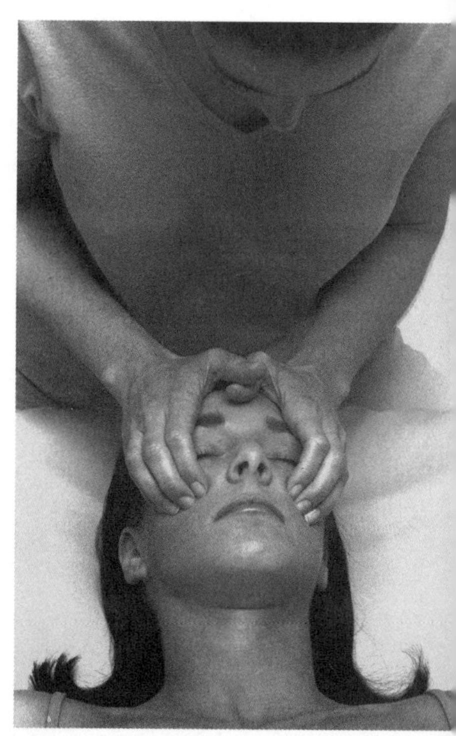

Fig 3-24

8. Place your first 3 fingertips on the jaw muscles, pulling the head toward yourself, and do a slow, deep counter-clockwise massage for 1 minute (Fig. 3-25). Then add the little finger for an additional 30 seconds.

9. Use a small amount of massage lotion, and take 20 seconds total time for this step.

a. Place your palms on the forehead (Fig. 3-26), and slowly slide them down over the face to the chin. Do it one time.

b. Then place the knife edge of both hands together on the middle of the forehead and press down firmly as you slide along the forehead over the temples to the ears (Fig. 3-27). Do this once.

10. Sit at the head of your client. Tap the center of the forehead with your fingertips for 40 to 60 seconds (Fig. 3-28). Yogi Bhajan tapped 81 times when he demonstrated this technique.

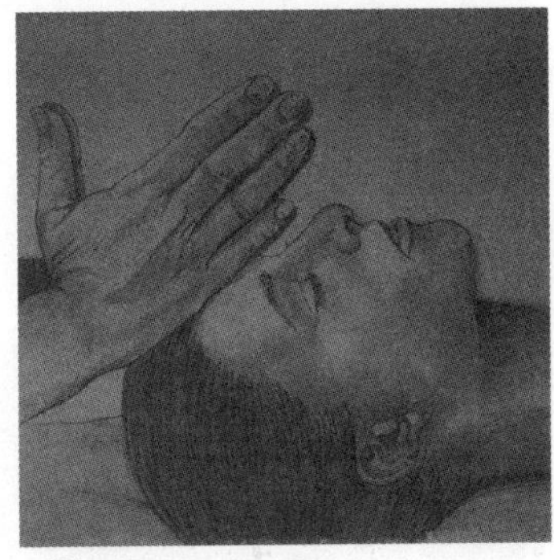

Fig 3-27

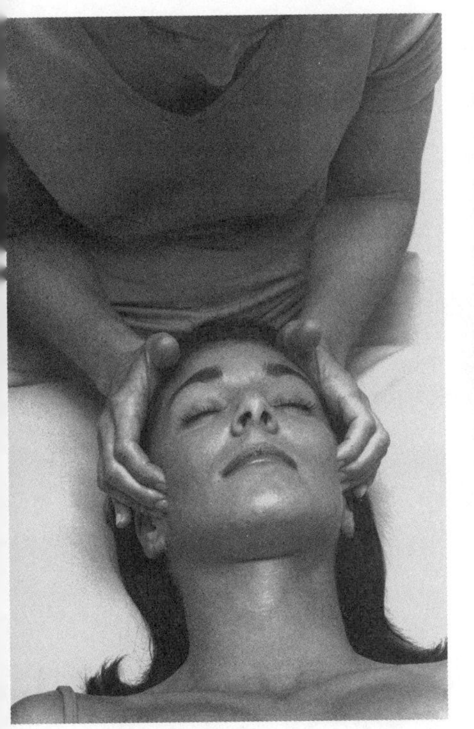

Fig 3-25

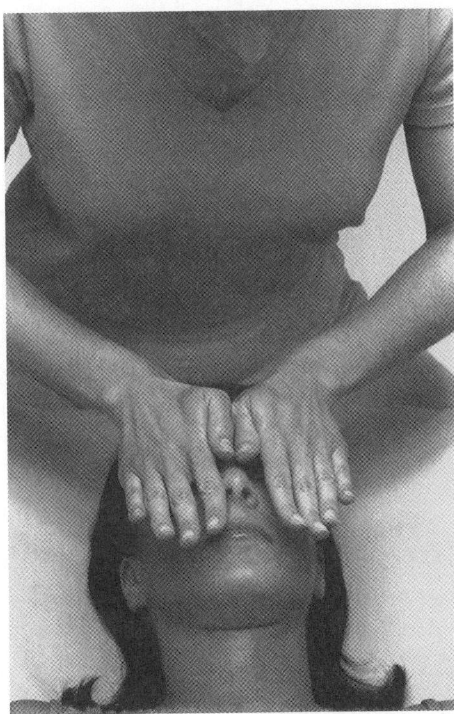

Fig 3-26

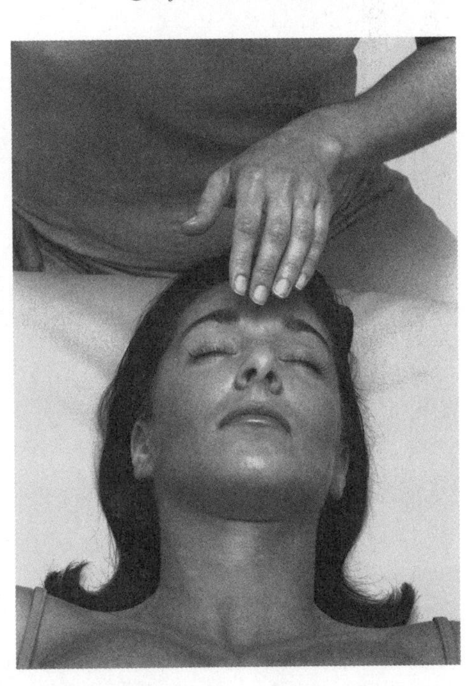

Fig 3-28

11. Have the client turn over, face down. Move to the left side and place the heel of your left hand on the left side of T-4. Place the heel of the right palm on the right side of L-5 (Fig. 3-29 and Fig. 3-29a).

a. Press straight down as much as you can with your right hand. Keep your right arm straight, using your body weight to produce pressure. Then slide your right palm 2 inches farther up the lower back muscles (still on the right side), pressing down again in the same manner. Repeat again 2 more times, moving your right hand 2 more inches up the back each time. Total time: 20 seconds.

b. Then change sides of the table. Place your right hand on the right side of T-4 as in the first part of this step. With your left hand on the left lower back muscles, repeat the same movements you did in the first part of this step, for about 30 seconds.

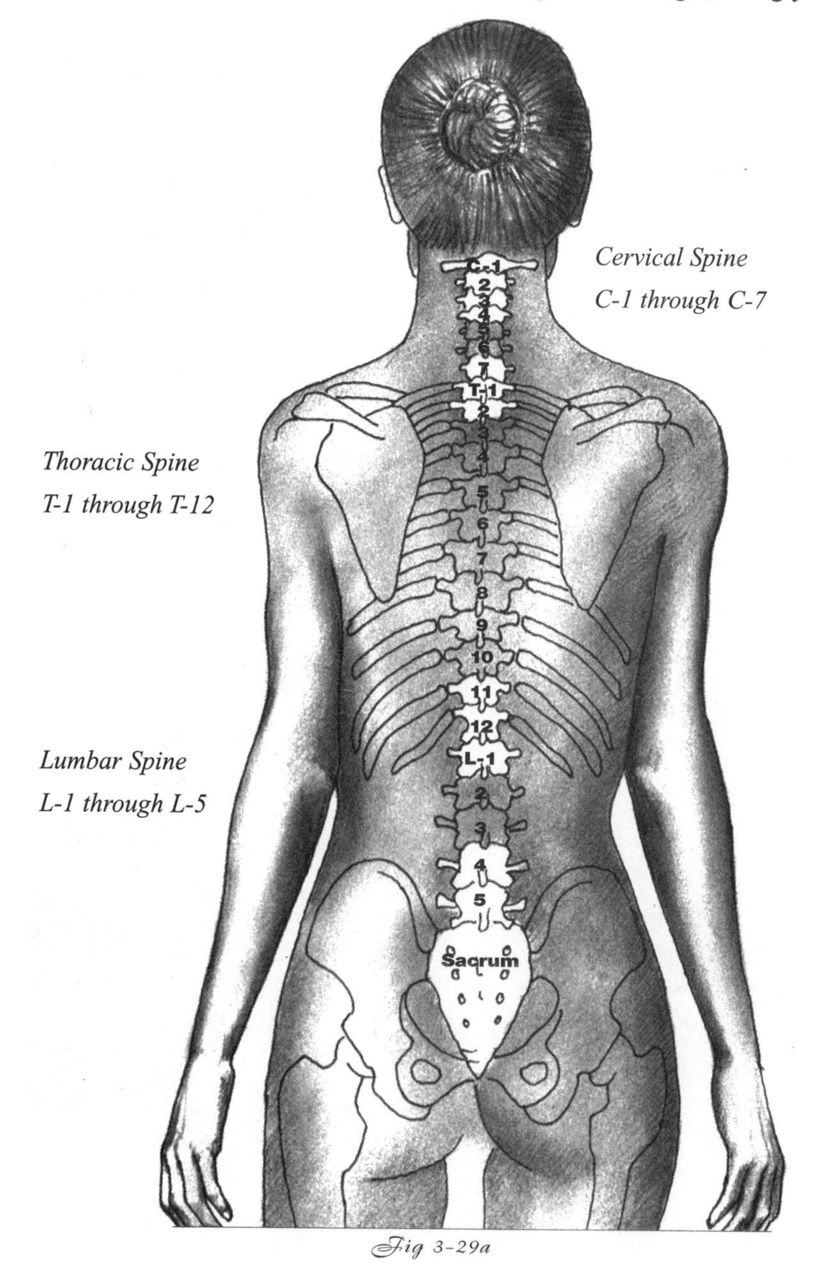

Fig 3-29a

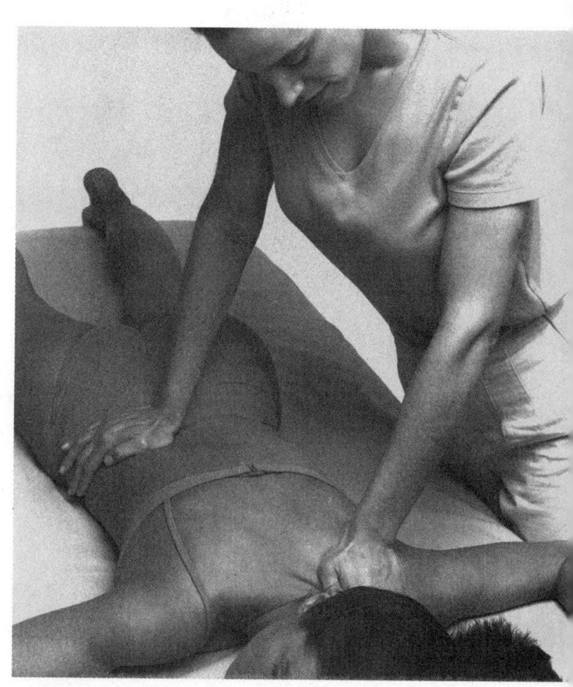

Fig 3-29

12. Move to the left side of your client. Your left palm covers the bony processes in the middle of the spine at T-4, fingers grasping the shoulder muscles. The right hand is palm-down on the sacrum, fingers curled on top of the tailbone (Fig. 3-30). Concentrate on your sacrum contact.

a. Keep your right arm straight as you push down with your body weight onto the sacrum. Make sure that you feel the body move as you push down. Use a slow, controlled "body-drop" movement.

Then shift to the left hand, and repeat the same downward push, using your body weight. Your right (sacrum) hand stays in place. You are performing a seesaw movement from one hand to the other. Seesaw back and forth for 15 seconds.

b. The left hand moves to position 2 (Fig. 3-30). You seesaw back and forth between the hands for 15 seconds again. Then move to positions 3 and 4 repeating the seesaw motion. Each position is 2 inches farther down the back toward the other hand. Time: 1 minute.

c. Move the left hand to the upper back, fingers grasping the shoulder muscles. Then repeat the movements with the right hand, moving up the spine and pressing on 3 areas:

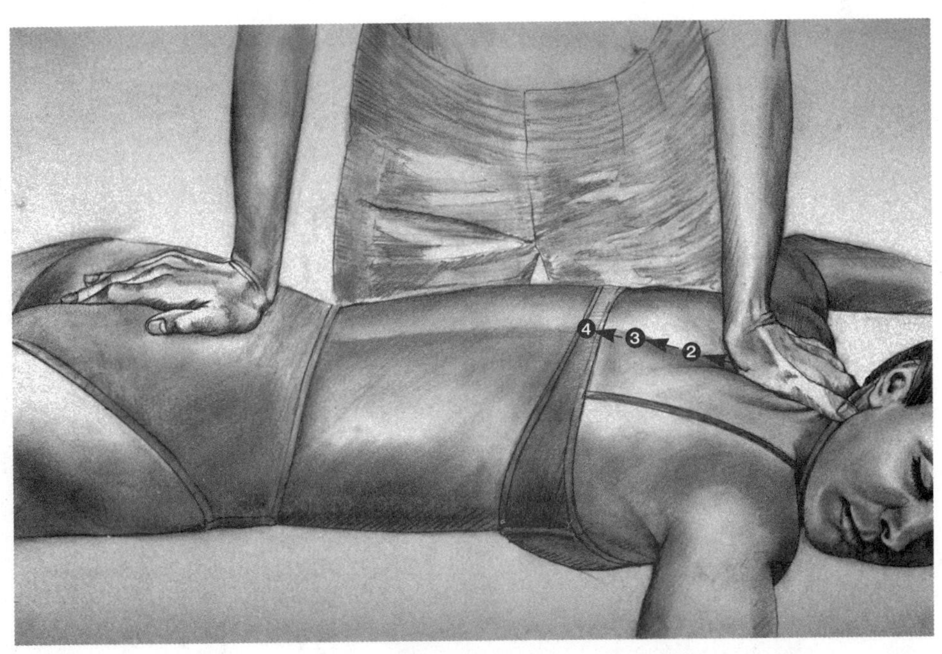

Fig 3-30

2 inches above the sacrum, 2 inches farther up the spine, 2 more inches towards the head (Fig. 3-31). Time: 1 minute.

Then repeat again, starting from the T-9 level, seesawing between your hands for 15 seconds, and repeating at positions 2, 3, and 4. Then move the left hand back to position 3, seesawing again for 15 seconds.

Repeat at position 2. Each time, your hand moves 2 inches more (Fig. 3-32). Take 1 1/2 minutes.

Move the left hand back to the lower shoulder blade (T-9). Use the seesaw motion for 15 seconds. Next move the right hand 2 inches farther up the spine to position 2, seesawing again for 15 seconds. Repeat at positions 3 and 4 (Fig. 3-33). Time: 1 minute.

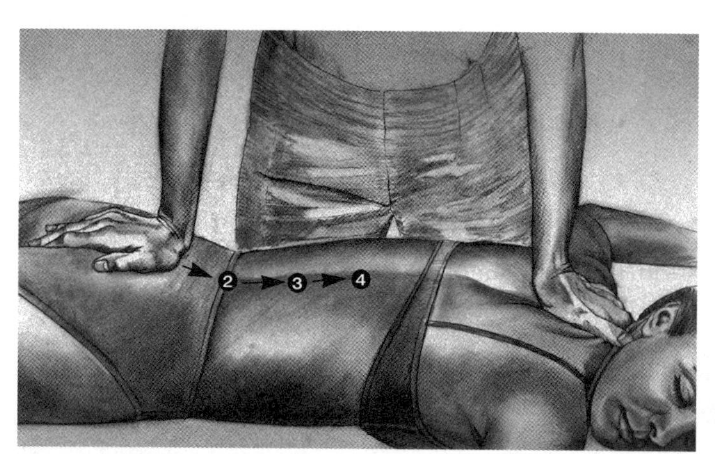

Fig 3-31

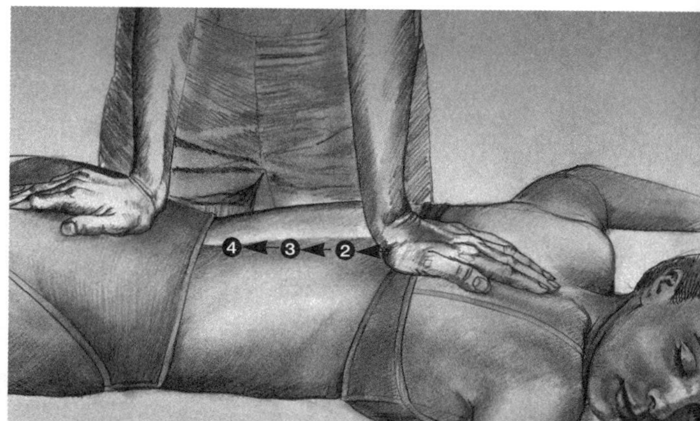

Fig 3-32

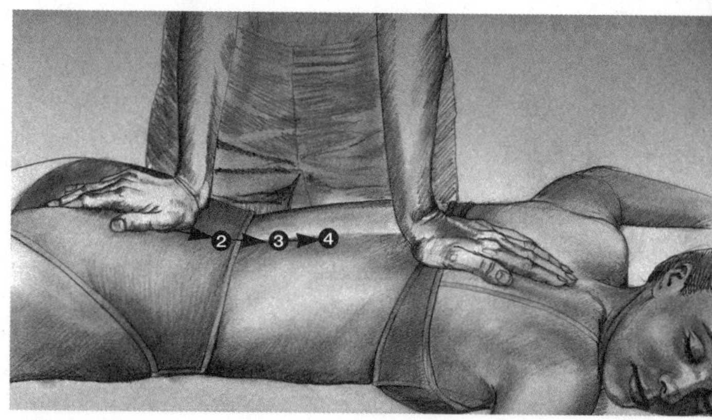

Fig 3-33

Surrender the Stress

(34 1/2 minutes)

IF YOU FEEL THAT A PERSON'S PROBLEMS ARE CAUSED BY STRESS, THEN THIS TREATMENT IS INDICATED. SO EVERYONE YOU KNOW WILL PROBABLY NEED THIS MASSAGE.

All regions, except in Step 7, are massaged for 3 minutes using a circular motion.

Practitioner intention: merge in subtle form with the particles of your client. Be there 100 percent, so much so that the boundaries between you dissolve—all of your being as one unit together. It will happen anyway. There is no difference between the two of you—you are only one.

1. Your client is lying face up. Sit at her head. Feel behind the fold of the ears until you find a dimple in the bone (Fig. 3-34). Massage this point in a rotary motion: first clockwise for 90 seconds; then counter-clockwise for 90 seconds.

2. With a heavy pressure, massage the ribs on the side of the body. Begin with your fingers touching the armpits, stroking up and down along the sides of the body using strong pressure (Fig. 3-35). Move from your starting position down the sides inch-by-inch, sliding over the ribs; moving up, then down in a rhythm you enjoy (Fig. 3-36). Finish at the waistline where the ribs end. Take 3 minutes. If you

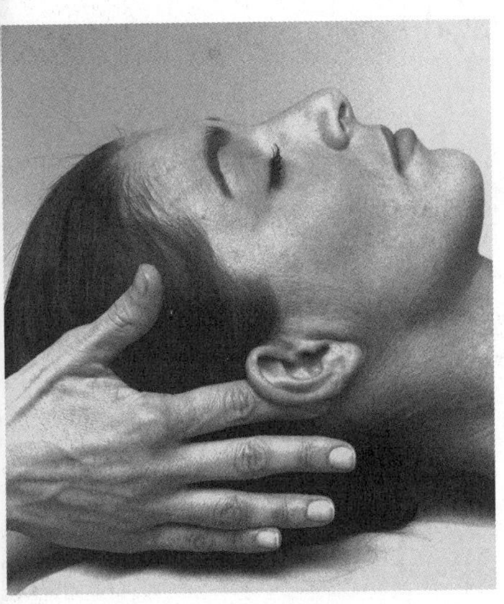

Fig 3-34

Fig 3-35

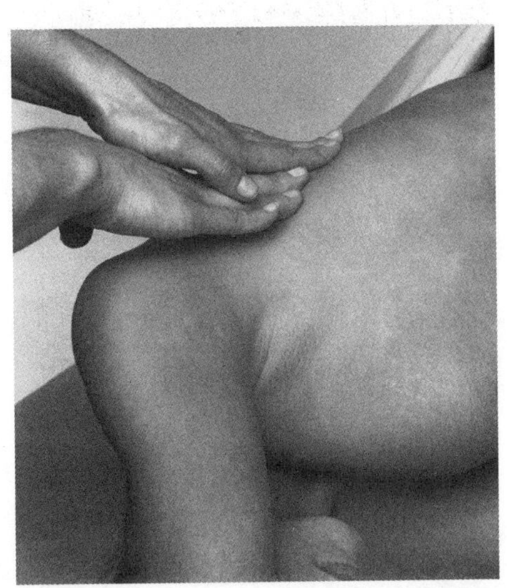

Fig 3-36

need to massage back up the sides to the armpits to finish the time, go ahead.

3. Massage the upper abdomen, using the knife edge of both hands. Push as deep as you can under the lower edge of the rib cage, doing both sides at the same time (Fig. 3-37). Use a variety of motions. Push with both hands at the same time, then alternate the left and right hands.

Remind your client to relax in rhythm with your pushing and pulling. Relaxation is achieved by breathing deeper, by sighing, by laughing, or by having your client pump the stomach in and out 5 times. Choose one or more of these actions, encouraging your client as you go. Continue for 3 minutes.

In Step 3, sensations can rise to the shoulders, arms, chest, or forehead. One side can be tighter than the other, and you may feel a lump when you apply deep pressure. When the abdominal muscles are tight it is difficult to go under the ribs.

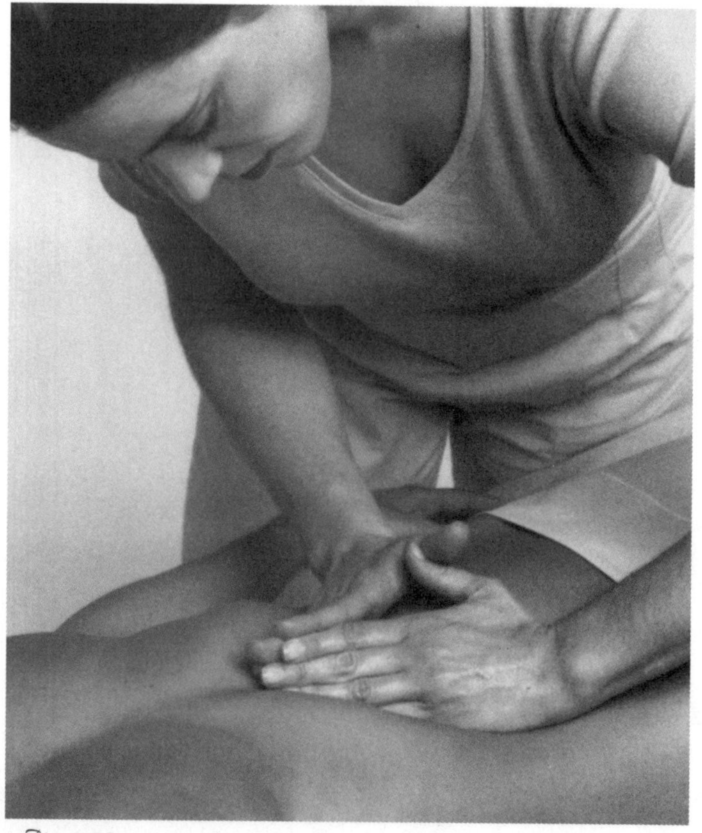

Fig 3-37

4. Massage the entire region inside the bowl formed in the lower abdomen by the front of the hip bones and the pubic bone for 3 minutes (Figs. 3-38 and 3-39). Standing near the thigh, facing the head, lean down into the groin area.

a. Keep your hands parallel to the sides of the triangle. Slide your hands back and forth. Move your hands closer together, continuing to stroke down towards the pubic bone, then back up the abdomen. Massage as much of the triangle as you can.

b. Next massage the areas you have not touched, using a circular motion with your fists. Use your fingertips if fists cause pain on tight or lumpy areas. (See General Caution for All Treatments.) You can change positions to face the client's feet when you need a new perspective.

c. Push deeply with both knife-edge hands into the lower abdomen, stroking the abdomen back and forth. Pull your hands back towards you, dragging the tissues; and then push back towards the pubic bone. Stay within the triangle as you move farther up the abdomen.

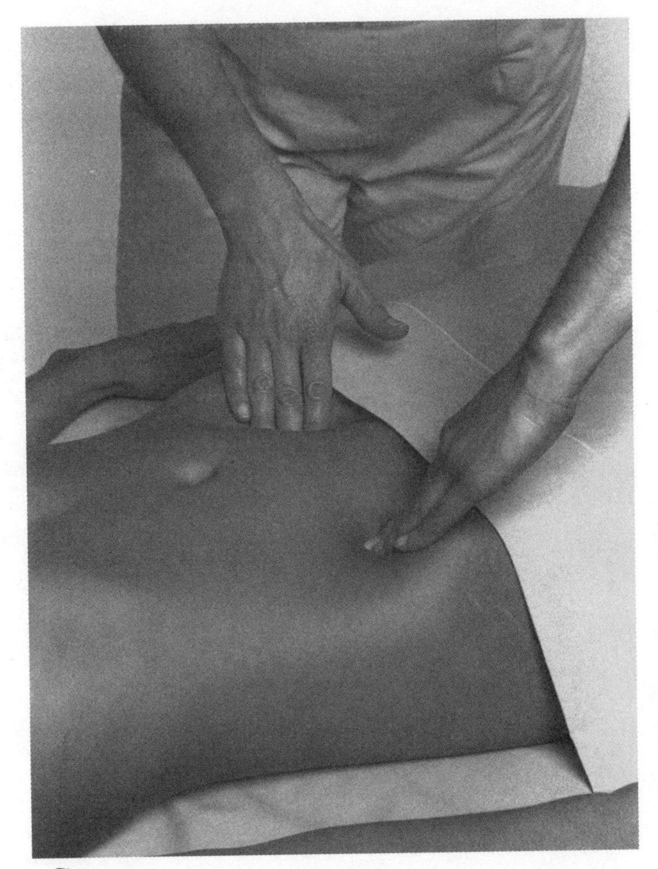

Fig 3-38

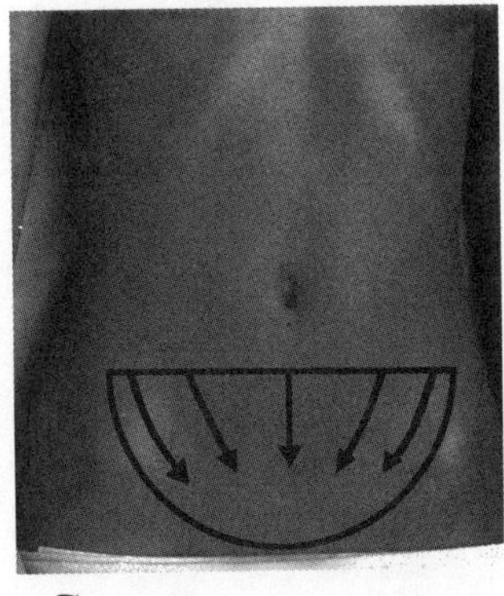

Fig 3-39

Step 4 is important when muscles at the ribs are rock hard or when one side is sore or painful from your massage in Step 3. Search to the right or left below the navel, and you will find tight spots to massage.

5. Most of the kneecap region is bony– the femur (thigh bone) joins the tibia and fibula (lower leg bones). There is not much muscle, so be careful in treatment. Massage for 3 minutes.

a. Massage the kneecap and surrounding tissue. Go all the way around the kneecap, from a few inches above the knee to a few inches below. Do this part with some firmness but be careful with the kneecap itself (Fig. 3-40).

b. Use your palms to massage either side of the knee caps, sliding down toward the feet then up toward the hip (Fig. 3-41). Warm the knee with your movements. Move your palms to the sides of the knees, continuing the same strokes. Now add some circular stroking. Then continue with one hand above the kneecap, the other below.

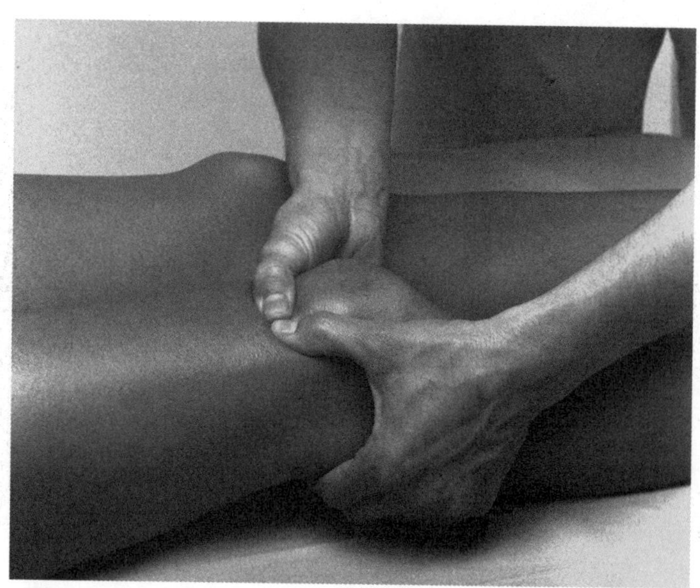

Fig 3-40

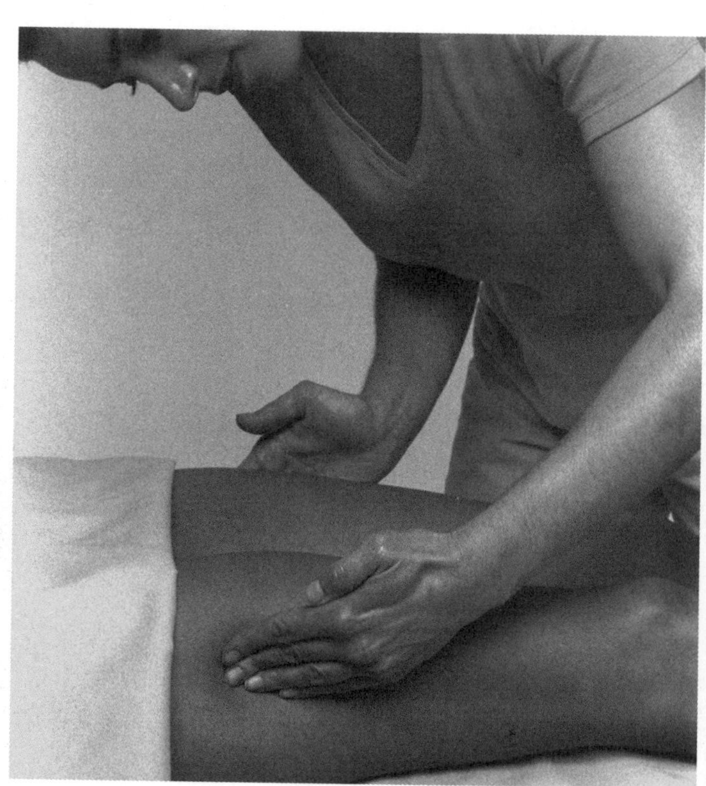

Fig 3-41

6. Your client turns over, facing down. Massage the Achilles tendons using 3 hand positions:

a. Start with both hands wrapped around one ankle, fingers underneath the ankle, the thumbs on top of the tendon, side-by-side. Then push the Achilles tendon down toward the floor, sliding from the heel bone 4 inches up the tendon (Fig. 3-42). Slide back down to the heel bone. Do this for 1 minute.

b. Use your thumbs and index fingers to squeeze the sides of the tendon, sliding from the heel bone up the leg 4 inches (Fig. 3-43). Next, stroke back to the heel. Move back and forth for 1 minute.

c. Wrap your hands around the Achilles tendon with your thumbs crossing. The fingers grasp the front of the ankle (Fig. 3-44). Squeeze your hands together, compressing the tendon, starting near the heel and working 4 inches up the lower leg for 1 minute.

7. Massage behind the knees—an area commonly overlooked. The area behind the knee is like an old storage closet that never sees the light of day.

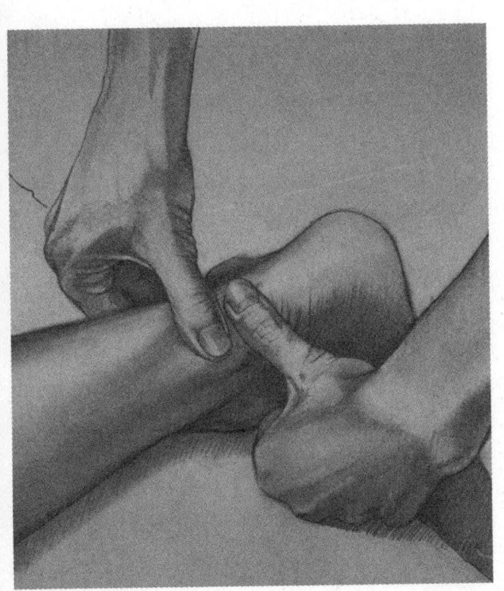

Fig 3-42

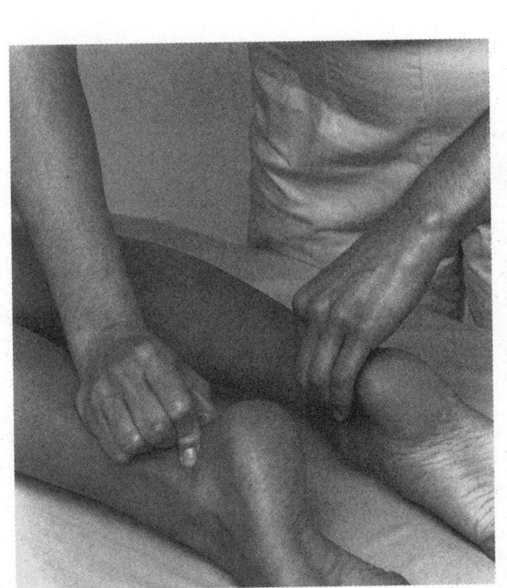

Fig 3-43

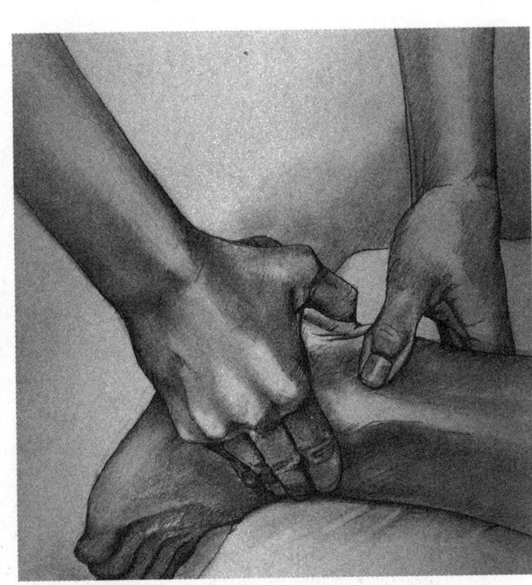

Fig 3-44

a. Using the heel of your hand, slide from below the knee into the soft center and above (Fig. 3-45). Then slide back down, turning around again, back and forth for 30 seconds.

b. Switch to your fingertips, sliding above the knee, then back below it (Fig. 3-46). Press the tendons on the outside of the knee and slide up and down in the center of the knee for 30 more seconds.

c. For 30 seconds more use your thumbs to slide and stroke through the back of the knee.

8. Massage the lower buttocks and upper thighs around the gluteal fold (Fig. 3-47) for 3 minutes. Massage from the inside corner of the buttocks near the tailbone to the outside near the hip socket. Move in 3-inch sections starting from the midline close to the tailbone. Use your fingertips to slide side-to-side, then up-and-down, in this 3-by-3 inch square of muscle tissue. Then move 3 inches towards the hip socket (the side of the body) repeating the strokes. Continue several times until you are at the hip socket. Massage both sides at the same time.

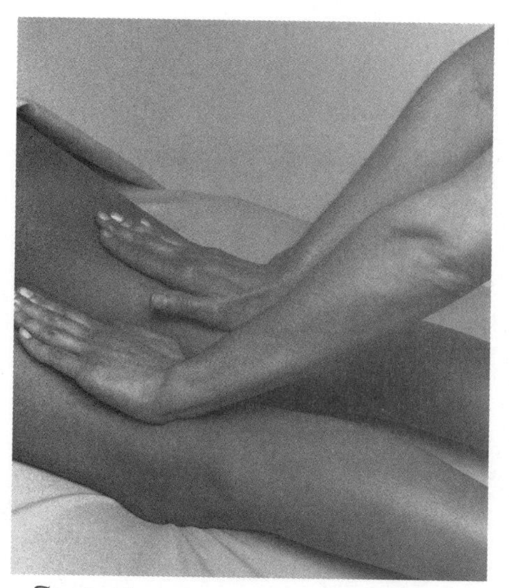

Fig 3-45

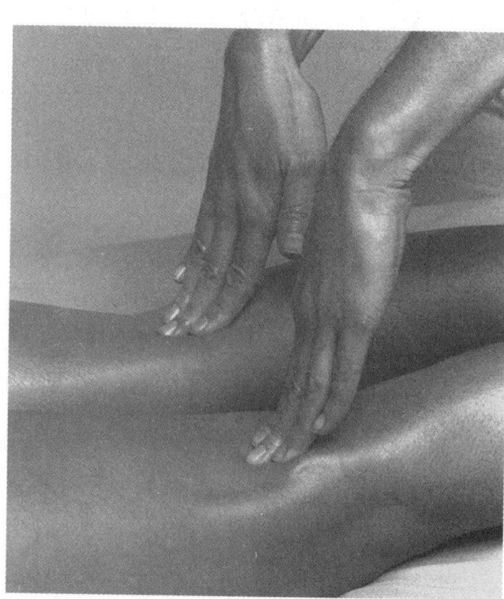

Fig 3-46

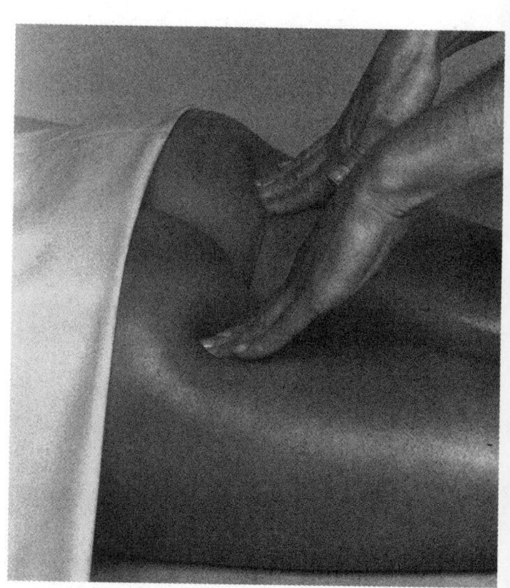

Fig 3-47

9. Massage the muscles next to the spine at the L-5 level (Fig. 3-48). This can be an area of deep tensions, where much structural pressure collects. Use your strength to massage deeply for the full 3 minutes. You can use your thumbs, the knuckles of your index and middle fingers, and your finger-tips to probe as deeply as possible. Or you can bend your arms, placing your hands near your shoulders, and use your elbows on the lower back muscles at the base of the back.

10. Use your fingers to slide along the back muscles from the base of the lower back (where you started in Step 9) all the way to the neck with medium pressure (Fig. 3-49). Do this 5 or 6 times in the 3 minutes you take for this step.

11. Massage from the shoulder muscles to below the shoulder blades using the fingertips, from the base of the neck to the 2 shoulder blades, with heavy pressure (Fig. 3-50). Make sure to stroke across the top of the shoulder blades, on the outside edge of the

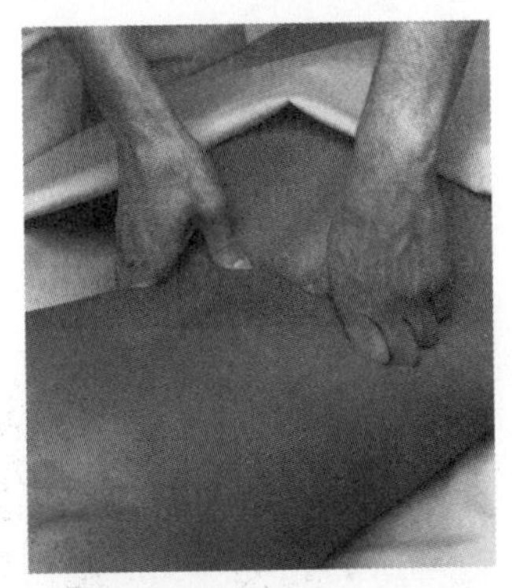

Fig 3-48

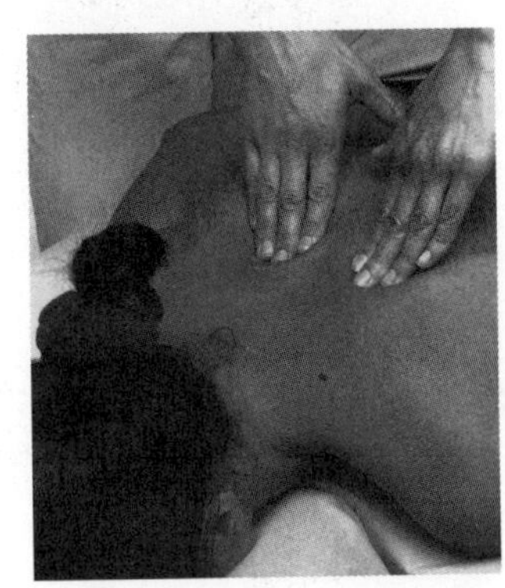

Fig 3-49

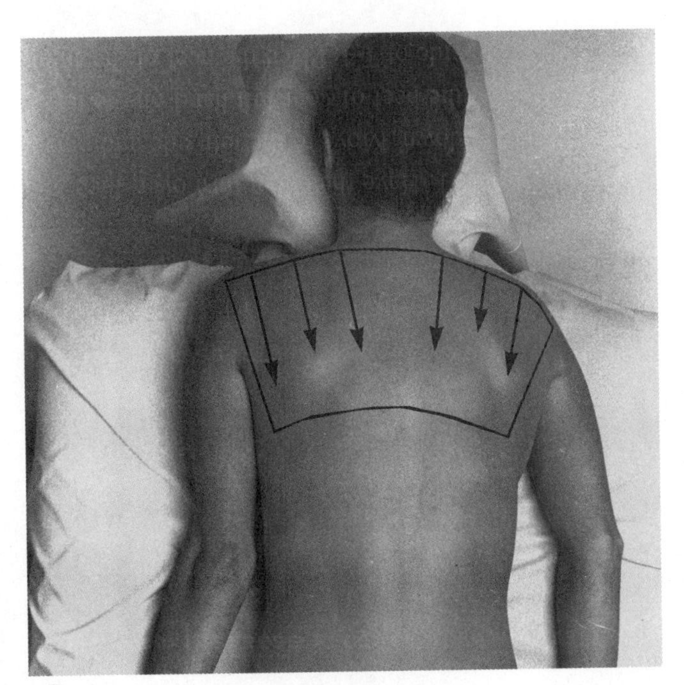

Fig 3-50

blades, as well as along the spine between the blades. Total time: 3 minutes.

12. Massage the soft tissues at the top of the neck and across the base of the skull for 3 minutes (Fig. 3-51). This is a free-form step, so massage the way you like.

Comment

In Step 3, when the abdominals are as hard as the ribs, the client may have one or more of these symptoms: migraines, stress headaches, stiff neck, throat problems, tight shoulders, liver or gall bladder problems, stomach symptoms, constipation, fatigue, tiredness of the whole body, or lower back pain. Repeating this treatment until the abdominals loosen alleviates these problems. Teach your client to do **long deep breathing** if you find much tightness at or under the ribs in this step.

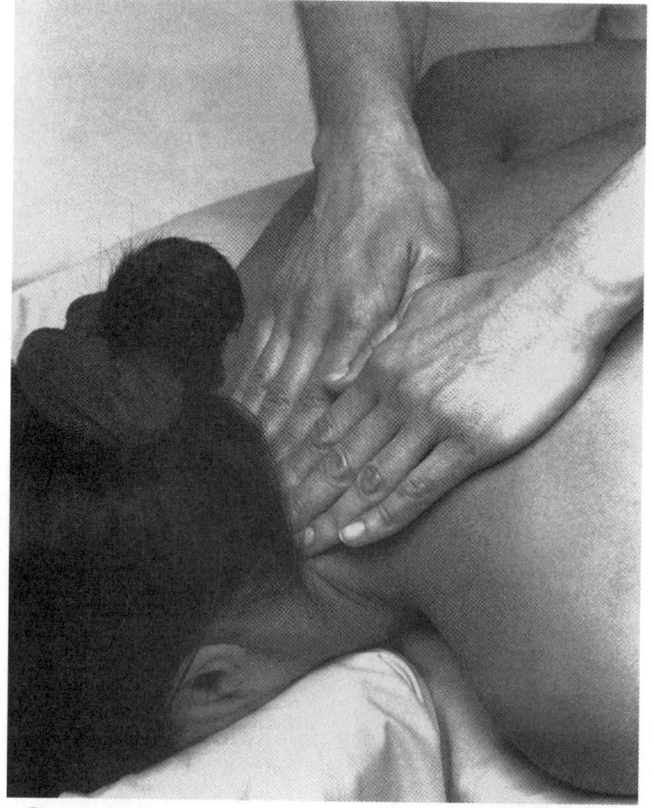

Fig 3-51

Quicktouch Treatments

Quicktouch treatments are brief—from 1 to 8 1/2 minutes long. They provide instant change and serve many purposes. They're simple, easy to do, and can be performed by anyone on a bed, a futon, a massage table, an adjusting table, or on top of a folded wool blanket on the floor. Most of them can be done with clothes on, and the results are surprising.

Quicktouch treatments:

- stimulate change and healing when time is short. A focused intent to heal concentrated over a short time can create magic. Certainly healing can begin in a Quicktouch Treatment. Healing experiences may occur in a matter of seconds, whether the touch is gentle or strong. I encourage you to develop strong beliefs about instant healing events.

- stimulate the glandular and circulatory systems for a quick change of mood and metabolism.

- help change the deeper processes in the body. For example, the Digestive Fire Quicktouch improves digestion and assists elimination.

- help you understand the mysterious way the body functions. For example, stimulating Stomach-41 is used in classical acupuncture to relieve excess mucous anywhere in the body—sinuses, joints, or muscles.

If you are a chiropractor, an osteopath, or a hands-on healer, these short treatments add value to the services that you already provide. In my profession (chiropractic) the doctor does not invest many minutes in a patient visit.
A chiropractic treatment yields results in 1 to 5 minutes. With a few exceptions the longest chiropractic treatment that I do is 15 minutes. So Quicktouch treatments augment my practice.

By contrast, many massage therapists do hour-long treatments, and specialized therapists may spend 1 1/4 to 2 hours on treatments. Even so, Quicktouch treatments can be used in these longer specialized treatments at the beginning, middle, or end. For example, you can use the Release Navel Tension Treatment to loosen the abdominal region during an hour-long massage.

Quicktouch treatments can also be used as "pre-healing" treatments or mini-massages, to warm up a patient before he sees a doctor. Massage therapists who visit office buildings for 10 to 20 minute on-site massages can also use them. Finally, Quicktouch treatments can be used by anyone to become more healthy, to increase the ability to relax, or to enhance sensuality in a relationship.

There are Quicktouch treatments for helping general pain and stiffness as well as for rejuvenating the body. They can relax the entire body. Or they can work on regions of the body: balancing the navel **chakra**[1] or adjusting the lower triangle (navel, lower abdomen, and hip regions). There are Quicktouch treatments for specific problems: relieving lower back pain, releasing chest or shoulder blade tension, and oxygenating the brain. And there are specific treatments for the feet, arms, shoulders, neck, and back.

Calming Quicktouch

(about 1 1/2 minutes)

IN FOOT REFLEXOLOGY, CHINESE MEDICINE, AND IN QUICKTOUCH TREATMENTS TOUCHING POINTS FAR AWAY FROM SYMPTOMS CAN BRING RELIEF. THIS FOOT MASSAGE TREATMENT IS AN EXAMPLE OF HOW MASSAGING THE FOOT CAN BANISH PAIN IN THE HEAD AND THROAT REGION.

The point massaged in this treatment is called Gushing Stream (ST-41) in Chinese medicine. It is on the stomach meridian. The stomach meridian starts under the eyes on the ridge of bone (infraorbital ridge) and travels down the body on both sides ending on the second toe. ST-41 is located on the front of the ankle in the depression between the two tendons of the big toe.

1. The client lies down on the back. Stand on the left side of the table and grasp the left toes with your left hand.

2. Now bend the foot and toes toward the floor as your right thumb massages in small circles between the tendons on the top of the foot (Fig. 4-01). Your thumb will just fit in this saddle. (If you want to be sure of the location of ST-41 have the client bend the foot toward the shin and watch the tendons protrude.) Massage for 40 seconds. Then switch to the right foot and repeat.

Comment

In my experience this treatment improves problems such as ankle pain, burning stomach pain, indigestion, sore throat, sinus problems, and headache. Other benefits mentioned by Yogi Bhajan include clearing the mind and helping to neutralize an overactive brain.

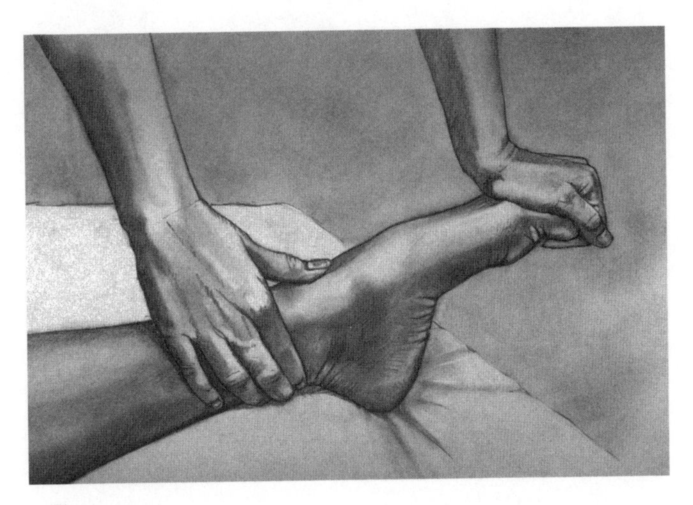

Fig 4-01

Lite Quicktouch Therapy

(about 1 minute)

This Quicktouch treatment helps spread the effects of other treatments over the entire body. Use it after an adjustment or a massage. You can help your client relax in a new way and integrate the experience of other treatments by touching lightly on different spots.

Move your hands slowly from head to foot, pinching softly here and finger-walking lightly there (Fig. 4-02). Then finish by running your hands palms-down, 6 inches above the body from the feet to the top of the head. This Quicktouch treatment is for 1 minute, though you can spend as much time as you want doing this subtle touching.

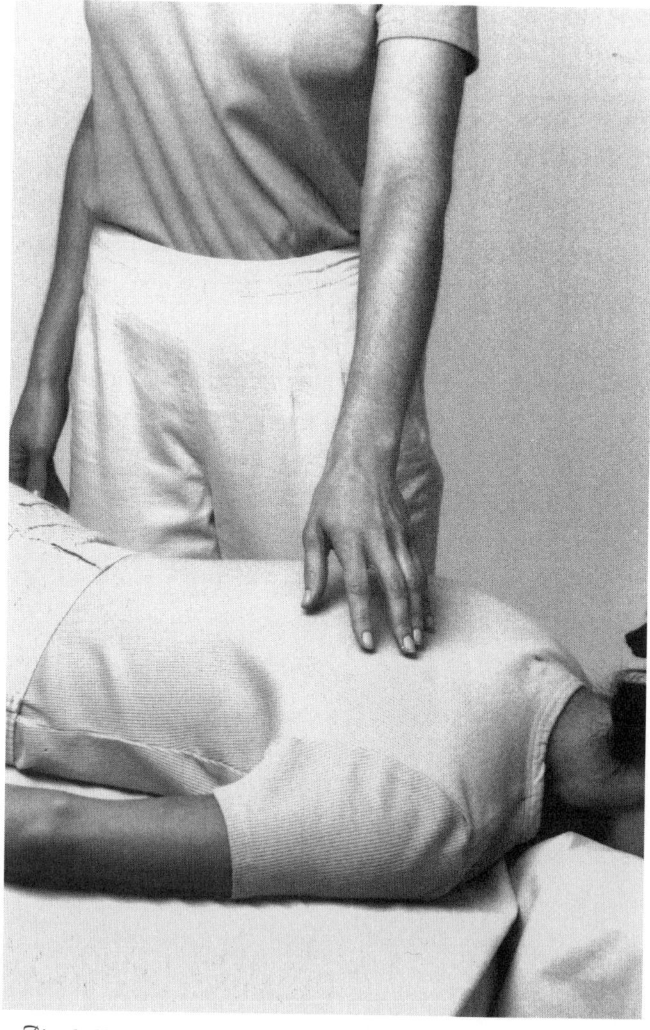

Fig 4-02

Arouse Vigor Quicktouch

(about 45 seconds)

In Step 1, this treatment helps release tension above and below the middle-back contact. The hand contacts are on either side of the spine at the T-11 and T-12 level. Steps 2 and 3 help relax the legs, the lower back, and the brain. If you have a massage table place your client so that the feet are over the end of the table. If you use the floor, place a thick pillow underneath the ankles so the foot has room to bend as you press down.

This treatment is over in a moment so be sure to do the steps with confidence. To expand your results ask your client to breathe deeply.

1. The client lies on the stomach. Stand to the left side of your client, placing both hands side-by-side in **collar mudra** at the lower middle back (Fig. 4-03). Your knuckles are on the right side of the spine, on the muscular ridge. Your thumbs on the left side press the muscles also. Lean down on your hand contact with strong pressure (equal on both sides) for 15 seconds.

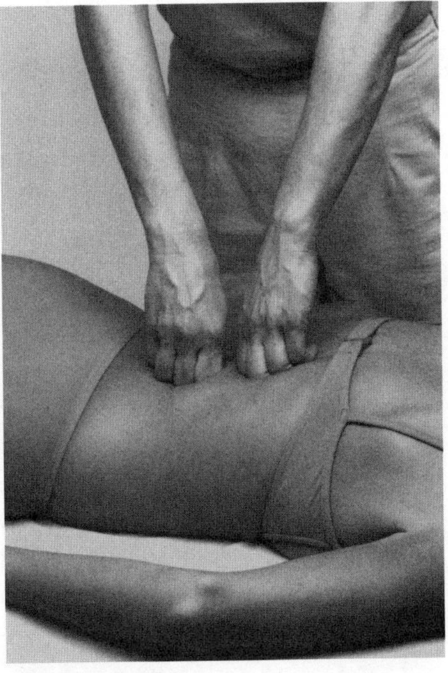

Fig 4-03

2. Place your thumbs on the calf muscle (2 or 3 inches below the knee, on the midline), and press deep into the tissue for 15 seconds (Fig. 4-04). Use your client's pain tolerance as a guide for the depth of your pressure.

3. Allow the client's feet to hang off the table (or put pillows under the ankles). Place the heel of your hands on the heel bones. Keep your elbows slightly bent, and push down with strength, stretching the Achilles tendon for 15 seconds (Fig. 4-05).

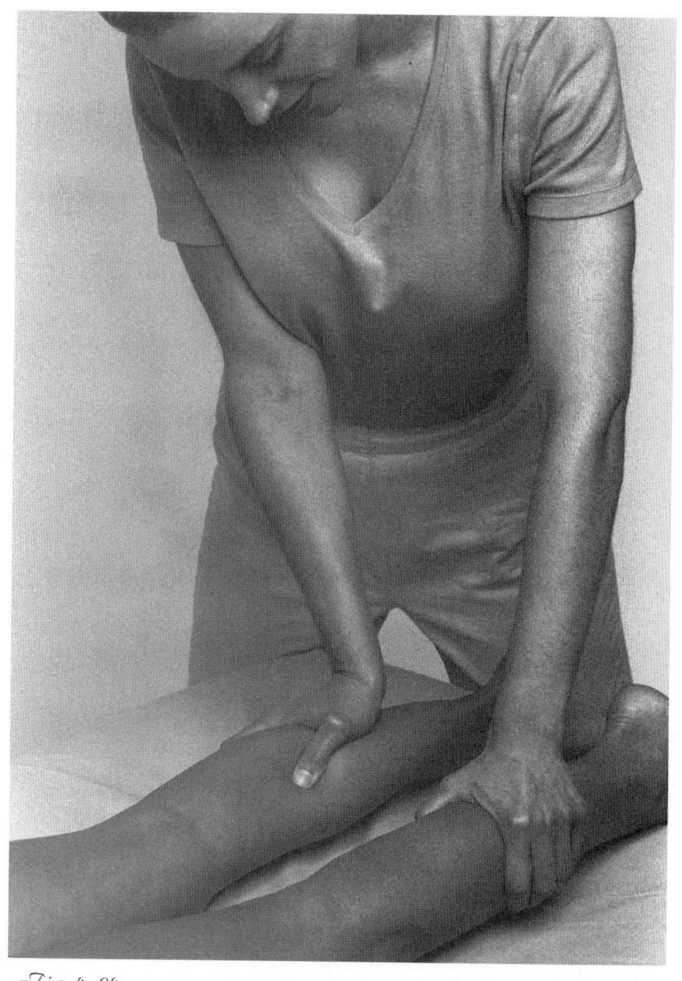

Fig 4-04

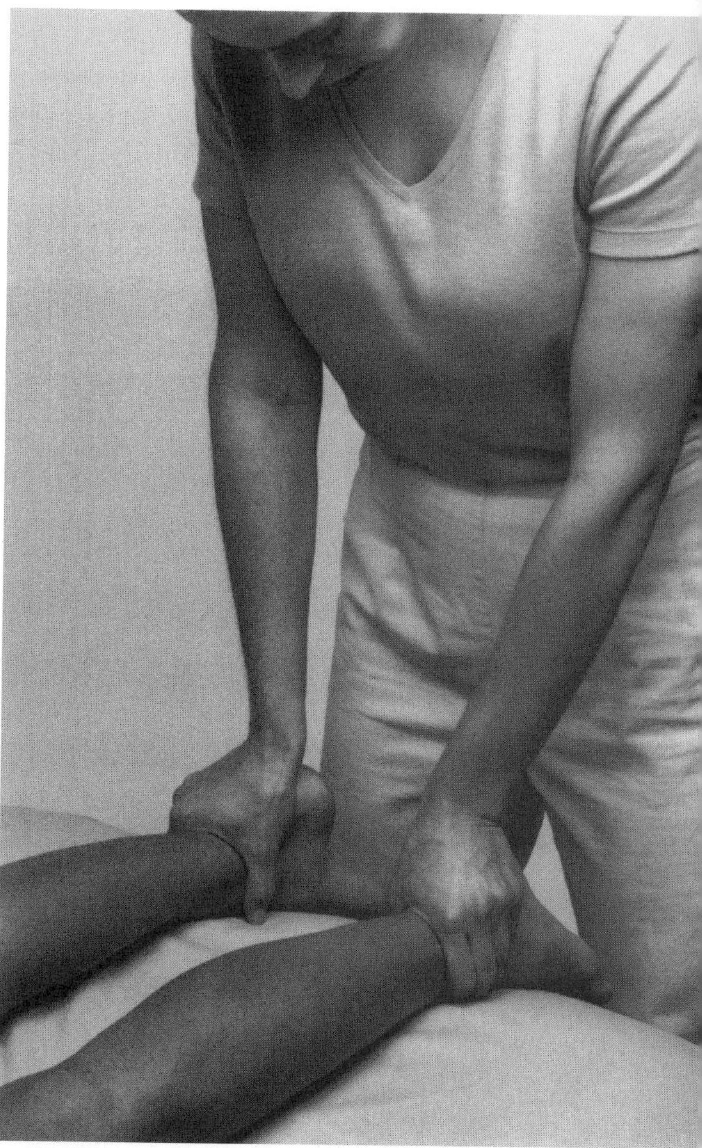

Fig 4-05

Head and Thymus Gland Quicktouch

(about 2 minutes)

"THIS TREATMENT IS FOR IMMEDIATE TENSION RELEASE, HELPFUL FOR PERSONALITIES WHO HAVE FEAR ATTACKING THEIR BODY, OR SUBCONSCIOUS BLOCKS THAT ATTACK THE BODY. IT IS AN ENJOYABLE RELEASE FROM SELF-NUISANCE. ALSO IN WOMEN WE HAVE FOUND THAT IT CAN HELP HEADACHES, EVEN MIGRAINES."

—YOGI BHAJAN[2]

The Head and Thymus Gland Quicktouch massage relaxes the face, relieves headaches, releases jaw tension, and helps relieve shoulder tension. This massage works well if you are treating office workers on site.

Having the head massaged is a sensual experience for many people who have tight jaw muscles and excessive tension in the scalp. It helps the client whose mind is filled with worry and too much thinking. It's no wonder that a tight scalp responds to being rubbed by caring hands. Nor is it surprising that the most common ailments we treat are headaches, migraines, and neck and jaw stress.

This treatment also stimulates the thymus gland. It is a small gland weighing 1 1/2 ounces just under the top third of the sternum. Known for thousands of years as the seat of life energy, a healthy, active thymus gland gives vibrant and positive health[3].

The regions of the head treated are: the temples; the upper lip point; the points next to the nostrils; the moon center (half way between the lower lip and chin); and the jaw muscles (that close the mouth). The jaw muscles control one of the most important joints in the upper body.

In all you will touch 13 areas of the client, each of them for 10 seconds. Some of them are important for the flow of the spinal fluid; others for proper motion and better jaw alignment. For a treatment time of 2 minutes and 10 seconds, do each step for 10 seconds, except Step 7 which takes 20 seconds.

1. Your client lies on the back. Be seated at the client's head for the entire treatment. Hook your forefingers on the ridge of bone above the eyes and adjacent to the nose (Fig. 4-06). Make sure your fingers are placed as deeply as possible without being on the eyes. Pull toward your body with pressure for 10 seconds.

2. Use your thumbs to press into the center of the temples with light pressure for 10 seconds (Fig. 4-07).

The temples are the sphenoid bone. The sphenoid bone joins with 12 other bones of the skull making it the pivot of all cranial motion. Some claim that if you influence the temples you move the entire skull. In Chinese medicine the center of the temples is called silken bamboo hollow.

3. Place your thumbs side-by-side on the midline of the head near the hairline, while the first 3 fingers of each hand press under the cheekbones (Fig. 4-08). If the client has a receding hairline or is bald, you can estimate the location of the hairline. With pressure move your fingers in circles for 10 seconds.

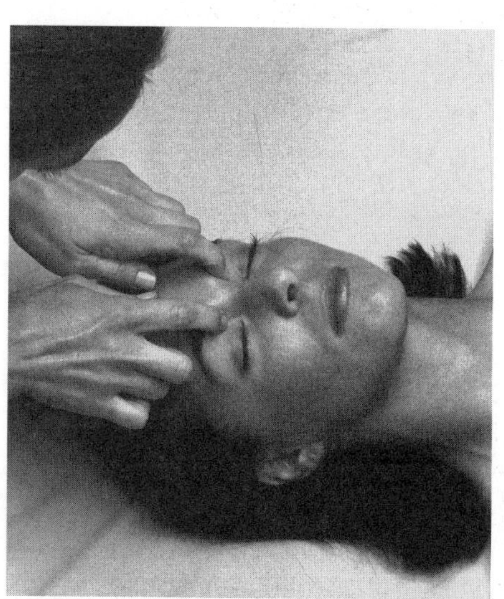

Fig 4-06

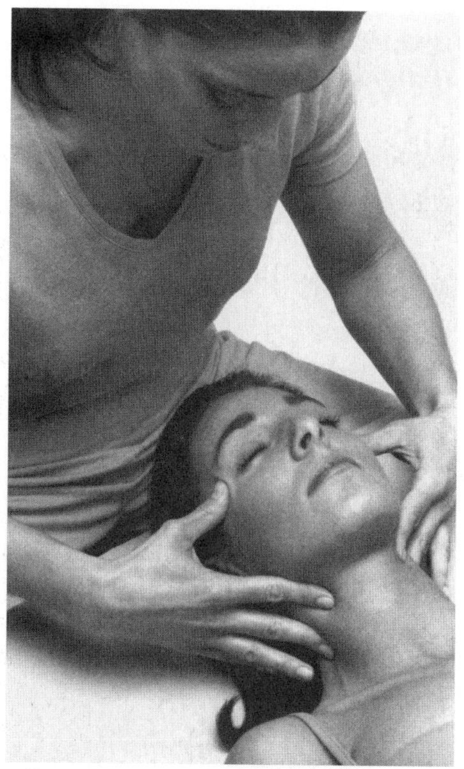

Fig 4-07

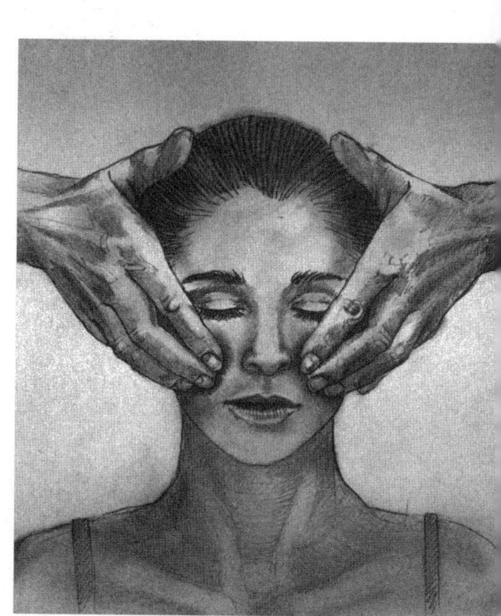

Fig 4-08

4. Place your thumbs adjacent to each nostril, while your fingers reach underneath the jawbone (Fig. 4-09). Firmly press your thumbs beside the nose, and press the fingers into the soft tissue under the jawbone for 10 seconds.

5. Place the heel of your hands against the side of the skull above the ears, and massage the jaw muscles by sliding your index and middle fingers back and forth with strong pressure for 10 seconds (Fig. 4-10).

6. Place the middle joint of your left index finger between the upper lip and the nose. At the same time, the middle knuckle of the right index finger presses halfway between the chin and the lower lip (Fig. 4-11). Press down with firm pressure on both points starting with a light touch, increasing in slow motion until you've reached the point of client pain tolerance. Hold for 10 seconds.

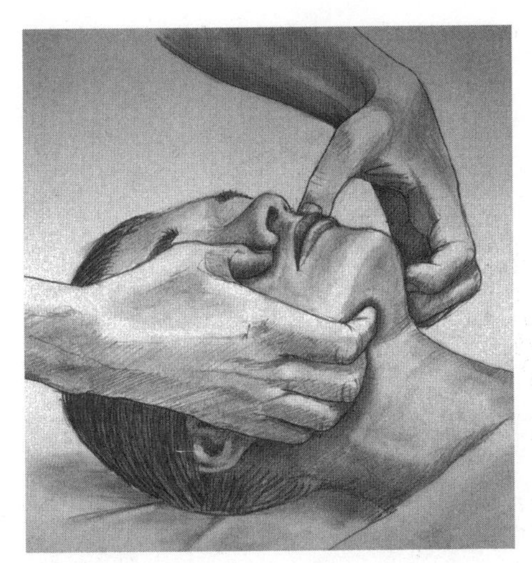

Fig 4-09

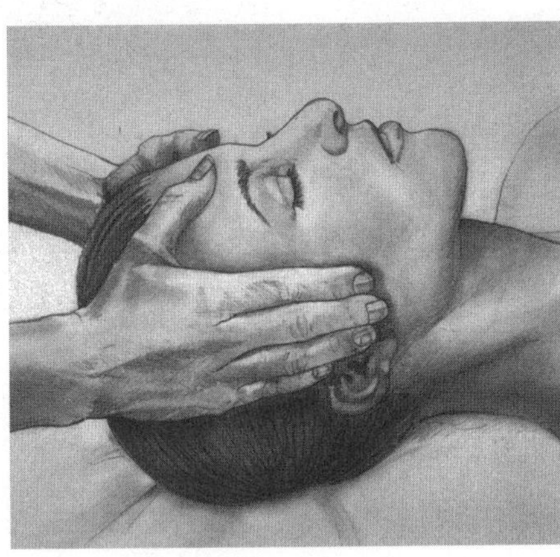

Fig 4-10

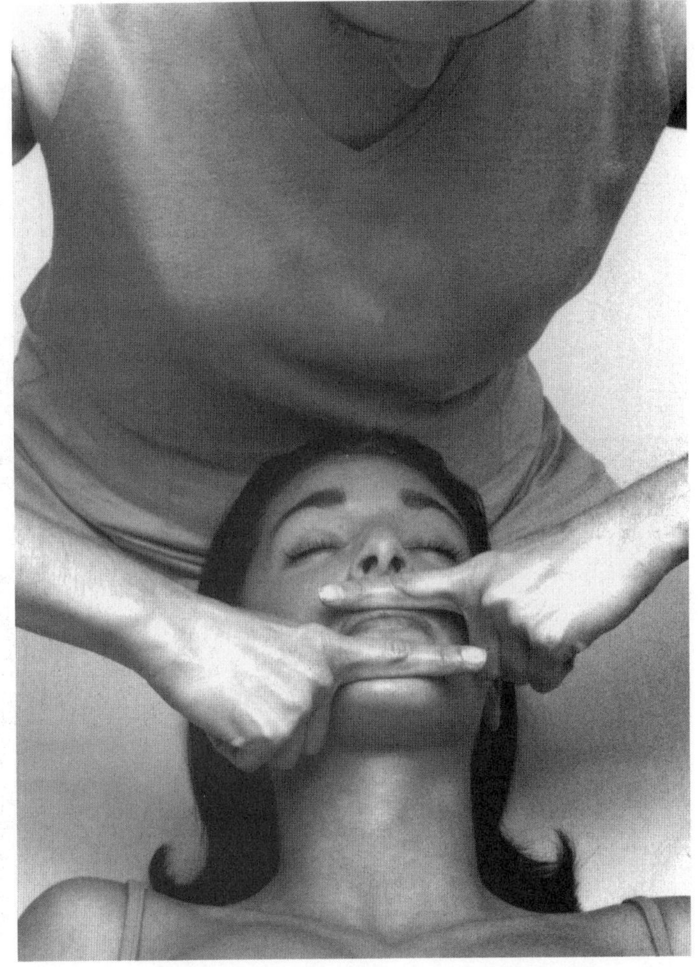

Fig 4-11

7. Place the 4 fingers of each hand underneath the jawbone and do 2 movements:

a. Pull straight towards your body using both hands equally (Fig. 4-12). This stretches the neck muscles. Hold for 10 seconds.

b. Slide your fingers back and forth underneath the jawbone in the soft tissue for 10 seconds.

8. Place your palms on the client's cheeks, with fingers pointing straight towards the feet. Massage the skin and muscles of the face by making a push-then-pull movement with your hands. As the right hand pushes toward the feet, the left hand pulls back in the opposite direction (Fig. 4-13) and vice versa (Fig. 4-14). Keep continuous contact on the face, massaging back and forth for 10 seconds.

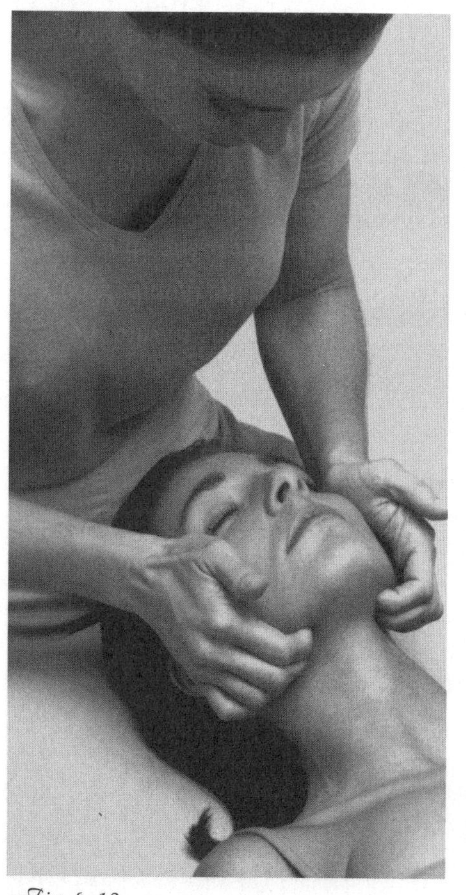

Fig 4-12

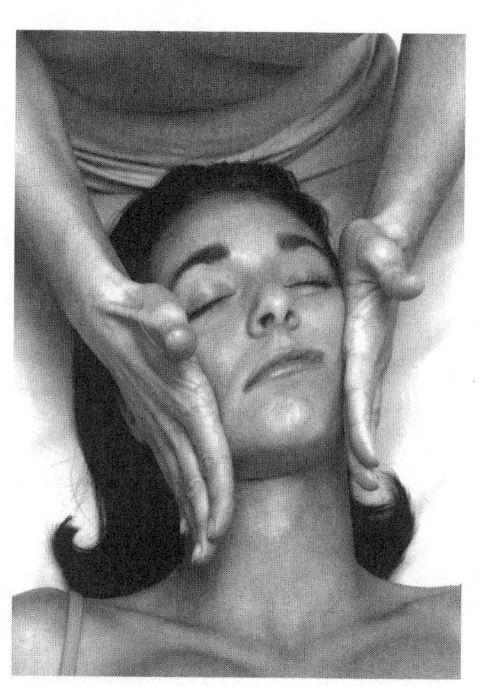

Fig 4-13

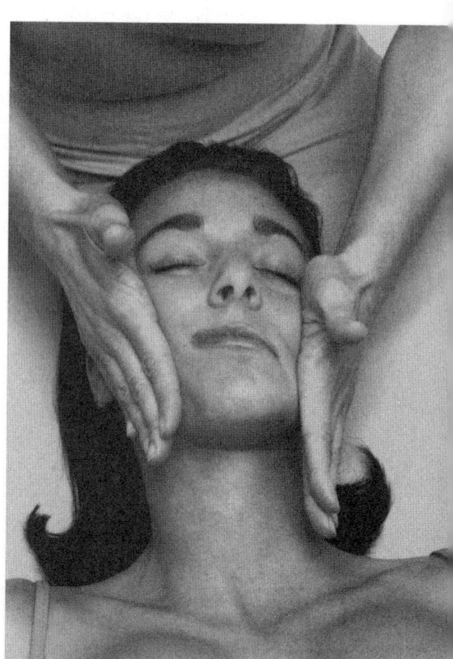

Fig 4-14

9. Place your thumbs above the eyebrows, as your forefingers press the cartilaginous flap above the ear where it opens into the canal (Fig. 4-15). Press in for 10 seconds.

10. Massage a small amount of massage lotion along the sides of your client's face if the skin is dry. Starting from the jaw close to the ear, use your thumbs to massage the jaw muscles and along the jawbone toward the chin. Slowly slide the thumbs along the muscle and soft tissue all the way to the chin, then return to the jaw (Fig. 4-16). Time: 10 seconds.

11. Be careful in this step. Talk to and reassure the client before you begin. Tell the client to breathe deeply; also, coughing is okay.

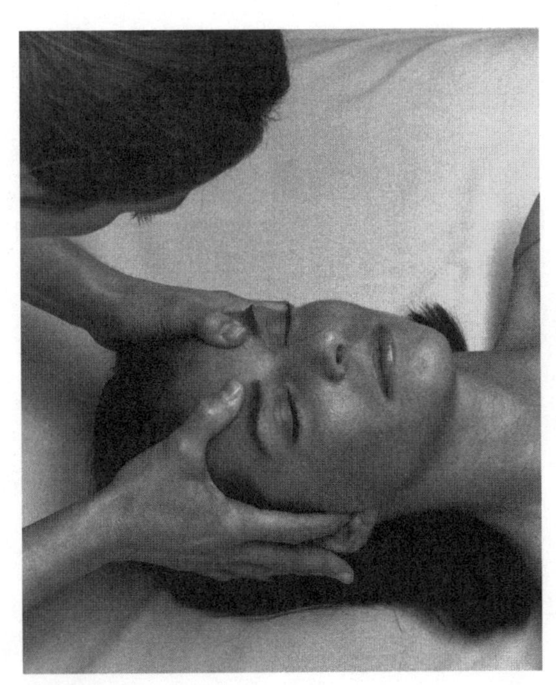

Fig 4-15

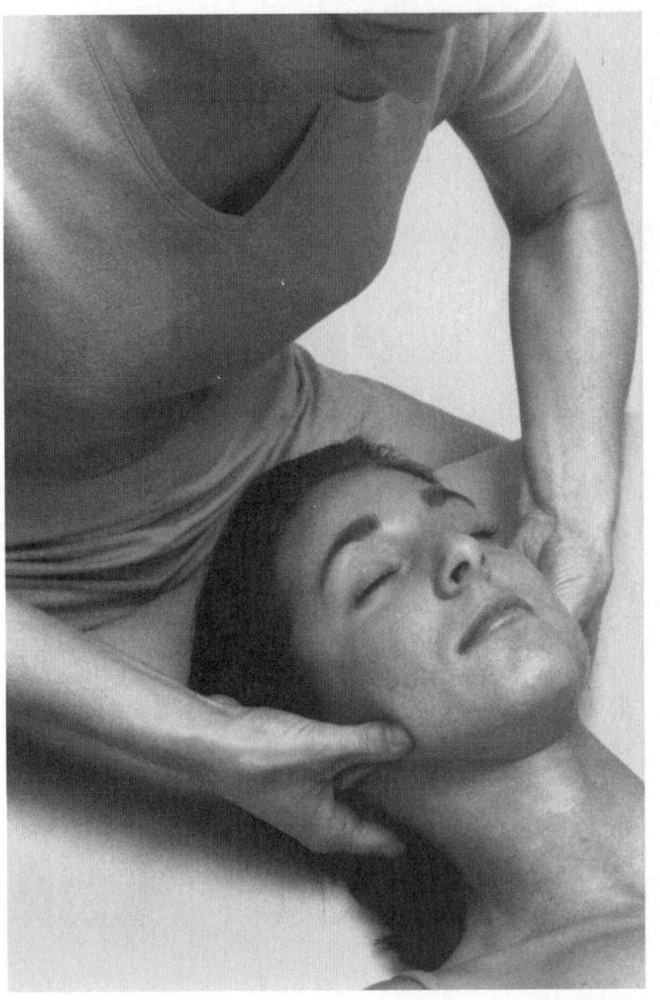

Fig 4-16

Using your dominant hand, push your thumb underneath the top of the sternum and behind it (episternal notch). Push towards the stomach for 10 seconds (Fig. 4-17). This movement stimulates the thymus gland.

12. Have your client lie down with legs hanging over the end of the table. Stand behind the client and place your palms over the upper arm muscles (deltoids) so that your fingers are on the tendons at the front of the shoulder joint. There is a groove here between two bones that your fingers can fit into. (This groove is for the biceps tendon.) Slide your fingers up and down inside this groove for 10 seconds (Fig. 4-18).

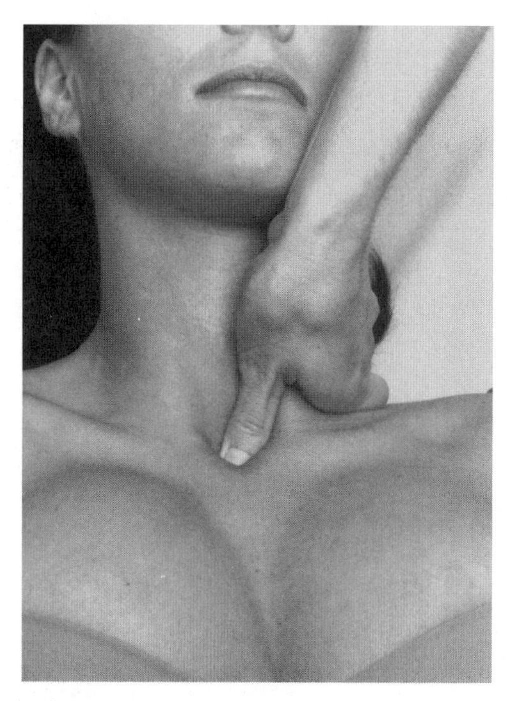

Fig 4-17

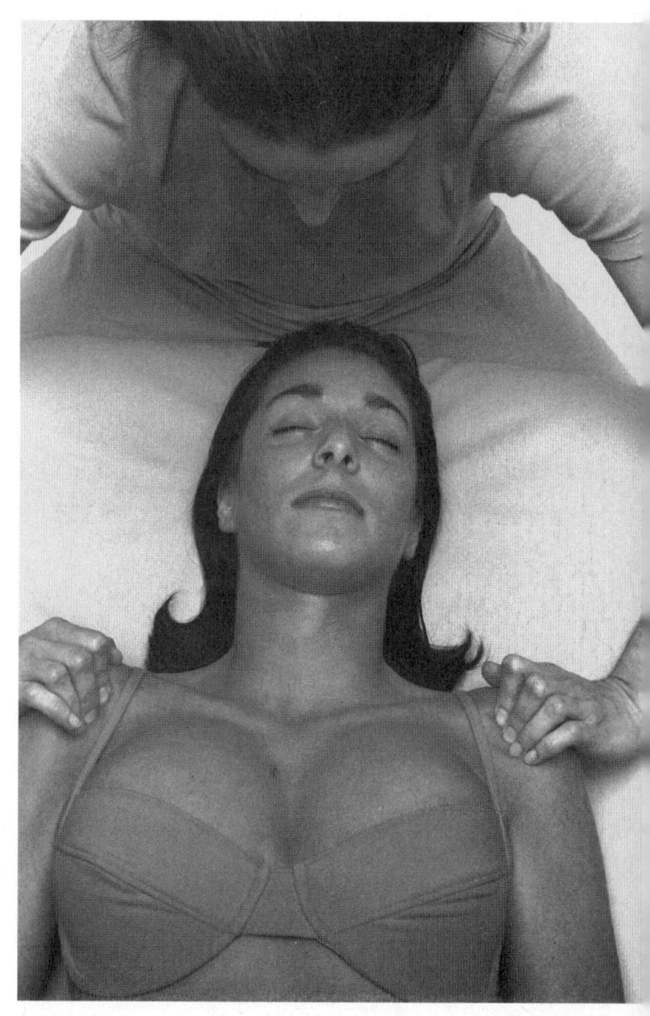

Fig 4-18

;ranial and Navel)uicktouch

about 1 1/2 minutes)

'HE CRANIAL AND NAVEL QUICKTOUCH :AN BE DONE FOR SOMEONE WHO NEEDS . FAST LIFT. IN ADDITION, THIS REATMENT BRIGHTENS THE EYES AND .ELAXES THE FACE, SHOULDERS, AND .BDOMEN. IT HELPS GET RID OF IEADACHES, MOISTENS THE THROAT, AND ;TIMULATES THE THYMUS GLAND. IT ALSO MPROVES DIGESTION AND INCREASES ;LOOD FLOW IN THE SEX ORGAN AREA.

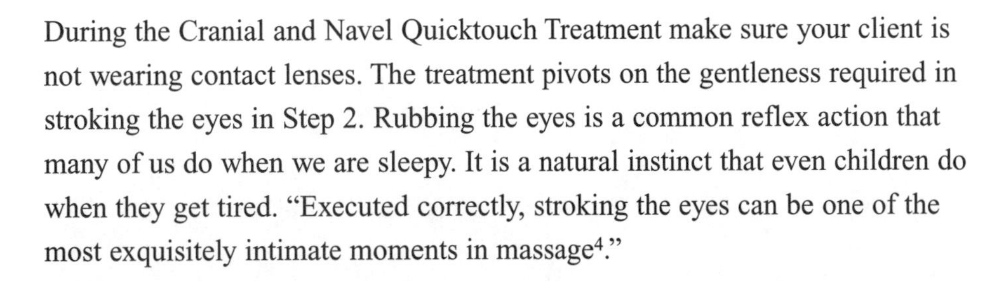

During the Cranial and Navel Quicktouch Treatment make sure your client is not wearing contact lenses. The treatment pivots on the gentleness required in stroking the eyes in Step 2. Rubbing the eyes is a common reflex action that many of us do when we are sleepy. It is a natural instinct that even children do when they get tired. "Executed correctly, stroking the eyes can be one of the most exquisitely intimate moments in massage[4]."

There is a reflex between the eyes and the heart. The muscles that move the eyes have a connection to the 10th cranial nerve, called the vagus nerve. When the eye muscles are massaged the vagus nerve is stimulated, slowing the heart rate. The heart rate will slow down 5 to 13 beats per minute. In some people the reflex is exaggerated, and the heart rate will slow as much as 50 beats per minute. This reflex has been used for centuries by martial artists and by skilled massage therapists to deeply relax their clients.

The times in the treatment steps can be extended to make the treatment 3 to 5 minutes.

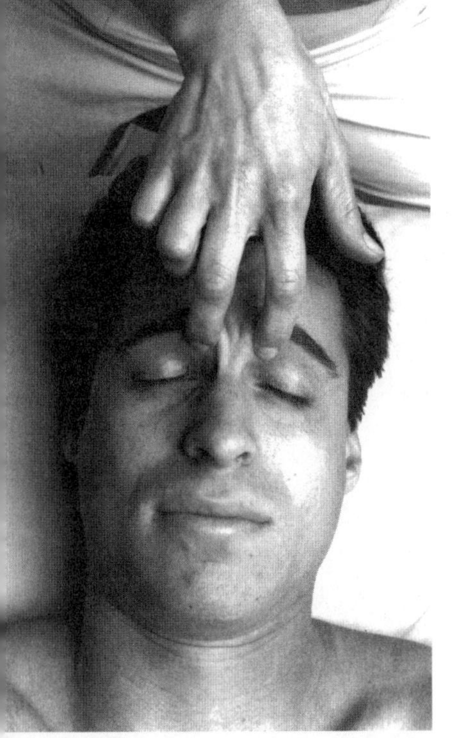

Fig 4-19

1. Sit at the head of your client, who is lying face-up. Using the index and middle fingers of your right hand, straddle the nose bone and make contact underneath the ridge of bone above the eyes. Your right index finger is on the left side, the middle finger is on the right side (Fig. 4-19). Pull towards your body firmly for 10 seconds.

2. *CAUTION: Be extremely careful doing this step. Use a light touch when you press the eyeball.*

Be sure contact lenses are removed. Treat both eyeballs at the same time, using your thumbs to very softly compress and massage around each eyeball for 10 seconds (Fig. 4-20). If the thumbs are awkward for you, use your fingertips.

3. Use your right thumb to press on the center of the upper lip below the nose using firm pressure for 10 seconds (Fig. 4-21).

4. Using your dominant hand press your thumb deeply into the notch of tissue just above the sternum (episternal notch). The thumb should sink underneath the sternum, while you have your client breathe deeply from the stomach (Fig. 4-22). There may be a cough reflex that occurs. Hold the thumb pressure for 10 seconds.

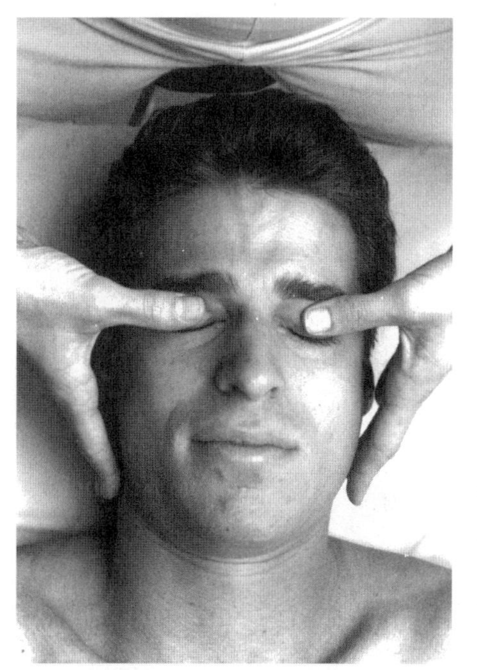

Fig 4-20

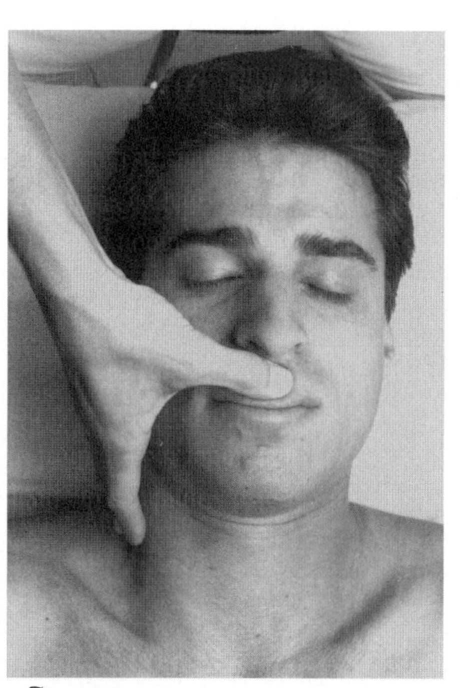

Fig 4-21

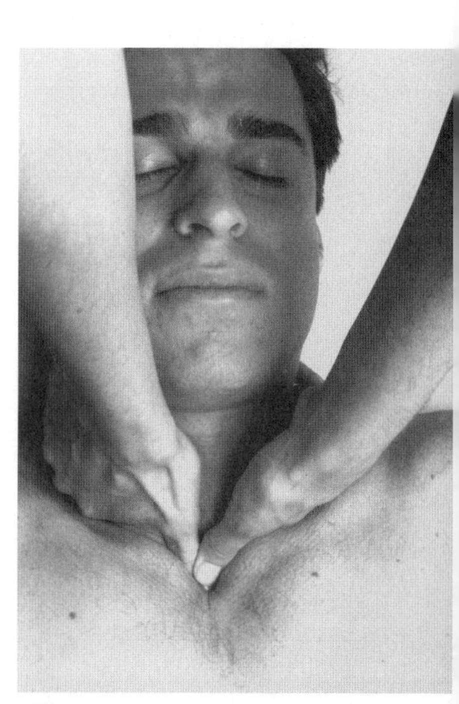

Fig 4-22

5. Place your fingers underneath the base of the skull. The head tips back as you do this (Fig. 4-23). Then pull the base of the skull away from the top of the neck for 10 seconds.

6. Move to your client's left side. Place your right hand on the sternum in **collar mudra**, knuckles on the upper sternum and the thumb on the lower sternum. The left hand is in a fist at the navel (Fig. 4-24). Press down on both hands for 15 seconds.

7. Keep the right hand on the sternum, and move the left hand to the pubic bone. Hold the pubic bone with your thumb pressed deeply into the lower abdomen directly above the bone. Your fingers are holding the top part of the bone. Push down firmly on both hands (Fig. 4-25). Use a light touch on the pubic bone if you treat a woman during the menses. Hold the contact for 10 seconds.

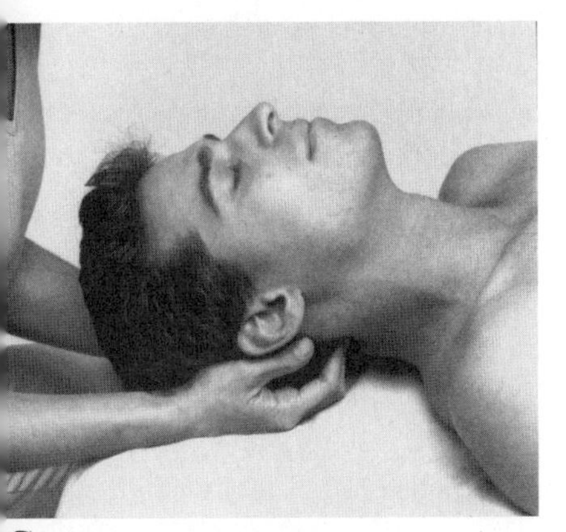

Fig 4-23

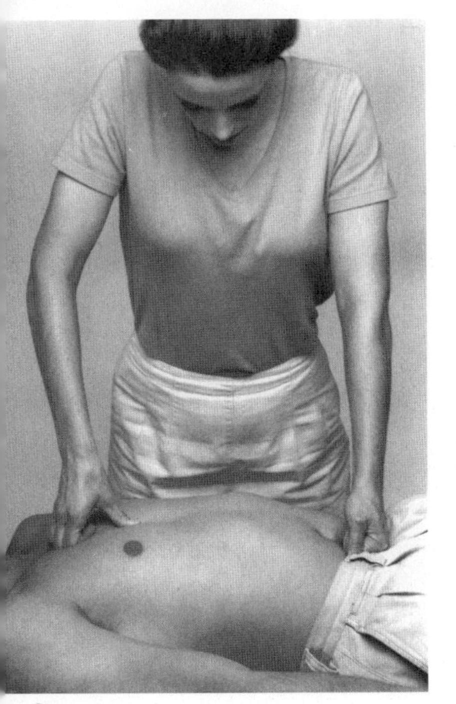

Fig 4-24

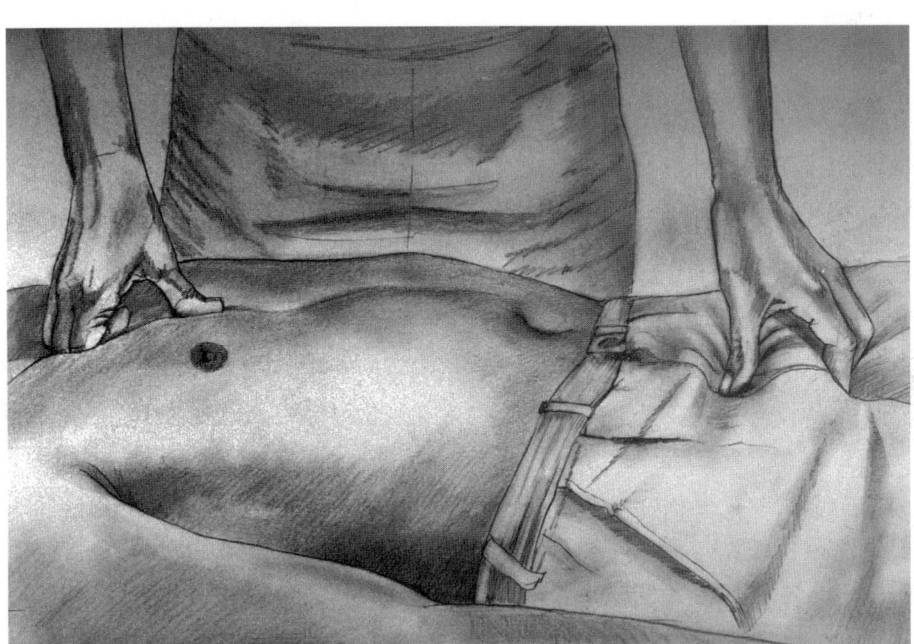

Fig 4-25

Comment

In Step 1, the temples are a sensitive part of the skull and part of one bone, the sphenoid. It is the only horizontal bone in the skull, forming a floor separating the brain from the mouth. The sphenoid supports the pituitary, the master gland of the body. This bone looks like a bird with outstretched wings, and treating it like this can put your client in flight.

In Step 4 the throat is cooled and the voice is soothed, to overcome coughing, hoarseness, and lung problems.

In Step 5, the neck traction is pleasurable and takes tension out of the neck and shoulders. There is something invigorating about feeling taller, having the neck stretched by someone else, a weightless feeling, that is unearthly sweet.

Steps 6 and 7 are an introductory **chakra** treatment. Chakra treatments connect one energy center to another. When the sternum (heart center) and navel (third center) are pressed, pranic energy rises to the chest, while the abdomen relaxes When a person feels two areas of the body at once a searching process begins. Inner questioning may begin. The person's curiosity can be aroused. What is this doing for me? Why am I so tight there? Let's see how I feel when this is over. Wow, what next?

I learned cranial technique from a chiropractor in Nebraska named Major DeJarnette. During the first 7 years of my practice I regularly travelled to Omaha for week-long seminars. "The Major," as he was known, used to say that a patient would notice an instant improvement because, "You have directed the cerebrospinal fluid into its proper channels." This fluid surrounds and cushions the brain. The brain floats in this pool that also travels down a small hidden canal in the center of the spinal cord.

Touching the cranium is something that I have incorporated in most adjustments that I do. After many years of practice my love for cranial touching is still strong because it brings results fast and patients report enjoying it.

'he Adept Neck)uicktouch

ıbout 2 minutes)

HIS TREATMENT IS SO SIMPLE THAT NYONE CAN DO IT. IT IS PASSIVE TRETCHING OF THE NECK, BECAUSE THE LIENT RELAXES AS YOU ROTATE THE ECK FOR HER. TURNING THE HEAD TO S MAXIMUM REMOVES OBSTRUCTIONS TO JLL ROTATION AND HELPS UNLOCK THE PPER NECK WHERE STRESS CCUMULATES. THIS TREATMENT ALSO ELAXES THE UPPER BACK AND BRINGS RESH BLOOD TO THE BRAIN.

1. The client lies on the back. Ask her to turn her head as far to the right as possible while keeping the shoulders on the table. Sit by the head. Place your left hand under the head, cradling the upper neck and the base of the skull. Put your right hand on the left side of the head, and press the head slowly down towards the table rotating the head and neck for a further stretch (Fig. 4-26). Hold in full rotation for 25 seconds. Repeat on the other side.

Take the client to the limit where you feel some resistance, and then turn the head a little more. This is a great help in increasing range of motion.

2. Use your thumb and forefinger to squeeze the client's nose shut, and push down at the same time for 10 seconds (Fig. 4-27). This pressure has a direct effect on the ***ida*** and ***pingala*** bringing **pranic energy** to the central spinal channel and the head. There are instantaneous effects: the pituitary gland will secrete; the sinuses will open; blood will rush to the face and skull; and the mind will clear of extraneous thoughts.

3. Now place your fingertips on the temples, massaging in circles for 1 minute (Fig. 4-28).

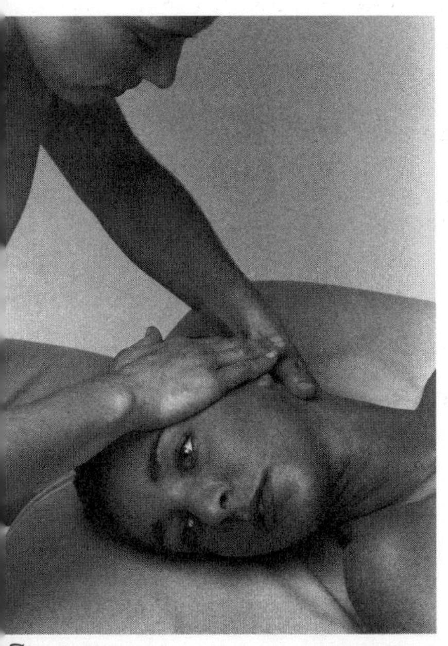

Fig 4-26

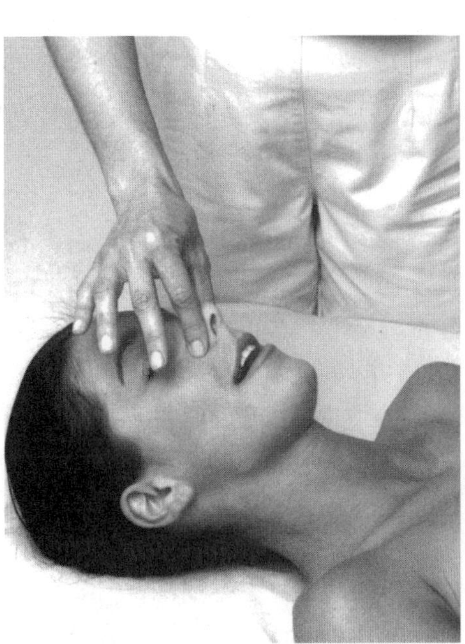

Fig 4-27

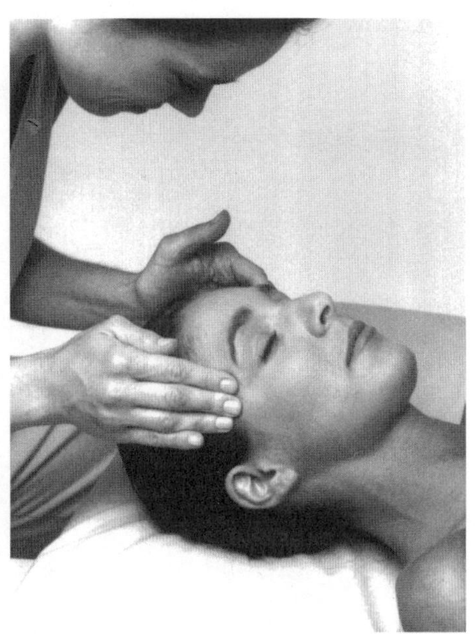

Fig 4-28

Comment

According to yogic scriptures, the neck is the vital portion of the spinal column. When rotated to the maximum the muscles will seek help directly from the local nerves. Then the nervous system responds to the passive muscle contortion and stretching. Because the neck rotation is held for more than a few seconds, nerve impulses travel to the liver, which sends fresh blood and stored sugar immediately. Also, the glandular system activates and sends hormones as part of a subtle self-defense mechanism. As a result the client relaxes in a unique way at the end of the treatment.

Warm-up Quicktouch

(about 2 1/2 minutes)

THIS IS A GOOD WARM-UP BEFORE A MASSAGE, A CHIROPRACTIC ADJUSTMENT, AN ACUPUNCTURE TREATMENT, OR A VISIT TO A PSYCHOTHERAPIST. EXTEND THE TIMES ON THIS TREATMENT WHEN POSSIBLE. YOU MAY BE SURPRISED WITH WHAT HAPPENS.

1. Your client is lying face up. Sit or stand on the left side.

a. Place your left palm above the navel on the abdomen. The left fingertips press under the ribs on the client's right side, and the left thumb presses under the ribs on the left side. Place your right fingertips underneath the body on the left side in the muscles of the middle low back (Fig. 4-29). Push with light pressure into the muscles using your first and second fingers of the right hand, then relax. Keep pushing and relaxing for 1 minute.

b. Move the right hand 2 to 3 inches lower and push in and out again with your first two fingers for 10 seconds.

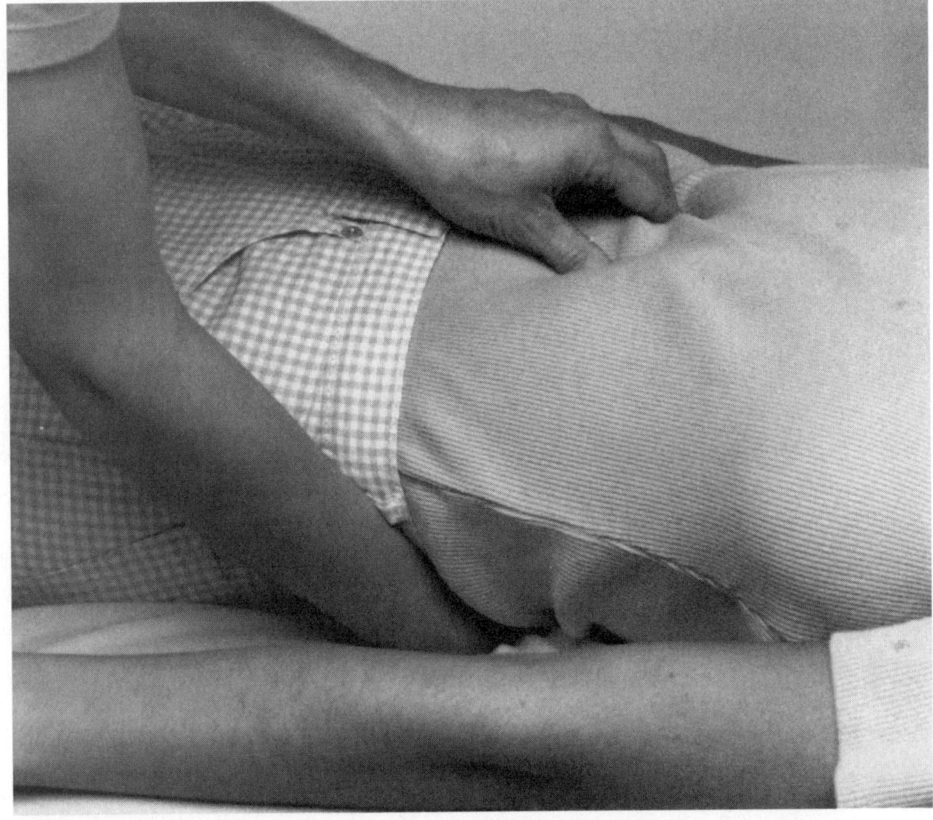

Fig 4-29

2. Face the head of your client. Place each thumb on the ligaments at the fold of the leg (at the inner thigh near the groin), with your left thumb to the right thigh and your right thumb to the left thigh (Fig. 4-30). Now press with firm pressure, using your body weight to lean on your thumbs for 20 seconds.

3. Standing to the side of the client, place your thumbs on either side of the sternum, an inch down from the episternal notch (Fig. 4-31). Using constant contact, seesaw back and forth shifting pressure from one side to the other for 30 seconds. You can use your body weight to help.

4. Move the thumbs to the space between the sixth and seventh ribs beside the sternum, resting your palms and fingers on the ribcage. Reach with your fingers to the ribs near the sides of the body and massage in the same seesaw fashion with alternating hands (Fig. 4-32). First squeeze with the fingers and press with the thumb of one hand. Then switch to the other hand. Go back and forth for 30 seconds.

Comment

By starting with the abdomen you help your client relax from the center of the body. The soft touch of Step 1 helps charge the solar plexus, while Step 2 affects the navel and second chakra. You finish at the heart center where better blood circulation is established. In addition, pranic energy is concentrated in the chest with Step 4.

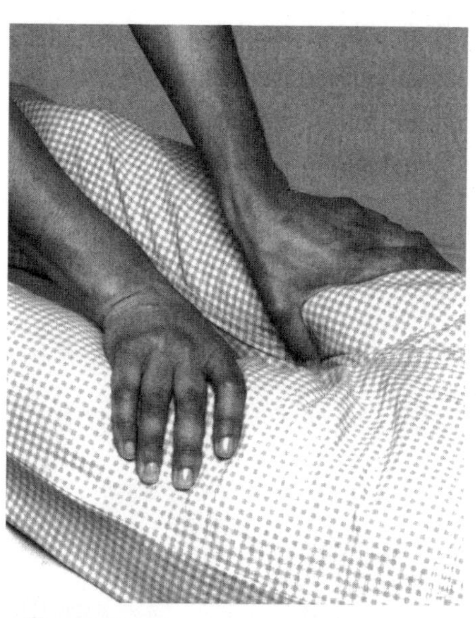
Fig 4-30

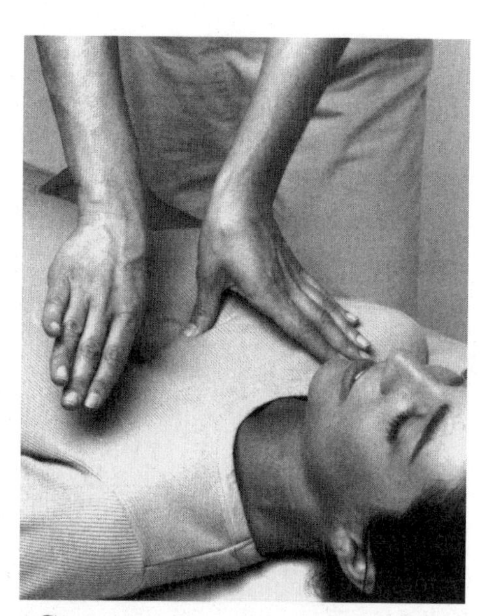
Fig 4-31

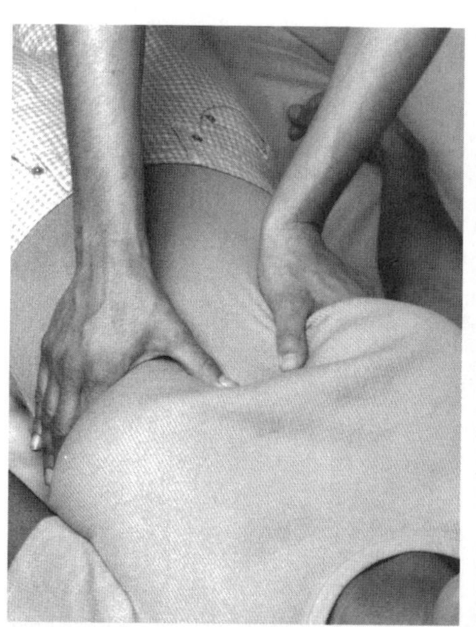
Fig 4-32

Bouncing-Balancing Quicktouch

(1 1/2 minutes)

"It is called Bouncing-Balancing. Man has his whole body printed in he C-1 vertebra. The body hologram is at C-1. And it never gets adjusted, doesn't matter what you do with it, until you come from underneath the base of the skull."

—Yogi Bhajan[5]

Use this treatment to begin a longer treatment or as a general stimulating treatment for the spine. It relaxes the diaphragm; it can calm an upset stomach; and it helps the liver and gall bladder.

1. Have your client lie face down. Both hands are in **collar mudra**. Place the right hand at the base of the skull with the thumb on the left side and the knuckles on the right. The left hand is at T-10 with the thumb on the right side of the client's spine; knuckles on the left (Fig. 4-33).

2. Lean into the body with firm pressure. Then rock back and forth using your body weight to provide alternating pressure to the hand contacts for 1 1/2 minutes.

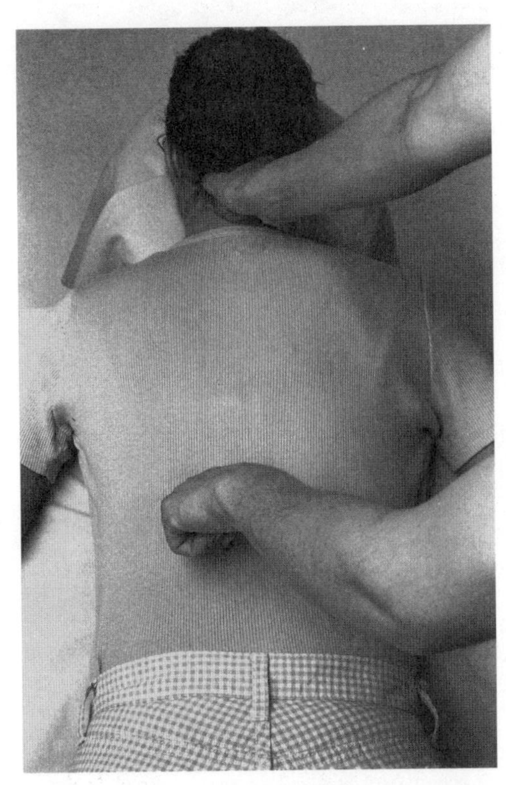

Fig 4-33

Ground the Soul Quicktouch

(about 4 minutes)

THE FOLLOWING TECHNIQUE CAN RELAX THE ENTIRE BODY. IF YOU ARE A CHIROPRACTOR, THIS QUICKTOUCH TREATMENT PREPARES A PATIENT FOR A BACK ADJUSTMENT.

1. Your client is face down. Stand to the right side. Find the center of the spine by using your hands as measuring sticks in the following way:

a. Place your right little finger at the base of the neck (C-7), your left little finger to the coccyx (Fig. 4-34-a).

b. Stretch your thumbs as far along the spine as they can go, then slide your forefingers to those two spots.

c. Keeping the forefingers in place, put your little fingers on these spots, stretching your thumbs toward each other (Fig. 4-34-b). The space between your thumbs is the center of the spine. It will be at or near T-10.

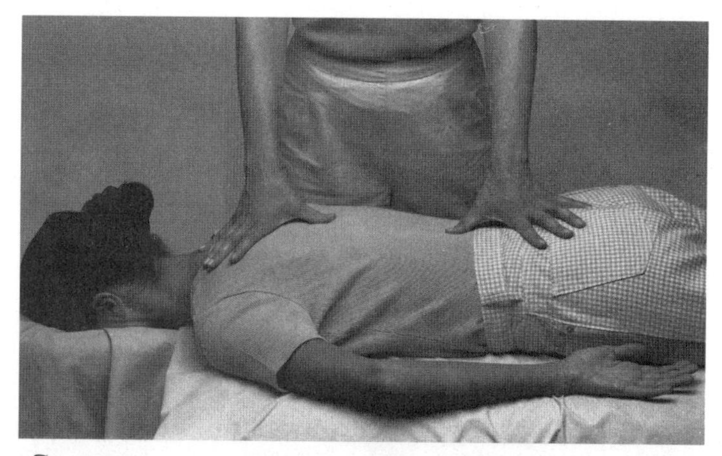

Fig 4-34-a

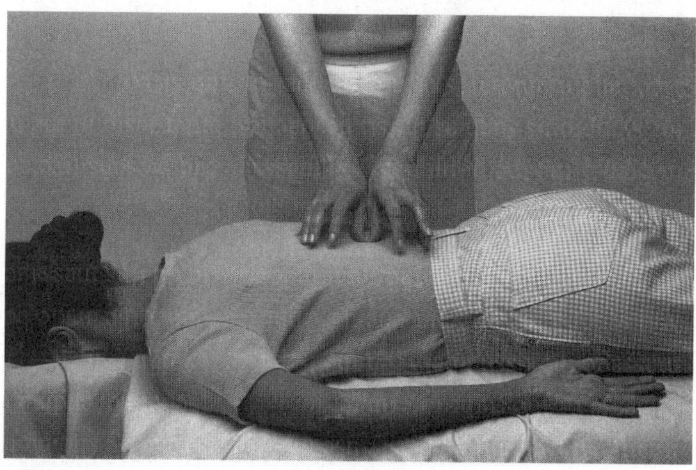

Fig 4-34-b

2. Place your thumbs on the back muscles at this spot (T-10) on the center of the spine (Fig. 4-35). Apply deep pressure, first on the right then on the left, rocking back and forth for a total of 30 seconds.

3. Keep your right thumb at the same point, rotating the hand so that the fingers point towards the client's head. Place the thumb of your left hand on the right buttock crease, pressing down on the hip bone (ischial tuberosity) underneath. Keeping contact with both thumbs, rock with your body weight back and forth. Have your client breathe deeply for 45 seconds as you do this step.

4. Keep the right thumb at the initial position on the right side of T-10. Move the left thumb to the left buttock crease toward the inside of the thigh (Fig. 4-36). Seesaw back and forth using your body weight for 20 seconds.

Move your left thumb to the same point on the right buttock crease and repeat for 20 seconds.

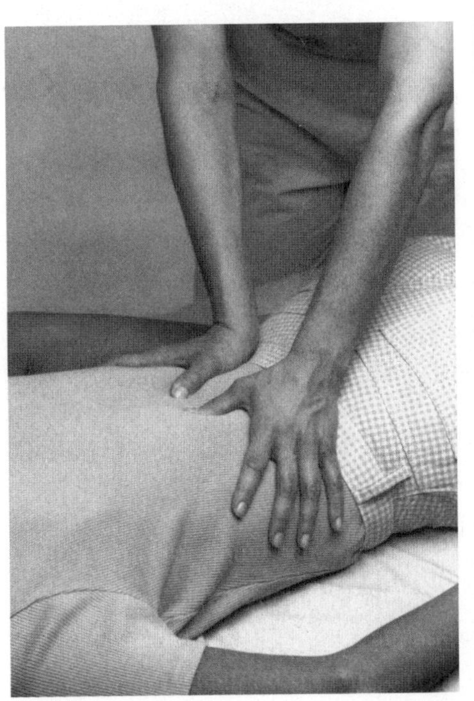

Fig 4-35

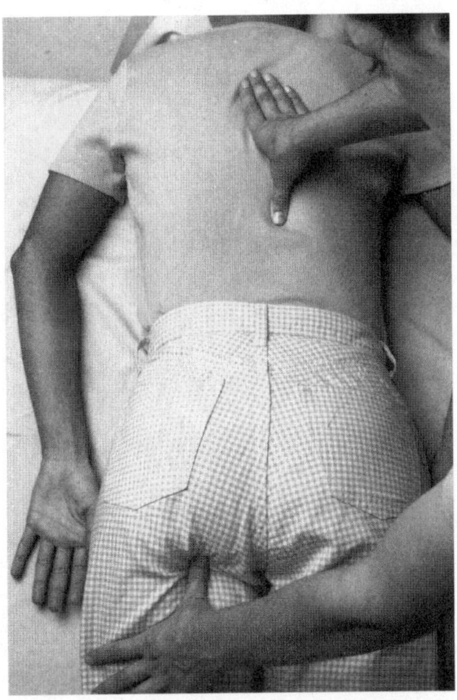

Fig 4-36

5. The right thumb stays on the right side of the spine at T-10. Move your left thumb to the right buttock crease. Apply deep constant pressure with both thumbs simultaneously for 20 seconds.

6. Make sure your client's head is straight down. Still standing to the right side of your client, put your right hand in **collar mudra** across the upper neck below the skull. Rotate your right hand so the right thumb is on the left side of the occipital ridge, knuckles on the right. Your left hand is still at the centerpoint (T-10) in **jacket mudra**, rotated so that your thumb is on the right side of the spine, index knuckle on the left side (Fig. 4-37). Rock back and forth in a slow rhythm for 90 seconds. Begin the rocking movement leaning on the right arm and hand, then lean on the left arm and hand.

You can change your hand positions in this step to make it easier for you to seesaw back and forth.

Comment

The middle part of the spine is where the heart resides, and pressure here feels good. So this treatment creates pleasant feelings at the center of the spine. It begins and ends at the central spine, around T-10.

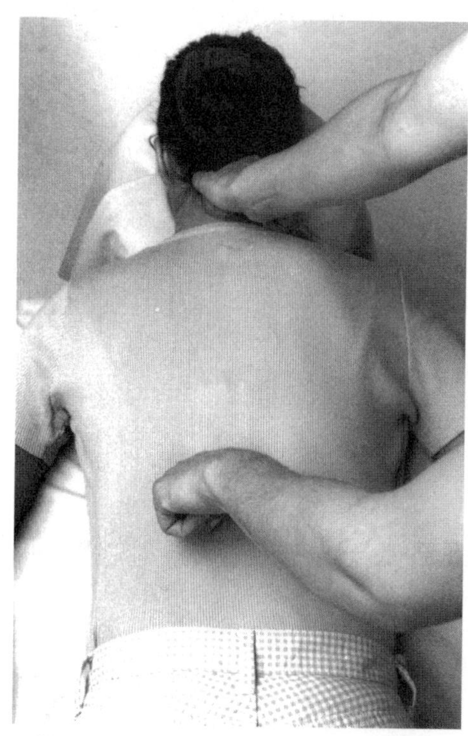

Fig 4-37

Resolving Navel Tension Quicktouch

(about 3 minutes)

"NOW WHAT DOES THIS NAVEL POINT DO? IT FORCES ALL THE ENERGY INTO CIRCULATION. TOTAL. WHEN THIS IS THE LAST POINT YOU TOUCH IN A TREATMENT, THIS WILL SEAL WHAT YOU HAVE DONE TO A PERSON."

-YOGI BHAJAN[6]

WARNING: This treatment is not done during a woman's menses. It is also not for young children, older debilitated individuals, pregnant women or people who have abdominal pain associated with tumors, masses, or chronic digestive problems.

The Release Navel Tension Quicktouch helps rid the body of physical and emotional tensions that collect in the navel region. It helps balance the navel pulse by moving it closer to the midline and to the navel itself. This treatment helps with dizziness, headaches, migraines, low back pain, stomach and digestive problems, and liver and gall bladder problems. I use this treatment when a patient has any of these physical symptoms: anemia, fatigue, poor appetite, constipation, stiff shoulders, or a tight neck. I will do the treatment 5 times or more until any tight spots in the abdomen soften or go away.

Please do this when your client has an empty stomach, 2 or 3 hours after a meal. Use your client's pain level to guide how much pressure to use. Start with light pressure and build it up if you can.

Have your client lie down on her back. Kneel on the table, straddling the client's thighs.

1. Place your fists on either side of her navel. Now push down into the abdominal muscles using both fists at the same time; then pull back (Fig. 4-38). With firm pressure continue this movement back and forth for 1 1/2 minutes.

2. Place your thumbs 2 1/2 to 3 inches on either side of the navel. Pushing the right thumb down into the stomach muscles, then pushing down on the left (Fig. 4-39), probe as deeply as your client can tolerate, as you continue alternating for 30 seconds.

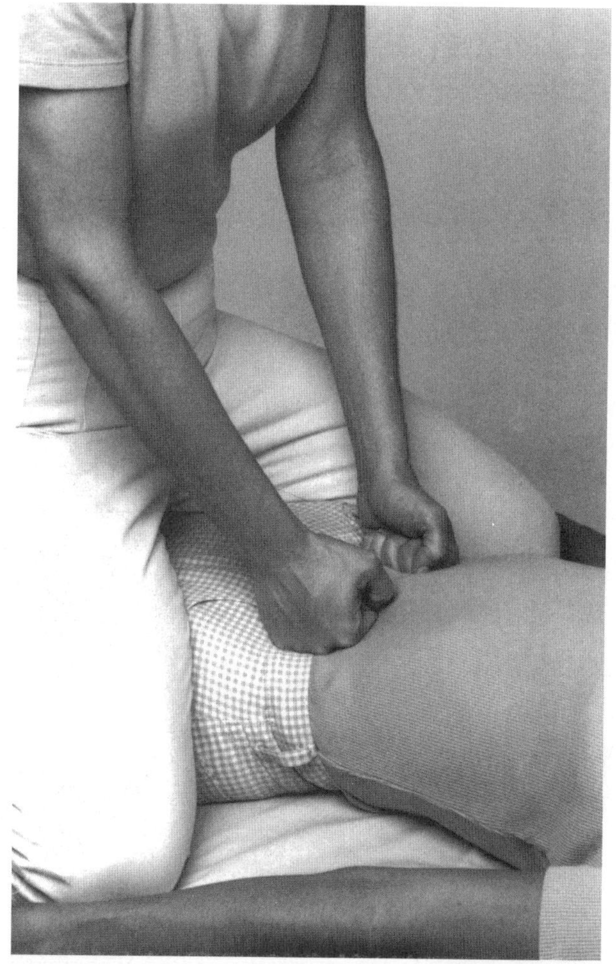

Fig 4-38

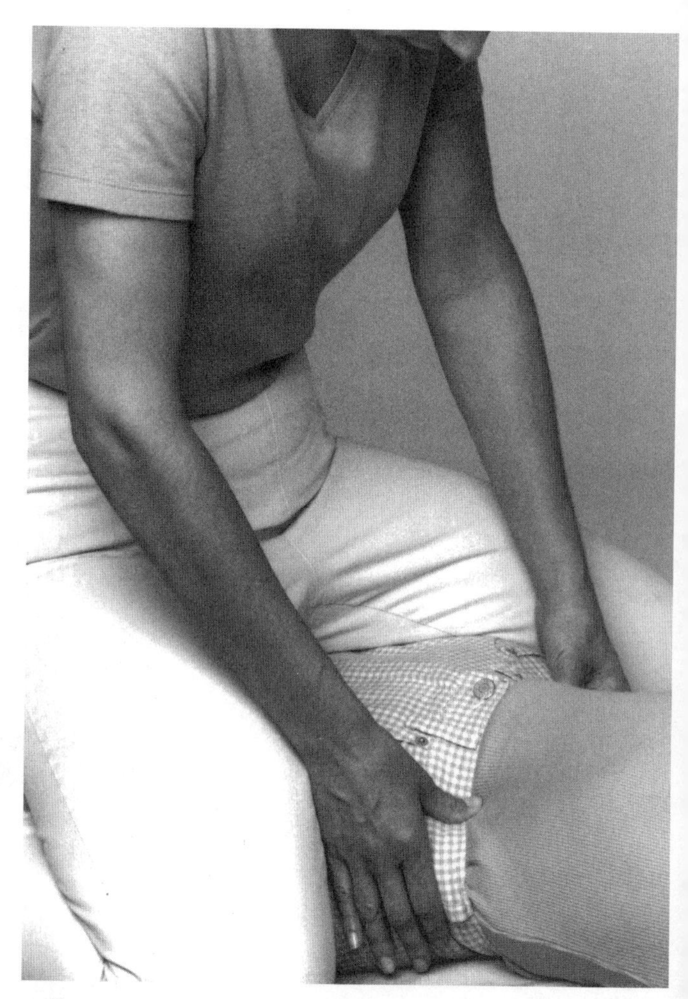

Fig 4-39

3. Place your fists side-by-side above the navel (Fig. 4-40). Now push down about 2 or 3 inches (or to your client's level of pain tolerance) for 10 seconds.

4. Make a fist with one hand and grasp that wrist with your other hand (Fig. 4-41). Starting slowly and building up to a brisk pace, push in and out at the navel for 1 minute.

Comment

There are several benefits to this treatment:

- You can relax a client prior to starting a longer treatment.
- You can seal what you have done in a previous treatment.
- You can improve the client's digestion and help regulate the movement of pranic energy in the abdominal area.
- You can help a client become calm, relieve anxiety, and disperse mental irritation.

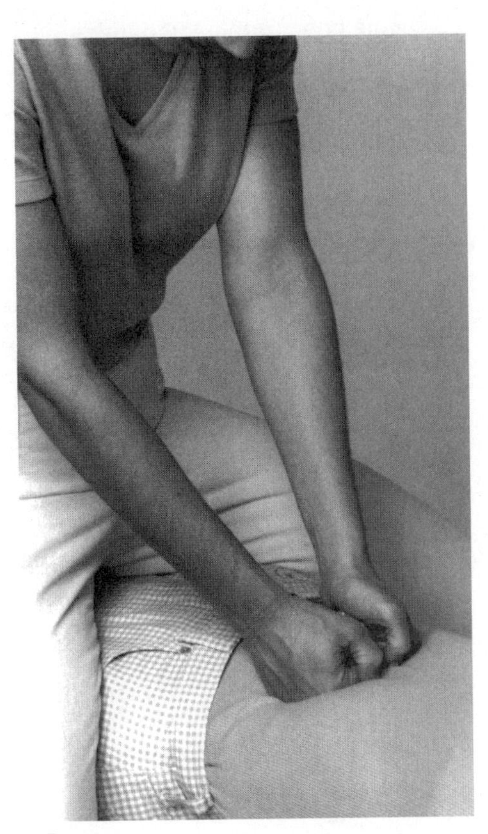

Fig 4-40

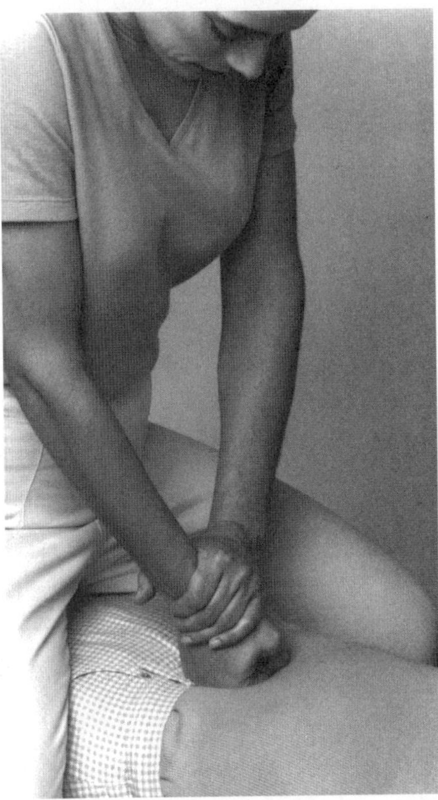

Fig 4-41

Navel-Heart Center Quicktouch

(about 3 minutes)

THE NAVEL-HEART CENTER PUMP RELAXES THE DIAPHRAGM AND BRINGS THE LIFE FORCE INTO THE HEART CHAKRA. ALTHOUGH BRIEF, THIS IS A POWERFUL TREATMENT.

Remember: the length of time needed to do a treatment is not necessarily proportional to the results. In my profession, chiropractic, an average of 5 to 10 minutes is spent with a patient. There are many chiropractors that I know who spend an average of 2 minutes with each patient and obtain good results. I urge you to be ready for good results. Have an eager desire to help and a belief that what you do is valuable.

The problems that have improved with this treatment include: diarrhea, urinary problems, and breathing difficulties. To help with irregular menses do the treatment during the cycle before the period begins.

1. Standing to the client's right side, place your right hand in **collar mudra**, knuckles on the left side of the pubic bone (ramus), thumb on the right side. Your left hand is on the sternum in collar mudra with the thumb on the lower third and the knuckles on the upper third (Fig. 4-42). Using your body weight seesaw back and forth with moderate pressure for 3 minutes.

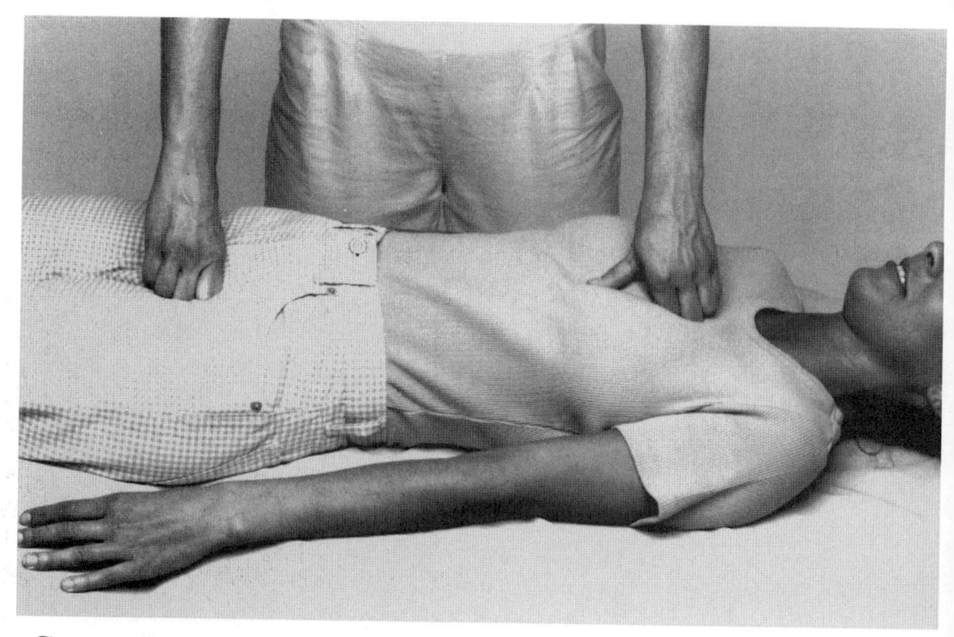

Fig 4-42

2. Sit near the head of your client. Curl your forefingers underneath the bony ridge above the eyes, adjacent to the root of the nose (Fig. 4-43). Now pull toward yourself with firm pressure for 10 seconds.

Comment

This treatment helps connect the lower chakras with the heart center. Remember that pranic energy (the life force) flows on both sides of the body, rising up from the pelvis. In Step 1 the rocking motion combined with the upper hand contact on the sternum helps bring pranic energy into the lung and heart cavities. Step 2 helps bring blood to the face and brightens the eyes.

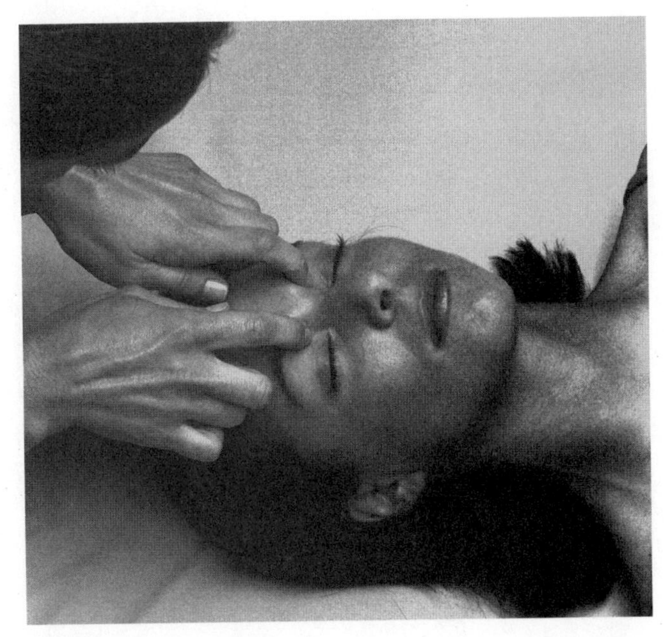

Fig 4-43

Willow Branch Quicktouch

(about 5 minutes)

THE NAME OF THIS QUICKTOUCH TREATMENT TELLS THE STORY: RELAXING, BENDING, AND BECOMING SOFTER. WILLOW TREE BRANCHES ARE SOFT, AND THEY FLEX EASILY IN THE STORM WINDS THAT BRING OTHER RIGID TREE BRANCHES TO THE GROUND.

This Quicktouch Treatment helps a client relax quickly. It's good for shoulder and neck tension. Patients that I have treated are surprised at how fast the good results happen. The percussion in Step 1 penetrates to the deeper tissues in the chest and abdomen. Wave-like effects travel through the intestines, stomach, liver, spleen, lungs, and heart. I find that many people want Step 1 to continue long into the evening. Percussion has compelling hypnotic rhythms.

1. The client is on the stomach. Use the knife edge of your hands, alternately striking either side of the spine in the back muscles (Fig. 4-44). Go from the neck to the base of the lower back and back again. Time: 3 minutes.

2. Your client is on the back. Wrap your fingers around the waistline and place your thumbs 2 1/2 inches to the sides of the navel. Press down into the abdominal muscles with your thumbs for 30 seconds (Fig. 4-45). Squeeze your thumbs and fingers together for added contact.

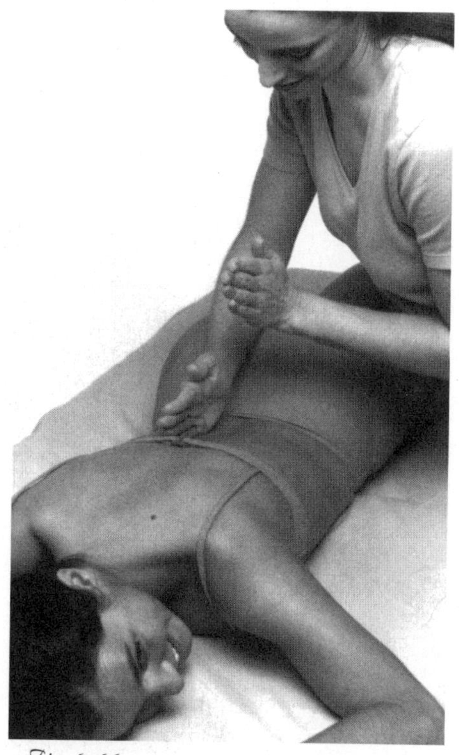

Fig 4-44

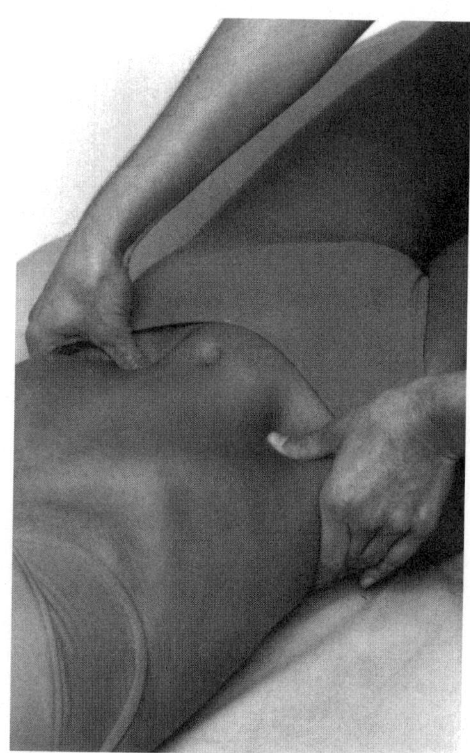

Fig 4-45

3. Your client is still face up, with the right knee bent, the right foot flat on the table. Standing to her right side, push your left thumb into the right lower abdominal muscles on a point 3 inches below the navel and 3 inches to the right side (near the inguinal ligaments). Simultaneously use the knuckle of the right forefinger to massage the tissue between the large and second toe on your client's right foot (Fig. 4-46). Slide the right index finger back and forth (1/4 to 1/2 inch) as you push down for 30 seconds.

4. Stand at the feet. Beginning with the right foot, massage around the ankle by placing both thumbs side-by-side on the front of the ankle. Make a long stroke by sliding the thumbs around the ankle, ending near the Achilles tendon (Fig. 4-47). The thumbs travel under the ankle bones. Take 1 minute to do this massage stroke 5 times.

Comment

In Step 3 the toe point that you massage can be sensitive and painful. It is used for symptoms such as thirst; headaches; bitter taste in the mouth; redness of the face; and nightmares or dreams that disturb sleep.

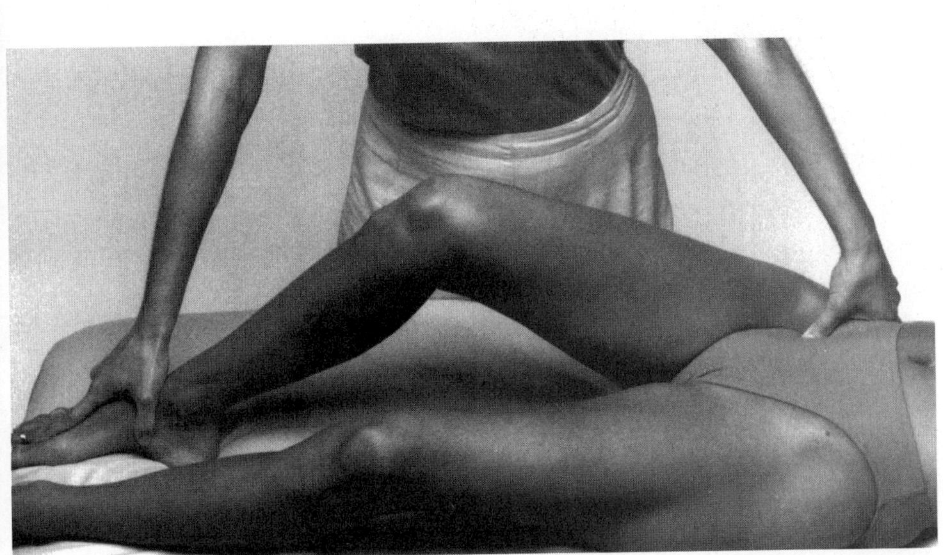

Fig 4-46

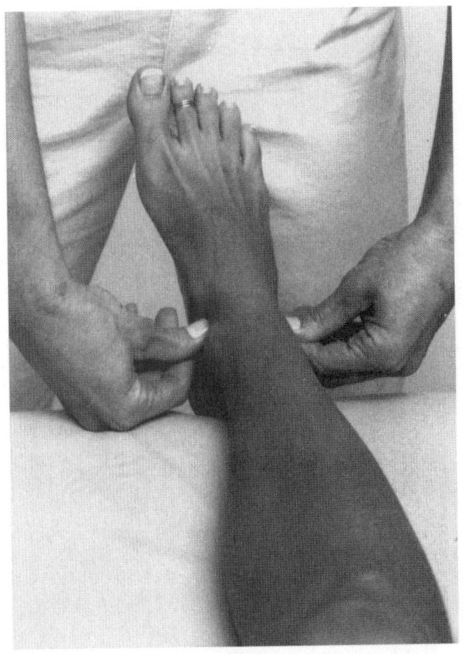

Fig 4-47

Laughter Quicktouch

(1 to 3 minutes)

"LAUGHTER—IT HELPS YOU 60 TIMES. IN PHYSICAL TREATING IT HELPS YOU MULTIPLY YOUR EFFECTS 60 TIMES."

—YOGI BHAJAN[7]

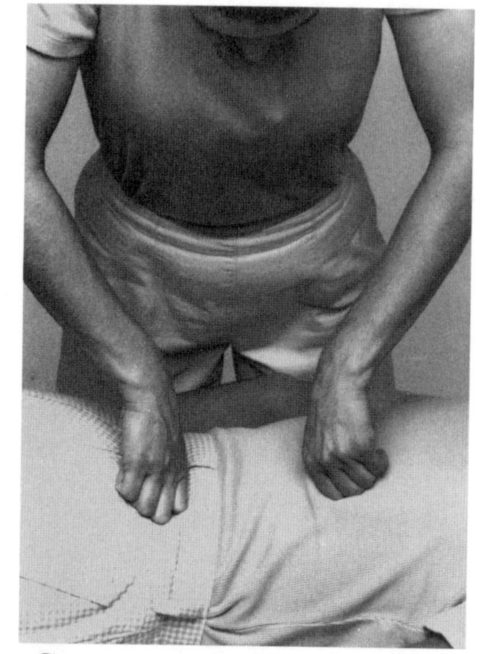

Fig 4-48

1. Stand on the client's left side with the client facing down. Use the **jacket mudra** with both hands. Contact the lower middle back with one hand: thumb on the left side of the spine, knuckles on the right. Make the same contact with the other hand 6 inches farther down the spine (Fig. 4-48).

Have the client belly laugh for 45 seconds. At first the laugh may be artificial, a forced attempt to laugh out loud at nothing in particular, with self-consciousness and self-restraint stopping it cold. Yet, if you persist you can help your client take off into laughter land. You may have to lead the way; laugh with the client ... or are you too serious? Encourage the client to keep doing it, with force, no matter how much hesitation or resistance.

Belly laughing is powerful, so get the client into it. Inspire the client to go from the fake laugh into the real thing. Have the client open the mouth and make the Santa Claus "Ho, ho, ho, ho, ho, ho, ho ...." belly laugh. Exaggerate to trigger more silliness. Change pace with a giggle: "Hee, hee, hee, hee, hee...." Do it until both of you break into uncontrollable laughter.

Laughter creates an environment for healing. Laughter relieves tension, breaks negative "holding patterns," and helps put problems in perspective. A good laugh actually changes blood pressure—the pressure rises during laughter but lowers below the starting point afterwards. Laughter reduces muscle tension and improves digestion. If you laugh so hard that you cry, releasing tears of past sorrows, you have accomplished some deeper healing. Laughter protects against the effects of negative stress by triggering the release of endorphins, the natural pain killers. And remember, he who laughs lasts.

Digestive Fire Quicktouch

(6 to 7 minutes)

BY DEEP, CONCENTRATED MENTAL ABSORPTION ON THE NAVEL, ONE GAINS KNOWLEDGE OF THE CONSTITUTION OF THE BODY[8].

This treatment helps balance the navel pulse, helps improve the digestive tract, and may relax your client into sleepiness. This treatment also helps to "set" the navel pulse on center, its ideal position for: maximum digestive power, increased stamina, and ability to relax. The navel pulse may not return to the exact midline of the abdomen where the belly button is, but it is easy to improve its location.

Before you start this treatment have your client lie on the back. Check the navel pulse (heartbeat) to find where it is the strongest. There are 5 locations: at the navel, above the navel, below the navel, to the left of the navel, or to the right of the navel.

Put your hand in **cone mudra** and push lightly down into the navel, feeling for the pulse. If you feel it, note it, and move your hand about an inch above the navel; press down lightly and feel for the pulse. Do this at each of the other positions so that you can find which one has the strongest pulse.

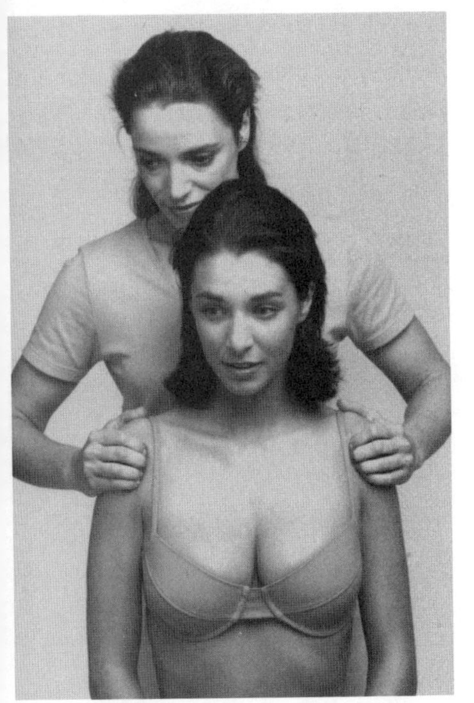

Fig 4-49

1. Your client is sitting up. Stand behind your client. Use your index and middle fingers together to massage the bony groove in the front shoulder with an up-and-down, side-to-side, and in-and-out vibrating motion for 50 seconds (Fig. 4-49). Move your hands up and down as fast as you can, keeping contact with the bony groove.

2. Hold the client's elbow. Now use both thumbs to massage the lower 1 1/2 inches above the elbow fold (biceps muscle) with a circular motion for 15 seconds (Fig. 4-50). Do one arm at a time and have your client pump the stomach as you do it. Total time: 30 seconds.

Stomach pumping is done by pushing the stomach out as far as it will go, then pulling it as far back towards the spine as it will go. The ribcage lifts up as the stomach is pulled back. It's a powerful, continuous movement back and forth which provides increased stimulation to the entire digestive tract.

3. Your client is face down. Wrap your fingers over the shoulder muscles (Fig. 4-51). Now press your thumbs on either side of the spine into the muscles at T-3 (upper back) using moderate strength as the client pumps the navel for 1 minute.

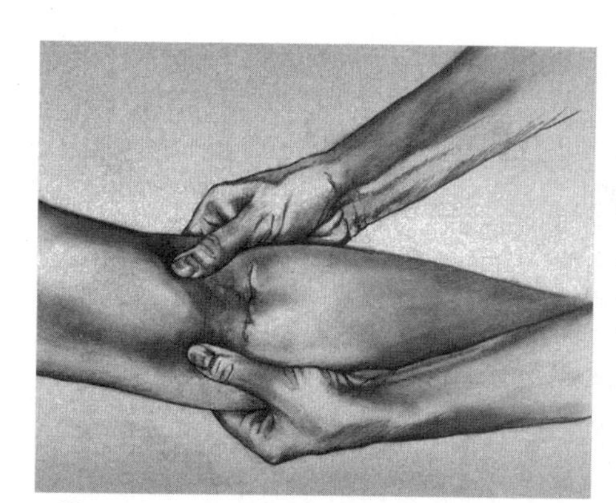

Fig 4-50

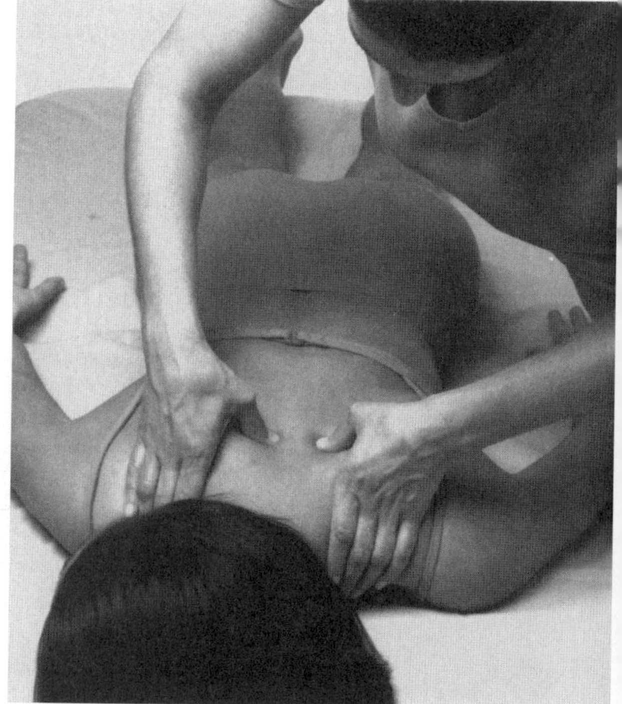

Fig 4-51

4. The client is seated, on a stool or the treatment table. You stand behind your client, leaning forward. Hold the client's forearms below the elbow, then push the arms down toward the floor with force for 30 seconds (Fig. 4-52). Ask your client to keep the spine straight when you push down—no slumping.

5. Now have your client lie face up on the table. Place your hand in cone mudra at the navel (Fig. 4-53) to feel the pulse: Ideally it is located on center, but it may displace in any direction. Has the position changed since Step 1? Is it the same? Is it on center at the navel? If it has changed for the better go on to Step 7. Make sure you have located it. Take 15 seconds.

6. Most commonly the navel pulse is to the left side, the approximate location of the abdominal aorta, the major artery in the abdomen. To help "set" the navel (to "balance" the pulse by shifting it closer to the body center), press the navel with up to 10 pounds of pressure, using cone mudra, for 1 minute (Fig. 4-53).

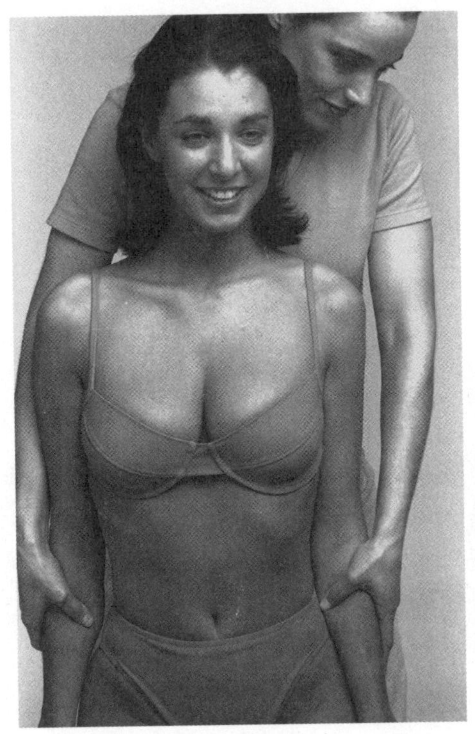

Fig 4-52

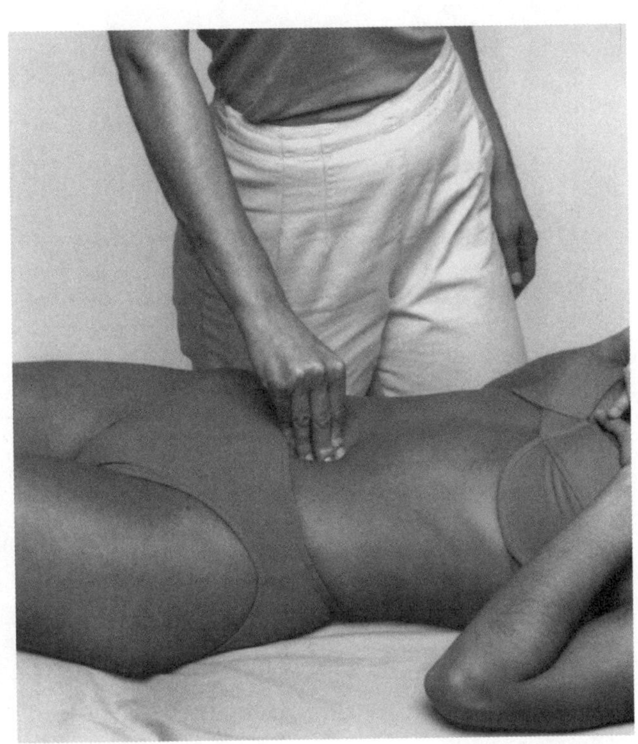

Fig 4-53

When you are finished, check to see if the pulse has moved closer to the navel. If it has moved closer, move to the next step. If it is at the same position as in Step 5 recommend following up with the client at another time, then move to Step 7.

7. The client is on the back. Place each thumb below the cheek bones, next to the nostrils, pressing down for 1 minute (Fig. 4-54).

8. Place your hands around the leg above the knee with the thumbs on the inside and the fingers wrapping around the outside (Fig. 4-55). Apply deep pressure for 20 seconds.

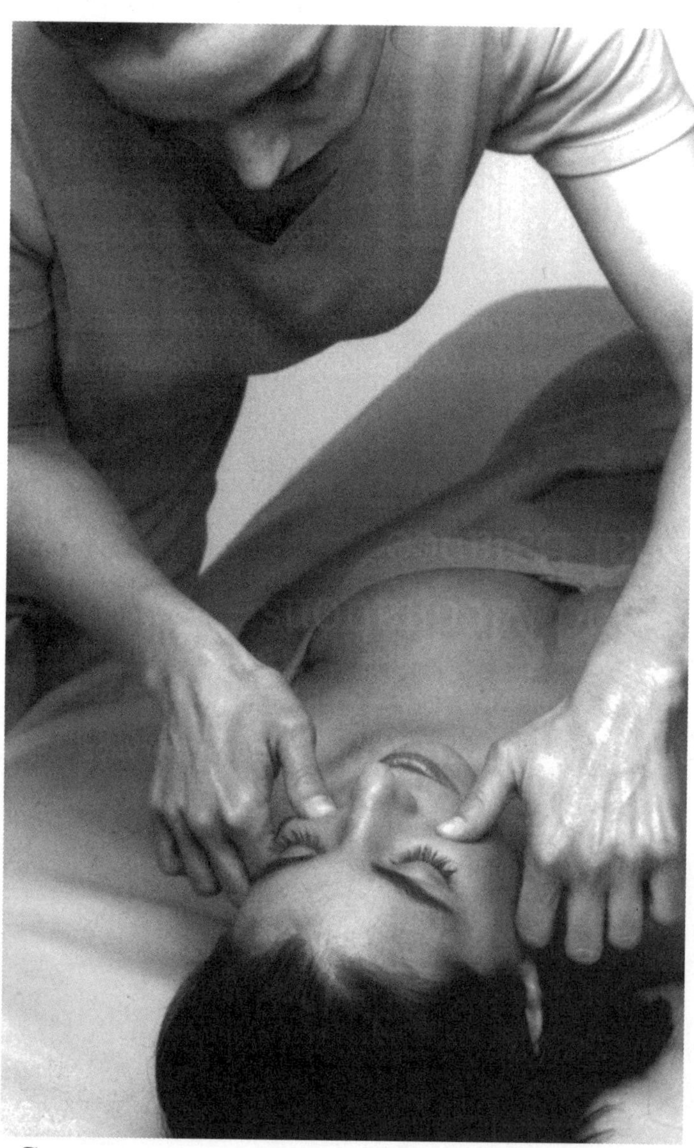

Fig 4-54

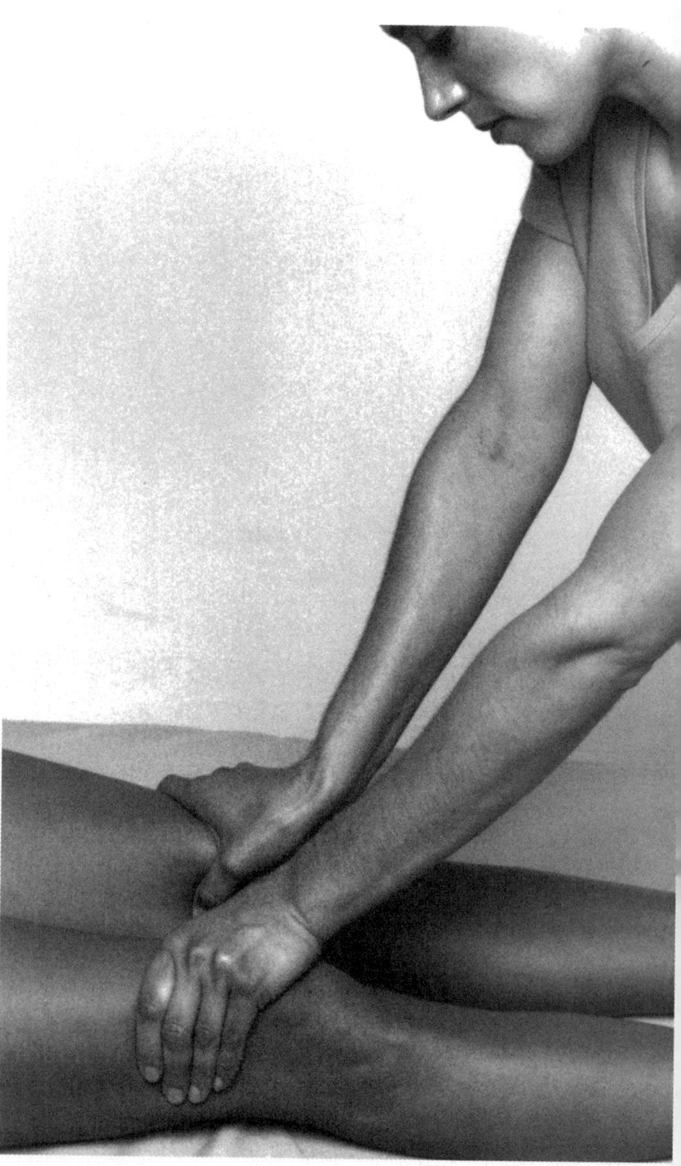

Fig 4-55

Wake Up The Feet Quicktouch

(6 to 8 minutes)

THIS QUICKTOUCH TREATMENT USES PERCUSSION OF THE FEET TO SEND WAVES OF HEALING POWER THROUGH THE LOWER HALF OF THE BODY. THE RHYTHM YOU CREATE FOR YOUR CLIENTS CAN PUT THEM IN A TRANCE OR MAKE THEM DROWSY OR SLEEPY EVEN AS YOU PERCUSS. THIS TREATMENT RELAXES THE HIP SOCKETS AND REJUVENATES THE FEET.

There are two versions of this treatment. Here is the first one.

Version 1

1. Have the client move toward the end of the table, lying on the back, holding the knees to the chest. Sit at the feet, make fists, and use the little-finger side of the hand to punch the balls of the feet (Fig. 4-56). Punch with alternate fists in a steady rhythm for 3 minutes.

2. Next, ask your client to straighten and raise the legs to 90 degrees with the arms folded on the chest, wrists crossing each other (Fig. 4-57). Then have the client bring the legs down from 90 degrees in slow motion until they are a few inches off the table, holding them there for 20 seconds (Fig. 4-58).

Fig 4-57

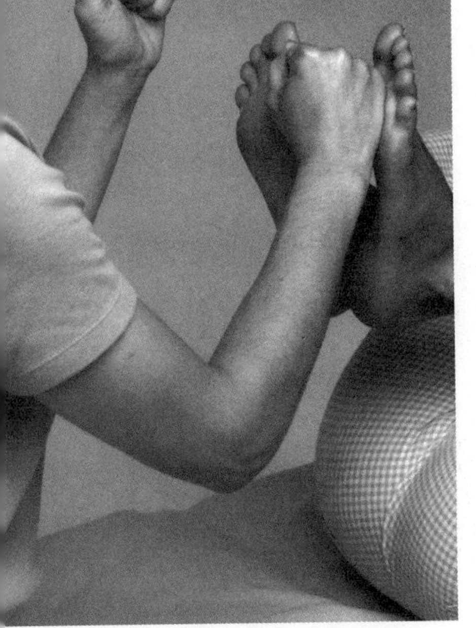

Fig 4-56

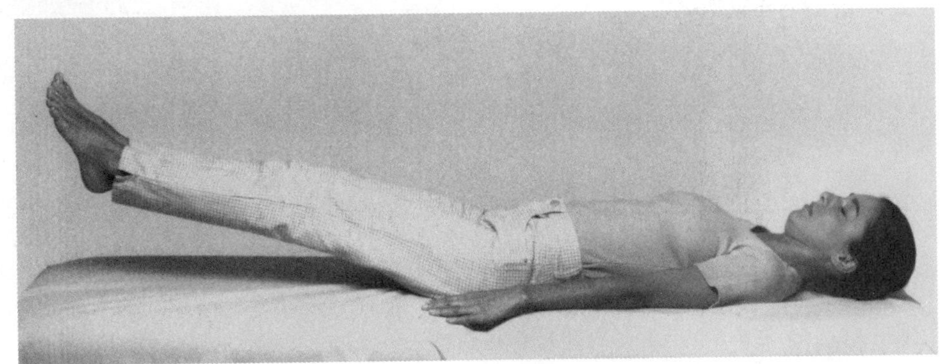

Fig 4-58

3. Have the client release the legs, relax on the back, and meditate on the image of red hot lava inside the spine for 1 minute.

4. Let the client relax and take a nap (Fig. 4-59) for 2 minutes, then have the client do a cat stretch to both sides. Cat stretch: bend the right knee and place the right foot on the table. Stretch the right knee over the left thigh keeping the shoulders on the table (Fig. 4-60). Then stretch to the opposite side. Cat stretch stretches the back and hips. Have the client get up slowly.

Advanced practice of Version 1. Step 1 for 13 minutes; Step 2 for 2 minutes. In Step 3 have the client bring the legs down to within a few inches of the table for 1 1/2 minutes, with **long deep breathing**. In Step 4 have the client nap for 5 minutes, then do the cat stretch to both sides. Total time: 22 minutes.

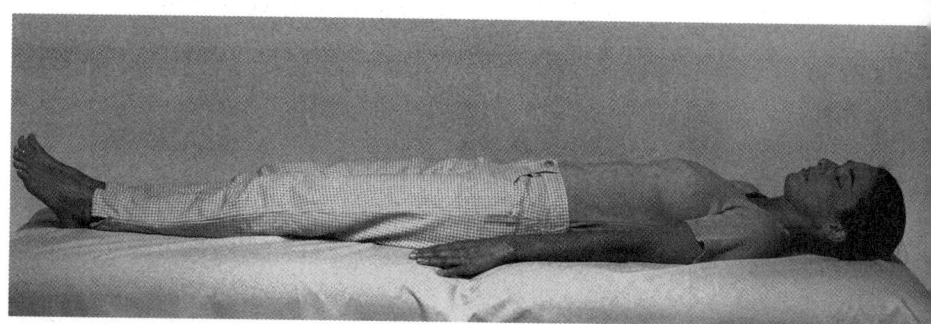

Fig 4-59

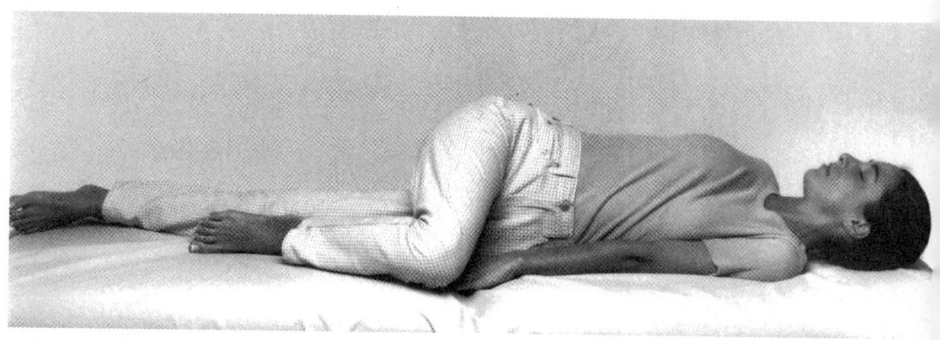

Fig 4-60

Version 2

1. Have your client lying face up near the end of the table, holding the knees to the chest. Sit at the foot of the table and, using your fists, punch the bottom of the feet with alternating fists for 1 minute.

2. Have the client straighten the legs. Now move to the client's knees. Using cupped palms, slap the knees first with the left palm, then with the right palm for 1 minute.

3. Move to the groin, with hands in a V-angle and cupped. Slap this lower abdominal region with alternating palms for 1 minute.

4. With slightly cupped hands, slap on the sides of the waistline with alternating palms for 1 minute.

Comment

This treatment is for creating a trance state in the client. However, by the end of the treatment the practitioner can be affected too. It is for enjoying.

Rhythmic percussion on the reflex areas of the feet stimulates the solar plexus, diaphragm, lungs, heart, esophagus, stomach, and liver.

Many comfortable feelings, memories, and dream states can be accessed during this treatment. Some people will go into a state of relaxation during the foot percussion. The relaxation is broken (or continues) with the leg lift exercise and entered again during the meditation at the end.

Supporting Mountain Quicktouch

(7 minutes)

THIS IS A GOOD OVERALL "TOUCH-AND-GO" BODY TREATMENT. HAVE SOMEONE YOU TRUST GIVE YOU THIS TREATMENT AND OBSERVE WHAT IT CAN DO FOR YOU.

In this Quicktouch treatment you can press on the acupressure points through loose clothing; however, the client needs to be able to move easily. Have your client wear sweat clothes, bathing suit, leotard, or casual wear—no tight jeans. Shoes, socks, and stockings are removed because you need to work on bare feet for best effect. If you do this treatment with clothes off, use massage lotion on the calf muscles, knees, and buttocks muscles.

1. Stand at the feet. Your client is face down, with feet hanging off the end of the table or with a towel rolled up under the ankles. Press deeply into the side of the Achilles tendon by placing your thumbs on opposite sides of the tendon and pulling in opposing directions (Fig. 4-61). Do this for 45 seconds, the last 15 seconds with near maximum effort. Then switch sides and repeat.

2. Your client is still face down. Start at the lower end of the calf muscles near the Achilles tendons. Massage both calf muscles simultaneously with the heels of your hands, sliding a few inches up, then back to your starting position for 10 seconds (Fig. 4-62). Move up the calf 2 or 3 inches and repeat the massage for 10 seconds. Then proceed farther up, repeating as many times as it takes to cover the whole calf. Total time: 45 seconds.

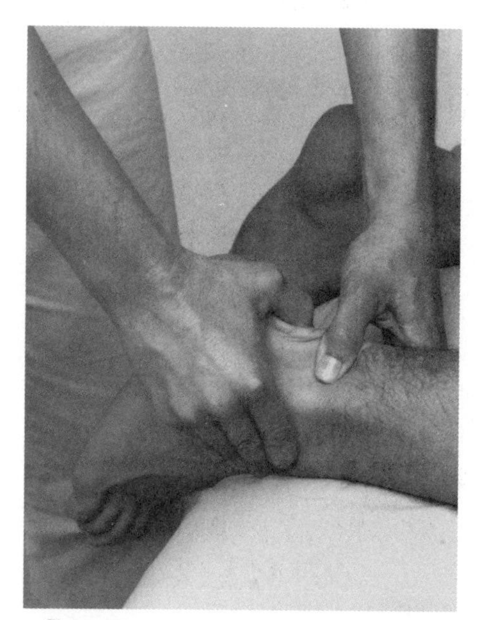

Fig 4-61

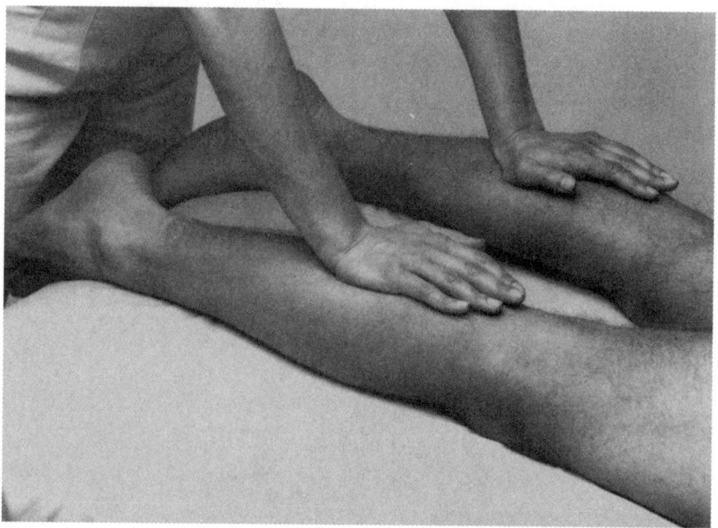

Fig 4-62

3. Then press down into the soft tissue behind the knee with the heels of your hands, sliding up and down for 45 seconds (Fig. 4-63).

4. Move your hands to the buttocks muscles, pressing down with the heels of your hands (Fig. 4-64). Do the same up-and-down movement as in Step 3 (Fig. 4-63). Do it with strength for 45 seconds.

5. Have your client stay face down. Massage the inside heels adjacent to the ankle bone with the thumbs for 35 seconds (Fig. 4-65).

This point is Kidney-6 (Shining Sea). Pressing it sends energy to the head. Kidney-6 is a major point with many functions. It benefits the eyes and throat, calms the mind, cools the blood, promotes the function of the uterus, and opens the chest[9].

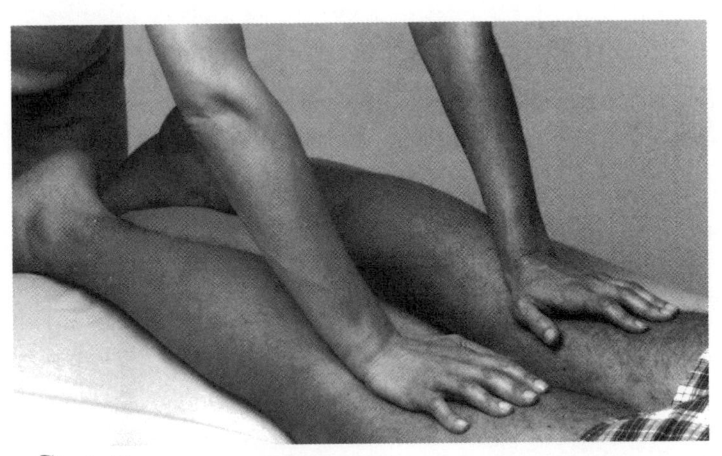

Fig 4-63

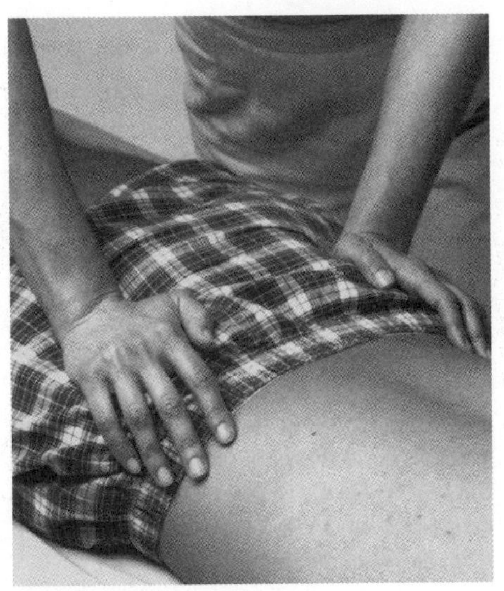

Fig 4-64

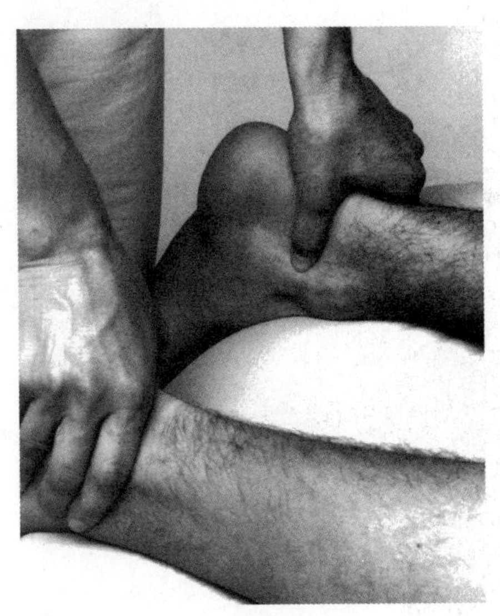

Fig 4-65

6. Measure a hand-width below the kneecap, and find a sensitive spot on the side of the leg, one finger-breadth from the center of the shinbone (tibia) in the muscle tissue. This is Stomach-36 (ST-36)(Fig. 4-66).

Massage ST-36 with your thumbs on top of each other for 30 seconds on each leg, one leg at a time. If your client feels sensations in the toes or the foot, you are using enough pressure. When something is felt there, let up on your pressure and go to Step 7.

According to Miriam Lee, massaging ST-36 stimulates hunger, increases digestion, increases the production of gastric acid, and helps food absorption. It also increases the flow of energy and oxygen to the head[10].

7. Stand to your client's left side. Grasp the lower edge of the pubic bone with the fingers of your right hand; the right thumb is above the bone. Now push into the lower abdomen for 45 seconds (Fig. 4-67).

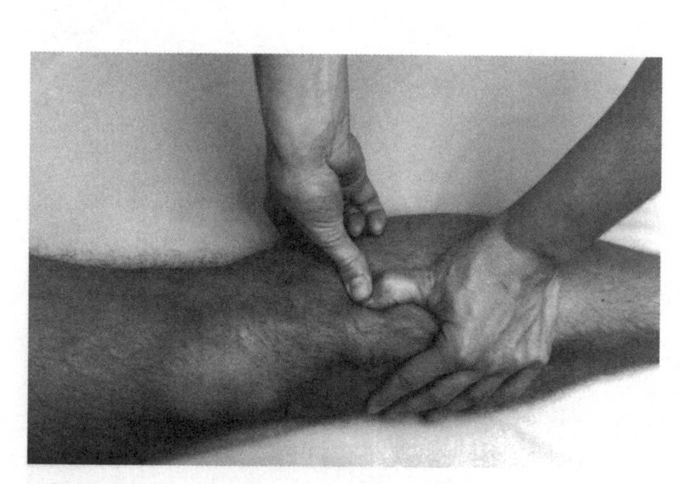

Fig 4-66

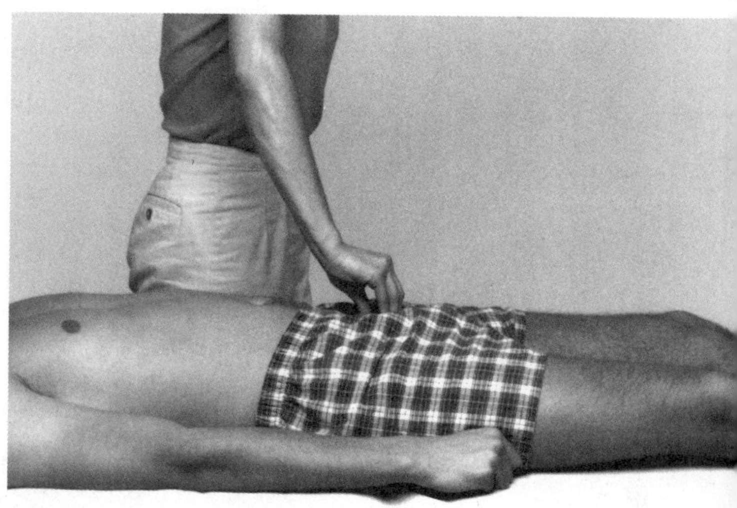

Fig 4-67

8. Use both hands. Press your fingers into the lower abdomen (above the ligaments connecting the pubic bone to the front hip). For 15 seconds, press deeply and release the pressure repeatedly (Fig. 4-68).

You can also use your thumbs, the knife edge of the hands, or the heel of your hands. This region is sensitive on some people. Use only light pressure on a woman who is menstruating.

9. Your client lies face down. Grasp the shoulder muscles with your fingers close to the neck. Repeatedly squeeze and let go, as your hands move from close to the neck across the shoulders (Fig. 4-69). Total time: 30 seconds.

10. Place your thumbs on either side of the spine next to T-3. Press with force into the muscles, and massage in small circles for 30 seconds (Fig. 4-70).

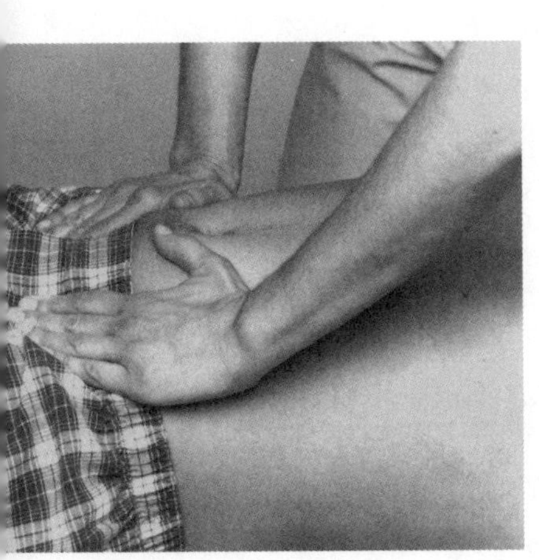

Fig 4-68

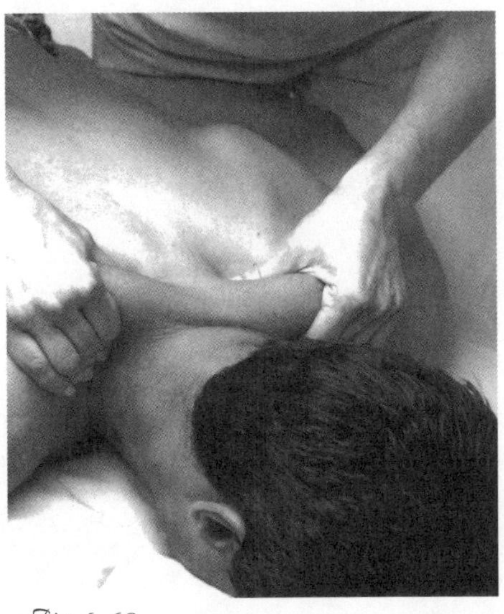

Fig 4-69

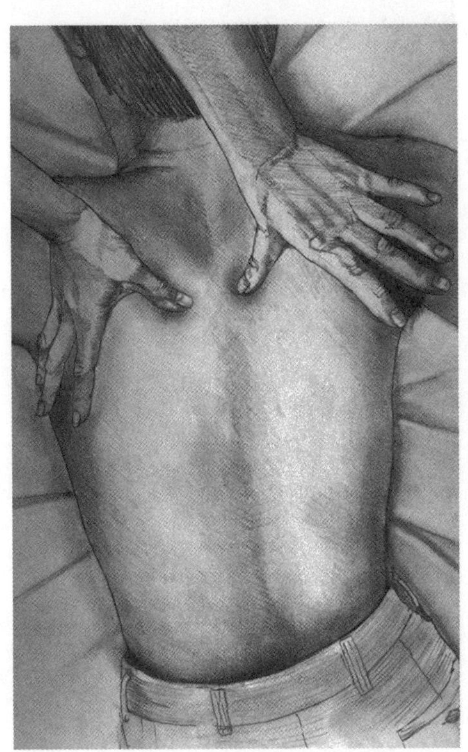

Fig 4-70

11. The client is still facing down. Bring the feet as close as you can to the buttocks. Grasp the ankles, leaning into the legs for 30 seconds (Fig. 4-71).

12. Stand by the side and have your client interlace the fingers behind the back. Slide your arms underneath the client's forearms and slowly lift them as high as you can (Fig. 4-72). If you are in doubt as to how far you can go without hurting the client, ask for feedback. Then stay at that level for 30 seconds.

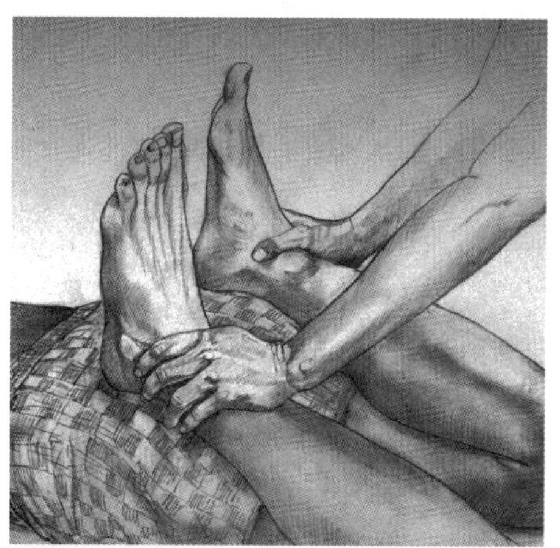

Fig 4-71

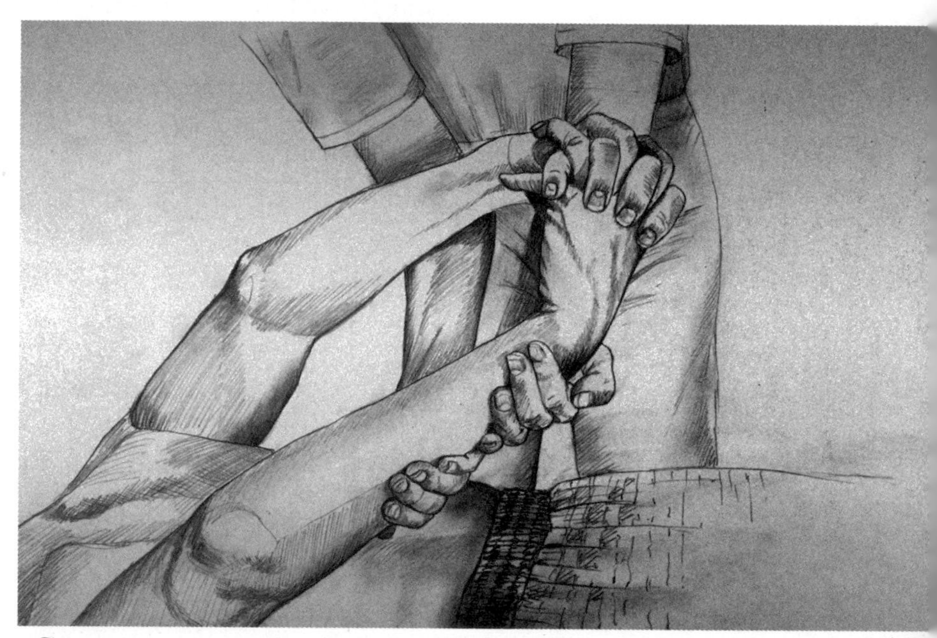

Fig 4-72

Bubbling Spring Quicktouch

(about 6 minutes)

YOU HAVE A RESPONSIBILITY AS A HEALER TO GIVE THE PERSON BACK TO HIMSELF. THAT IS HEALING. GIVE THE PERSON HIS ORIGINAL SELF."

—YOGI BHAJAN[11]

The beauty of this foot treatment is in the rhythmic way you tap the foot. Many of the foot reflexes are stimulated, so there is usually deep relaxation in store for your friends or clients. It is a Quicktouch Treatment that stands by itself, and it is a pleasant way to finish a longer massage.

Here is an easy method to help someone have relaxing sensations and comfortable feelings while lying down. You will stimulate many of the primary foot reflexes for the first time. Giving the stimulation evenly, continuously, and in a steady rhythm creates monotony so that sleepiness and deep relaxation can be the outcome.

1. Your client lies face down. Stand to the left side, and bend the client's left leg up to 90 degrees. Hold the ankle with your left hand while you tap the bottom of the foot with your right hand. Start at the toes, tapping with the knife edge of your right hand, working towards the base of the arch where it joins the heel. (Do not tap the heel itself.) Continue to tap from there back to the toes (Fig. 4-73). Do this for 2 minutes, then for 1 more minute tap with more force on the front third of the foot.

Repeat the procedure on the other foot for 3 minutes. Total time for both feet is 6 minutes.

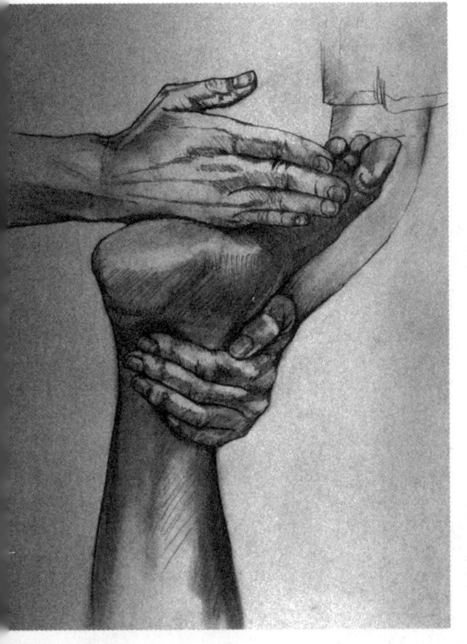

Fig 4-73

Sugar and Salt Quicktouch

(about 4 1/2 minutes)

"YOUR ENTIRE DEPRESSION IS AN IMBALANCE BETWEEN YOUR SUGAR AND SALT."

—YOGI BHAJAN [12]

The Sugar and Salt Treatment stimulates the flow of life force in the lungs and in the central spinal cord. It also releases tightness in the jaw.

Located at T-4, the sugar point is on the left side of the spine; the salt point is on the right[13]. These points on the upper back represent opposite tastes—sweet and salty. "Sweet" is expanding; it adds to body tissues and has calories. "Salty" is contracting and concentrating, and the two balance each other. Pressing on both sides at once is the key in this treatment.

Your client lies face down.

1. Locate the sugar and salt points adjacent to T-4 on either side of the spine: sugar on the left, salt on the right (Fig. 4-74). To find T-4, go to the prominent vertebra at the base of the neck (C-7) and move down the spine 2 to 2 1/2 inches.

Using your thumbs to press on both points at the same time, massage the points for 30 seconds.

2. Have your client turn over, face up. Sit behind the client's head. Place the side of the large knuckle of your left index finger below the nose and massage the upper lip, side-to-side (Fig. 4-75). Your finger stays in contact with the skin dragging it back and forth for 30 seconds.

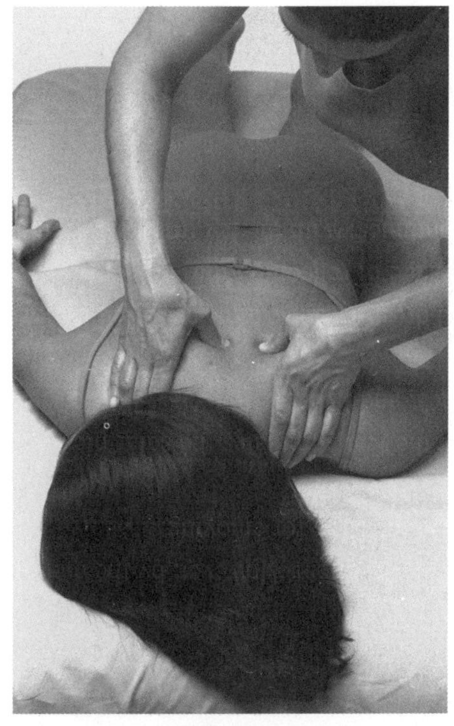

Fig 4-74

Fig 4-75

3. Do the same massage on the center of the chin below the lower lip for 30 seconds (Fig. 4-76).

4. Curl your index finger underneath your client's chin, and place the palm of your other hand on the top of the head. Pull up on the index finger and tilt the client's head back with your other hand. Hold the position for 1 minute (Fig. 4-77).

5. Place the palm side of the second knuckle of your left forefinger above the upper lip, with the palm side of the second knuckle of your right forefinger below the lower lip (Fig. 4-78). Press down for 30 seconds.

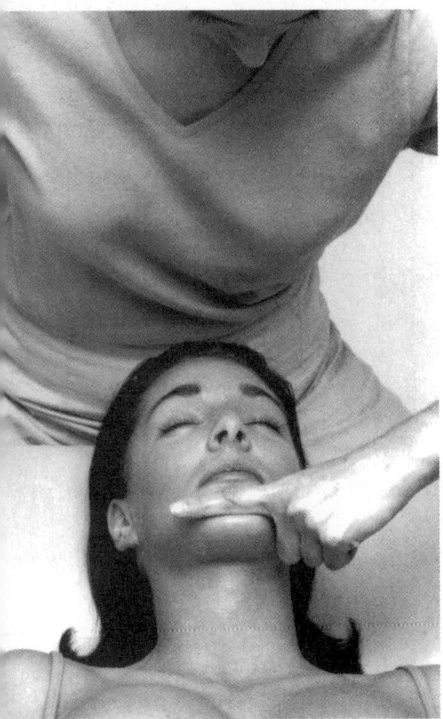

Fig 4-76

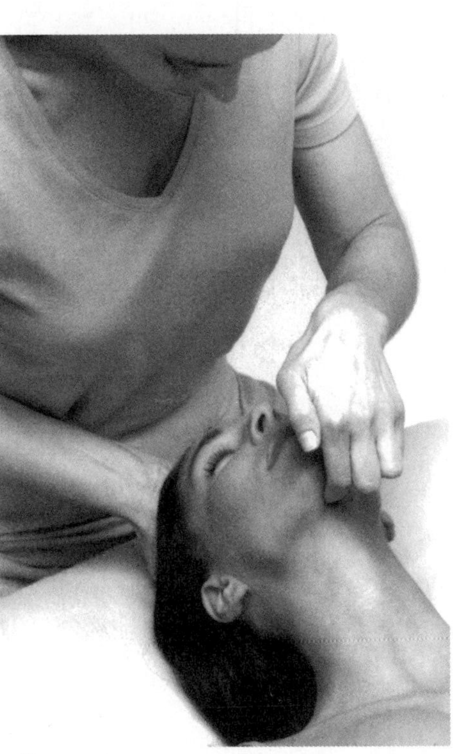

Fig 4-77

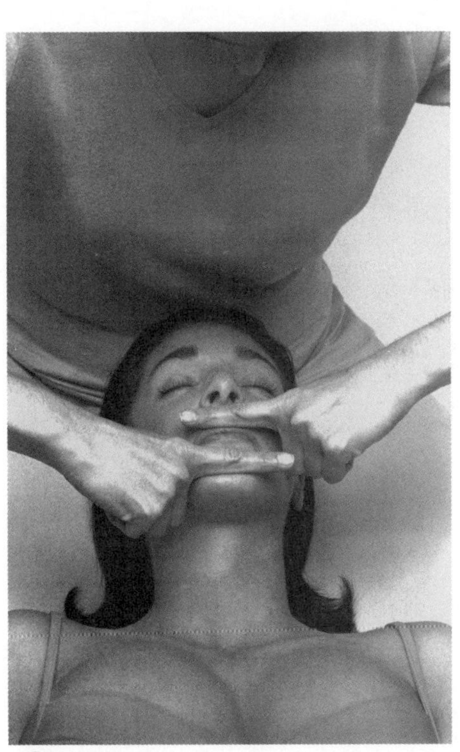

Fig 4-78

6. The client is sitting up. Stand at the head of the table behind the client. Interlace the fingers of both hands underneath the client's chin, and pull back towards your body for 30 seconds (Fig. 4-79).

7. The client is lying face-up. Apply pressure with the pad of muscle at the base of your thumbs onto the jaw muscles, pushing in and out, for 1 minute (Fig. 4-80).

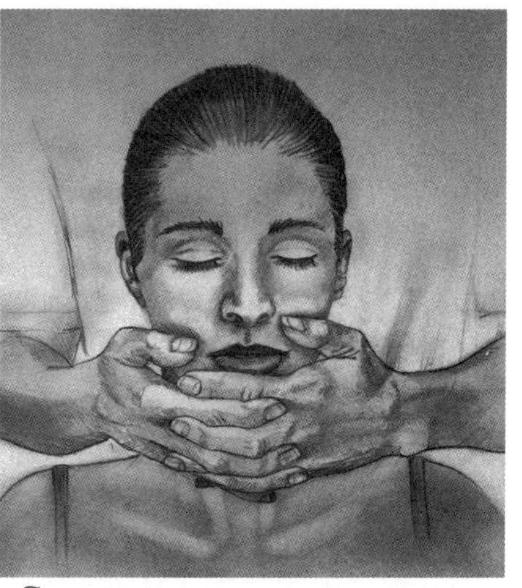

Fig 4-79

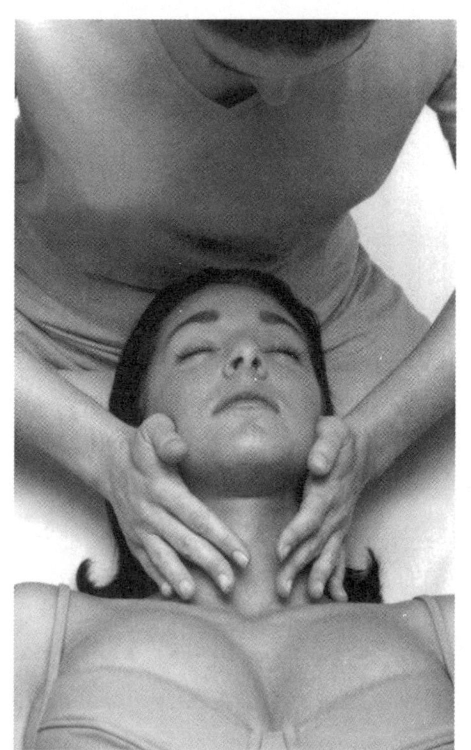

Fig 4-80

Comment

The Sugar and Salt Treatment stimulates the upper back at T-4, the two connecting points for the lungs. In Chinese medicine the lung is the source of our physical and emotional protection. If the lung is weak we are vulnerable to infections and the negative thoughts and emotions of other people[14].

The points on the upper and lower lips and chin stimulate the central spinal core energy. Any time the skin on the midline is touched the primal life force is contacted, whether it's on the lips, the chin, the sternum, the abdomen, or the perineum.

The treatment ends through helping the jaw muscles to relax. The jaw is an area where many people have tension. Commonly there is extra tightness that has found its way to the jaw muscles from clenching the teeth at night, grinding the teeth, or holding extra tension unconsciously during the day. Frustrated self-expression that has not been released through exercise, talking, singing, or therapy will create more jaw tightness.

Treatments and Meditations for Emotional Balance

"In the West we have a psychological quirky behavior. And we have emotional personalities. Do you know where it comes from? It comes from our structural tension. Can you understand? And each time there's a structural defect, in that coordinating area, in the biological living tissues, the stress creates a psychological problem. It's a fact. And this fact was known 3,000 years ago. So under no circumstances does a person who comes to you for adjustments, come only for physical treatment. He has a deep psychological problem and biological pain.

—Yogi Bhajan[1]

Depression

Much of the US population has emotional problems needing attention. Marriage and family counselors, psychiatrists, psychotherapists, hypnotherapists, social workers, and many others offer help. Most of the problems concern depression. Thirteen percent of the US population is diagnosed as depressed, and that is only the official number of diagnosed cases. But the actual number may be closer to 50 percent.

Depression is a medical illness with clearly recognizable symptoms such as: lack of hope, listlessness, indecisiveness, absence of cheerfulness, feelings of inadequacy, and withdrawal from social contact. Depressed people may lack self-confidence and self-esteem. They may have poor ability to concentrate and have negative expectations. Some depressed people dwell on thoughts of suicide and death.

Depression includes major depression, manic-depression, dysthmia, and it costs the US economy $43.7 billion annually. Suicide costs the economy $7.5 billion. Direct-care, including therapy, medication, and psychiatric services costs $12.4 billion. Costs from morbidity are $23.8 billion. Morbidity includes lost income due to absenteeism and reduced productivity. Depression costs more than stroke, epilepsy, multiple sclerosis, and cerebral palsy put together[2].

Depression often strikes during a person's most productive years, between the ages of 25 and 44. Roughly 70 percent of all depressed adults are under the age of 45, and 72 percent of those are in the labor force[2]. In a world-wide trend, over a third of the women from 18 to 22 years old showed significant depression[3]. In young men the risk of depression is rising to the same level as it is among young women[4].

Despite the grim statistics, depression has a higher success rate for treatment tha many other illnesses. Depression is most often treated with drugs such as Prozac Side-effects may include insomnia, heart palpitations, dependency (whether psychological or physical), more depression, and even suicide.

Whether people seek professional help for depression is debatable. At least 3 out of 10 of my patients have mental and emotional conflicts contributing to their disease. So, depression may be lurking under the surface of whatever complaints your client is communicating to you: insomnia, stiffness in the lower back, tightness in the neck and shoulders, or feelings of stress and anxiety.

Can you help depression and other emotional problems? Yes, you can be part of the steps that your client takes to recover energy and stamina. Remember that these treatments can relieve tension, boost self-esteem, heighten a sense of well-being, and even reduce depression. Your healing touch can alleviate the pain and soothe the battle wounds. You can restore blood circulation that neutralizes the anger and rage. You can assuage the grief and sadness. You can help your clients live more comfortably with themselves. You can rekindle a sense of self-confidence in the person with wounded self-esteem.

However, I never begin to treat a patient with the idea that I'm curing an emotional problem. I enter the treatment room ready to treat the physical body. It is always a physical touch procedure. After the visit, I expect that the person's vitality and love of life will be increased.

The most important truth to deal with initially is the symptom that has motivated the person to seek care. To get the broadest and most revealing symptomatic picture, ask questions. How long have you had pain there? How much pain?

On a scale of zero to ten—where zero is pain-free and ten is excruciating pain—what score do you give? Is it constant or does it come and go?

Does the pain travel to other areas of your body? Do you experience hot or cold sensations associated with it? Is this a new development or have you had it before? Is the pain from a physical injury? Or do you think it is related to stress or emotional tension?

When it is appropriate to counsel a person about emotional stress, I do it. There are times when the patient only wants to talk and is satisfied with my undivided attention and conversation. When it is evident that patients need more than brief counseling, I refer them to a psychotherapist.

Kindle the Golden Stove Treatment

(about 9 minutes)

IF YOU ARE UNEASY AND DO NOT KNOW EXACTLY WHERE TO START WITH A CLIENT WHO EXHIBITS EMOTIONAL TENSION, THIS TREATMENT IS A PLACE TO BEGIN.

TREATING THE CLIENT FROM THE ABDOMEN CAN CREATE RELAXED FEELINGS AND RID THE BODY OF MANY IMBALANCES.

The Golden Stove is one name the ancients gave to the region below the navel. It is also called the **kundalini** point, the residence of the coiled serpent of human potential, or the center point—the center of gravity in the body. The kundalini point is found 1 1/2 inches below the navel and is at the level of the fifth lumbar vertebra. It is an area that can warm the entire body when properly stimulated.

The Japanese call this point *hara*. The *hara* is like a sea of generative force and vitality that gives us the ability to adapt and change. Discovering the *hara* means finding an inner balance point, and it implies feeling more centered psychologically as well as physically[5].

The primary effect of this treatment is heating the body. When the kundalini is aroused from this area below the navel the entire body can heat up.

1. Your client is lying face up.

a. Use 3 or 4 fingers to tap at the kundalini point (1 1/2 inches below the navel) with a steady rhythm (Fig. 5-01). Begin with a soft percussive movement for 30 seconds, then double the intensity using the

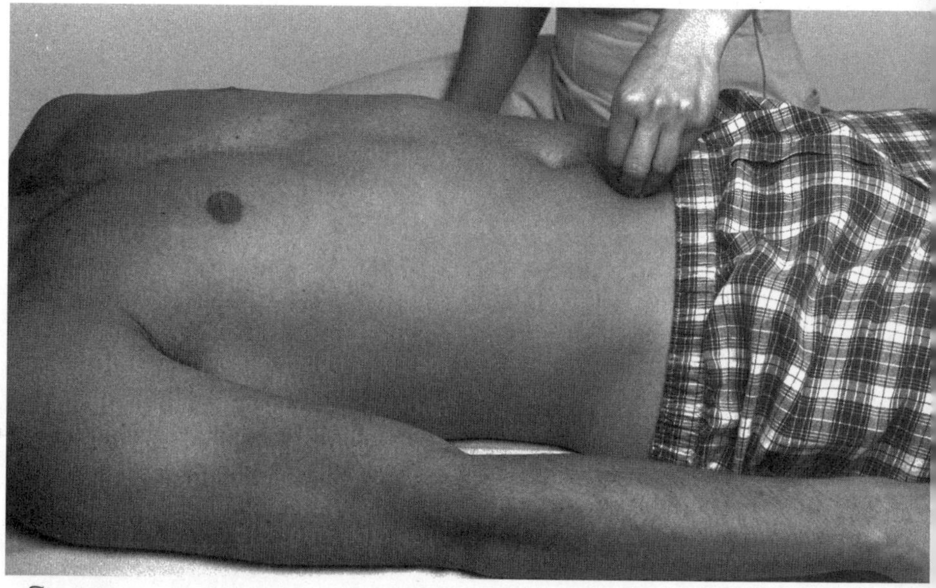

Fig 5-01

client's pain tolerance as your guide. Continue for 2 1/2 more minutes.

b. Have your client lift his legs 2 feet off the table as you continue to tap 1 1/2 inches below the navel with a fast, strong rhythm (Fig. 5-02) for 1 1/2 minutes.

If the legs come down before the time is up, continue percussing, and ask the client to lift the legs again as soon as possible to complete the 1 1/2 minutes. Remember, the longer you tap at the kundalini point, the more heat will be generated.

2. Use the fingertips of one hand to tap the sternum with a steady rhythm for 30 seconds (Fig. 5-03).

3. Continue to percuss the upper chest muscles on both sides, using your fingertips (Fig. 5-04). Tap using both hands at the same time for 1 minute.

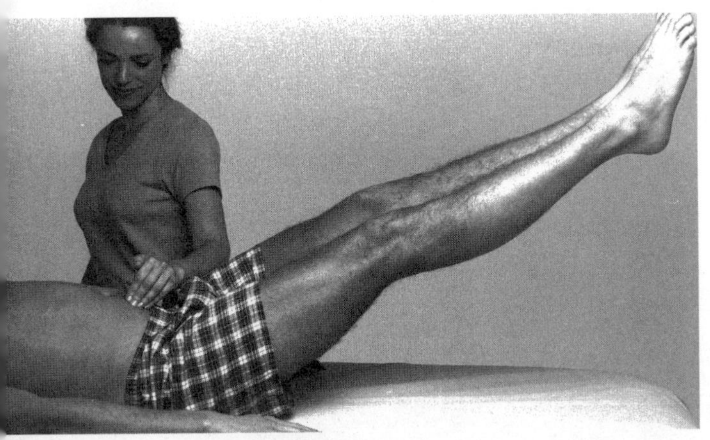

Fig 5-02

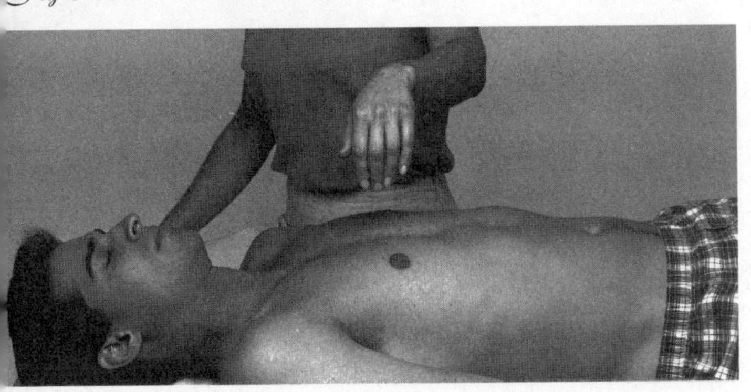

Fig 5-03

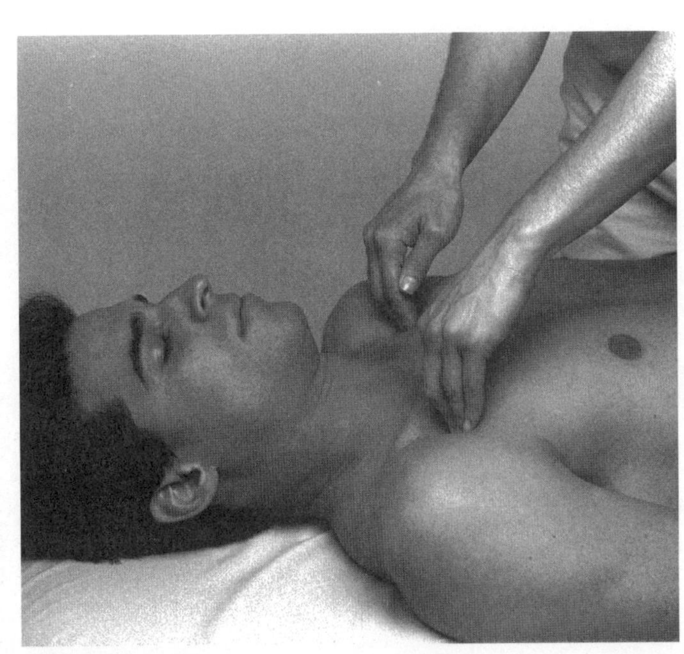

Fig 5-04

4. Then hold each of your client's wrists; clap the fingers together using a fast motion for 30 seconds (Figs. 5-05 and 5-06).

5. Place your client's hands on his chest, one on top of the other, and ask him to relax (Fig. 5-07). Time: about 3 minutes.

Here is a sample of the kinds of suggestions to give your clients as they begin to rest: "Heal yourself by entering a state of deep relaxation.... Direct your white blood cells to heal you.... Direct your red blood cells to feel good...."

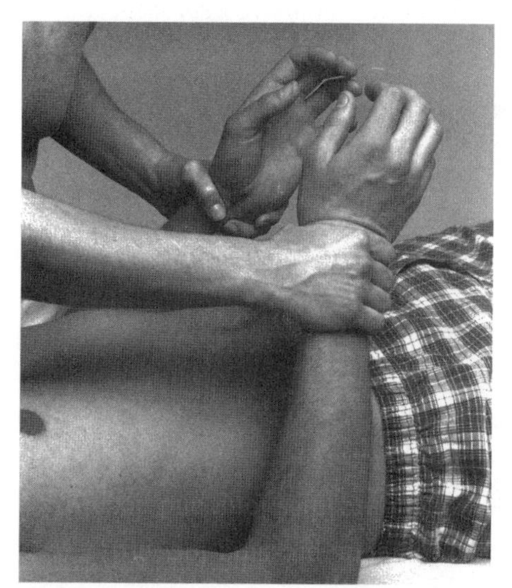
Fig 5-05

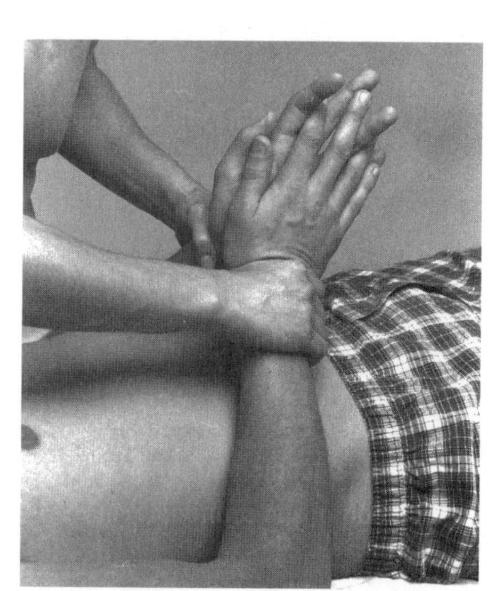
Fig 5-06

Fig 5-07

Advanced Practice
(about 14 minutes)

1. The client is lying face up.

a. Percuss the kundalini point (1 1/2 inches below the navel) for 1 minute using a soft and steady rhythm. Then change to a stronger and faster movement for 6 more minutes.

b. Have the client lift his legs 2 feet off the table for 2 minutes as you continue percussing. Then have him lift his legs higher for 1 minute while you keep percussing the same point.

2. The client's legs are down. Have him relax while you tap the sternum with the fingertips of one hand for 1 minute.

3. Switch to tapping the upper chest muscles on both sides for 1 minute.

4. Hold the client's wrists and clap his fingers together rapidly for 20 seconds.

5. Place the client's crossed hands on his chest, and ask him to relax. Now give the client healing suggestions.

Comment

Your goal is to bring your client out of his head and out of his heart, down into the center of his body. Get him away from the turbulent emotions that disturb the heart.

Remember, use the client's pain tolerance as a guide for how strongly you percuss. And the longer you tap at the kundalini point, the more heat will be generated.

Massage for Security and Connectedness with Earth

(10 to 11 minutes)

USE THIS TREATMENT FOR LOWER BACK PAIN, HIP-JOINT PROBLEMS, KNEE PAINS, AND ANKLE PROBLEMS.

1. Your client is face up. Place both hands below the knee side-by-side and palms down. Press your thumbs into the front portion of the calf muscles at the curve of the shin (tibia). At the same time press your fingers into the outside part of the calf muscle (Fig. 5-08). Do each leg for 1 minute.

2. Have your client turn over face down. Gently press your thumb into the coccyx area for 10 seconds (Fig. 5-09). To find the coccyx (tailbone) go to the center of the **sacrum**. Then travel a little farther down the sacrum until it curves forward like a hook, and push there.

3. Use your fists to punch the buttocks for 2 minutes (Fig. 5-10). Stay on the soft tissue—do not punch the bones.

4. Pound the feet with alternating fists for 2 minutes (Fig. 5-11). Do both feet at the same time.

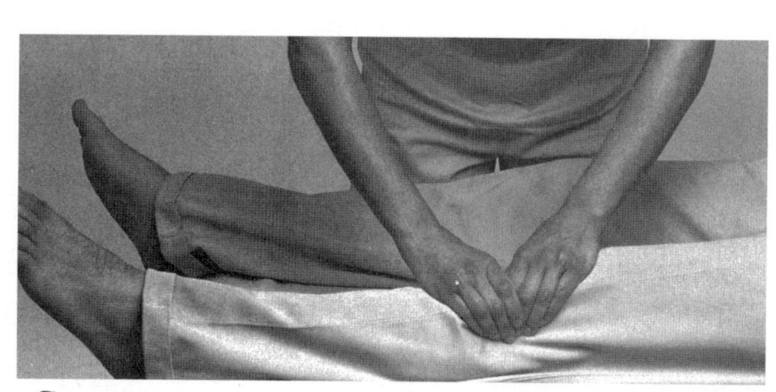

Fig 5-08

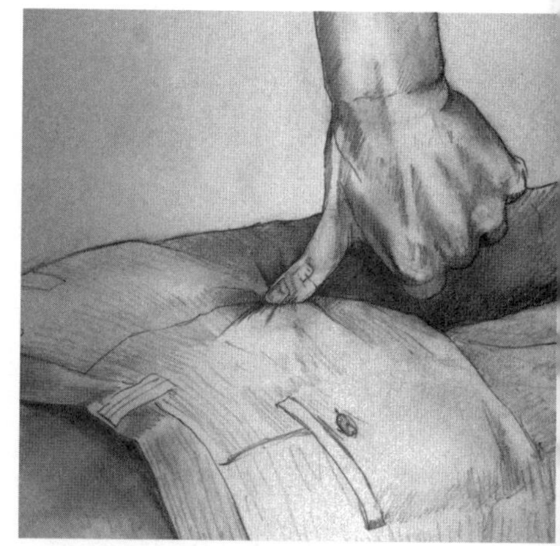

Fig 5-09

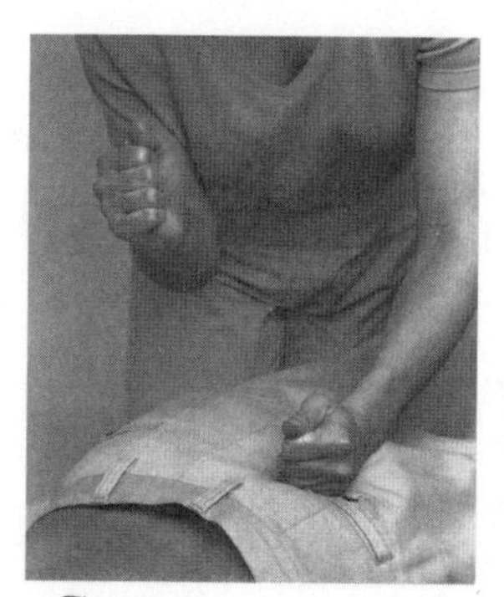

Fig 5-10

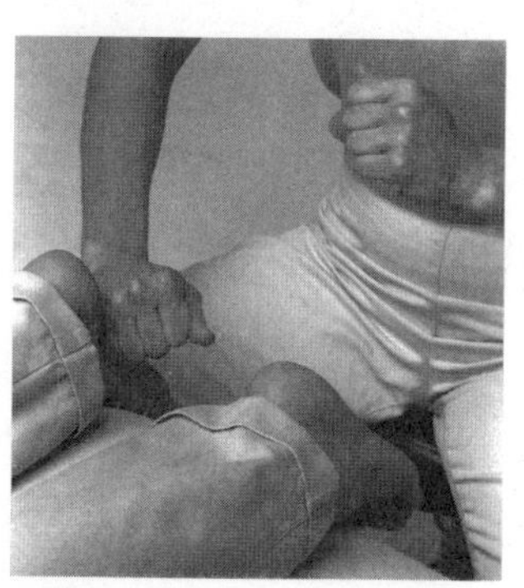

Fig 5-11

5. Push the thumbs deeply into the midline of the calves for 1 minute (Fig. 5-12). Do both calves at the same time.

6. Use both thumbs to apply heavy pressure to the middle back, adjacent to the lower shoulder blade at the T-6 area (Fig. 5-13). Total time: 1 minute.

7. Place the thumbs on each side of the spine in the muscles at L-5 musculature and deeply massage in small circles for 1 minute (Fig. 5-14).

8. The client turns face up. Place the thumbs above the groin region (Fig. 5-15). Press straight down into the lower abdominal muscles for 1 minute.

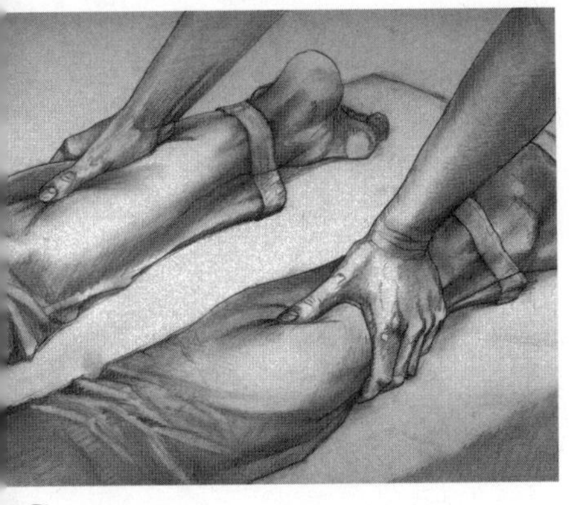
Fig 5-12

Comment

This treatment works on the lower body helping a client to be calm and connected to the earth element within the body. When the earth element is functioning well there is a sense of security and belonging. All food is digested and eliminated well.

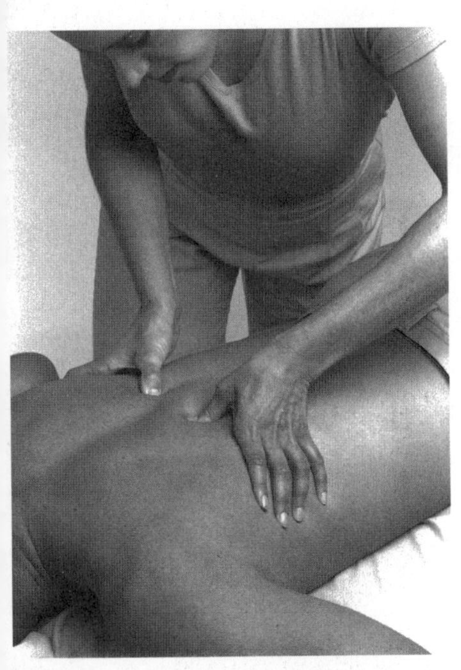
Fig 5-13

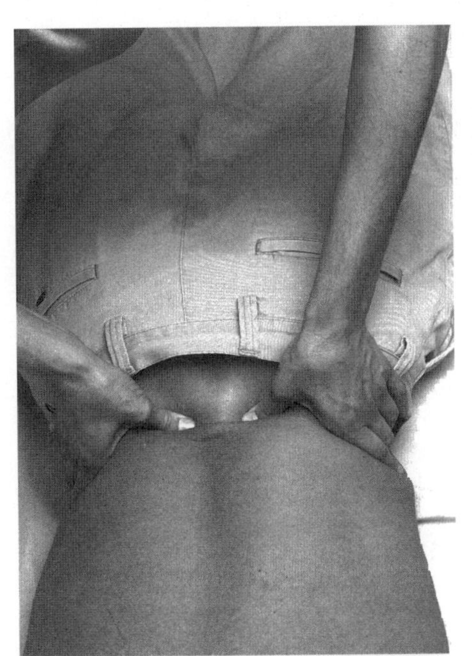
Fig 5-14

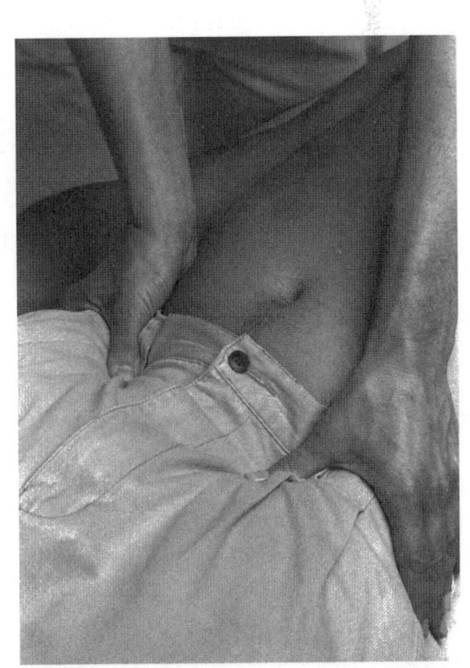
Fig 5-15

Cranial Adjustment for Restoring Courage

(2 1/2 to 3 minutes)

THIS FAST, EFFECTIVE TREATMENT IS DONE ON THE HEAD AND SHOULDERS. WHEN YOGI BHAJAN TREATED A MEMBER OF THE AUDIENCE, HIS PRAYER FOR THE PERSON DURING THESE STEPS WAS TO OVERCOME FEAR AND BE LION-HEARTED. I BELIEVE THAT IT IS ESSENTIAL THAT YOU TAKE A POSITION OF RESTORING HEALTH AND HELPING ELIMINATE TOXIC EMOTIONS. YOU WILL AWAKEN THE POSITIVE COUNTERPART TO THE NEGATIVE EMOTIONS.

I use this treatment as a body balancer, to connect the left and right sides, and to connect the upper and lower body. A common comment: "Can you do that some more?"

1. The client is seated. Stand behind the client with your elbows out to the sides, so that your palms can push the sides of the skull while your middle and ring fingers cover the eyes. Place your index fingers on the forehead. The back of the client's head rests against your stomach (Fig. 5-16). Pull back on your hands for 40 seconds.

2. Place your left index finger across the nose hooking the right side. Your right index finger hooks over the nose beneath the left index finger. Curl the other 3 fingers of both hands under towards the palms. The thumbs are on the sides of the head above the temples (Fig. 5-17).

Rest the back of the client's head on your stomach or chest. Now pull both index fingers in opposite directions as you pull the client's head toward your body while your last three fingers press the cheeks. Time: 25 seconds.

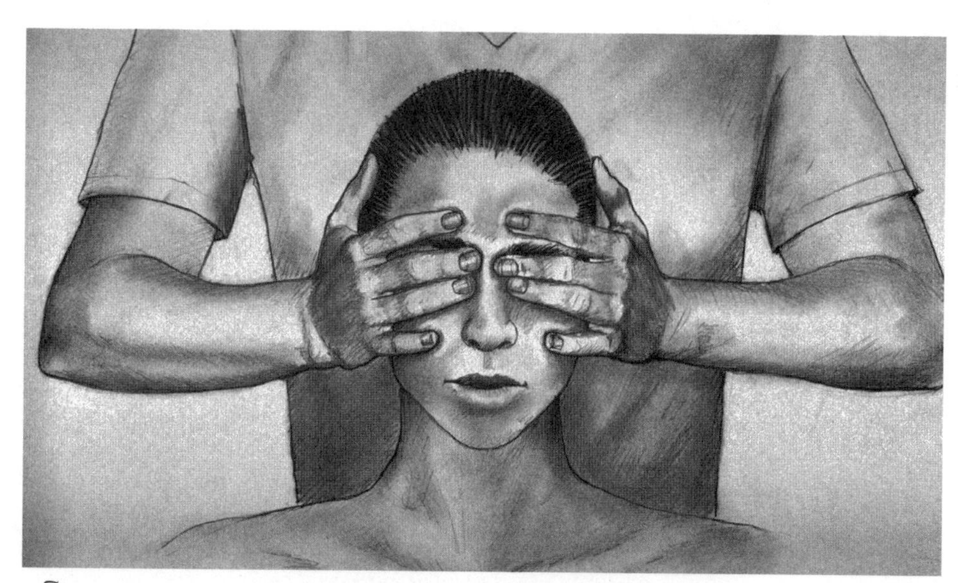

Fig 5-16

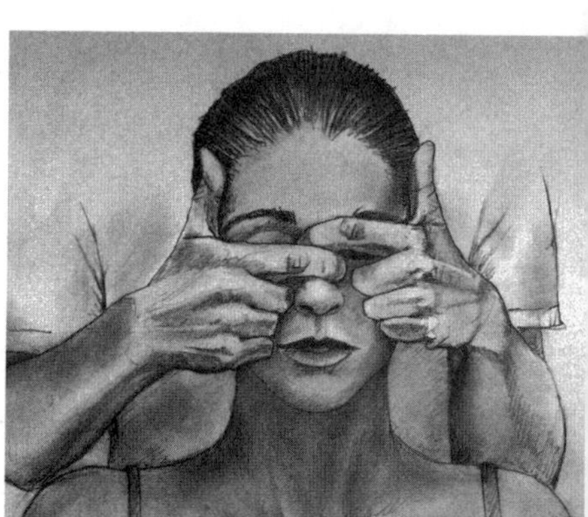

Fig 5-17

3. For this step, the client's head needs to be considerably lower than yours. Try having the client sit on a stool, or if you use a treatment table you could kneel on top of the table. The back of the client's head is on your stomach. Place all 4 fingertips underneath the cheekbones and lift the head holding steady pressure for 15 seconds (Fig. 5-18). The head will tilt back with the lift pressure.

4. Support the client's neck with your right hand. Place your left hand on the right side of the client's face and rotate the head as far to the left as you can using both hands for 15 seconds (Fig. 5-19). Now reverse your hand positions. Then repeat the movement, rotating the head to the right side. Total time: 30 seconds.

5. Rest your left hand on the client's shoulder. Press the right forefinger into the episternal notch. The forefinger can be pressed behind the sternum from this position (Fig. 5-20). Have the client cough 2 or 3 times. Then ask the client to cough again with mouth open and tongue out. Total time: 15 seconds.

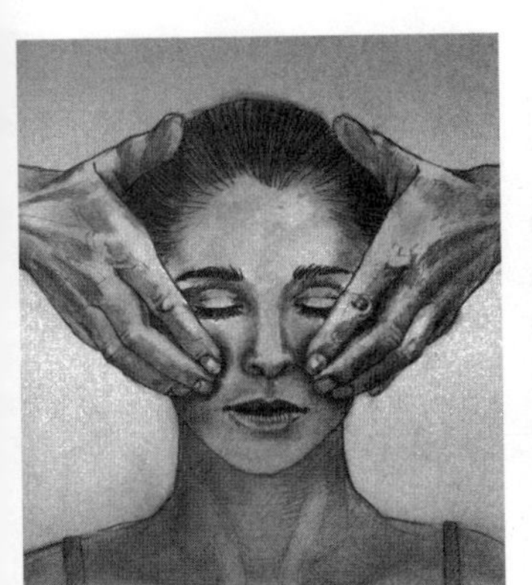

Fig 5-18

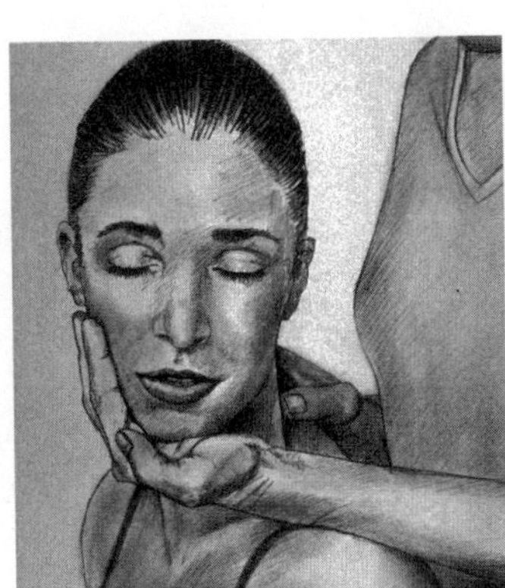

Fig 5-19

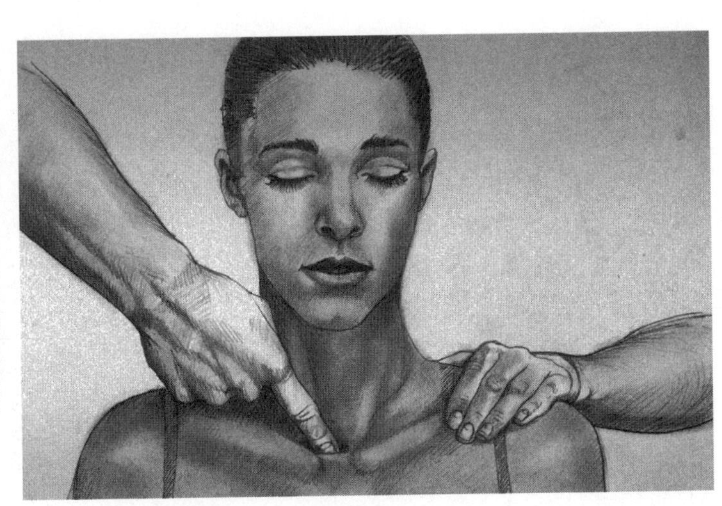

Fig 5-20

6. Grasp the shoulder muscles with heavy pressure for 20 seconds. Then release your grasp and push down on the shoulders with the heels of your hands for 10 seconds (Fig. 5-21).

Comment

This treatment is a new style of cranial adjustment in the seated position. When this treatment was first demonstrated, Yogi Bhajan treated a doctor in the audience whose father had died of a brain tumor when the doctor was 19 years old. The doctor reported having fears of similar health problems coming to his own life. And he felt a stifling relationship with his mother. As he treated the doctor, Yogi Bhajan said that taking courage into the future was the healing way to go.

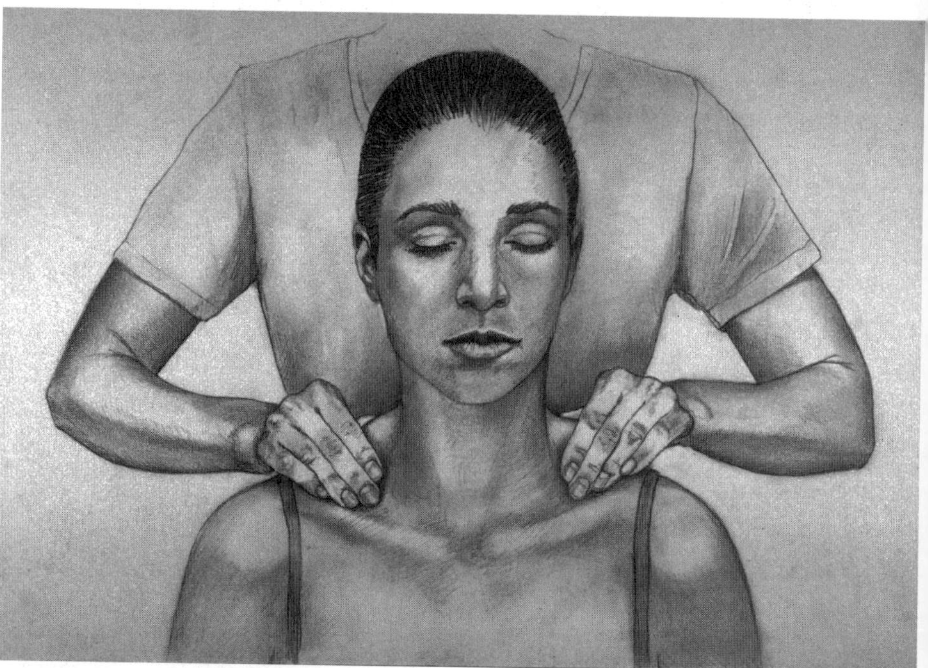

Fig 5-21

Cranial Adjustment for Reaching the Heavens

(19 to 20 minutes)

UNLESS YOU HAVE HAD THIS TREATMENT DONE TO YOU, YOU CANNOT GRASP THE INTENSITY AND BEAUTY OF WHAT TAKES PLACE. IF YOU FEEL THAT YOUR CLIENT NEEDS TO COMPLETELY ALTER HIS OR HER STATE OF CONSCIOUSNESS, THIS IS ONE TREATMENT YOU CAN USE. PLEASE DO ALL THE STEPS INCLUDING THE MEDITATION (STEP 7).

1. You are standing behind your seated client. Place your index fingers on the cheekbones. The middle fingers are just below the cheekbones, and the ring fingers are on the jaw muscles (Fig. 5-22). Rest the back of the client's head on your chest. For 3 minutes, slide your fingers simultaneously back and forth toward the **midline**, then away.

2. Interlace your fingers together across the forehead. Pull the head back into your chest or stomach with strong pressure for 3 1/2 minutes (Fig. 5-23).

3. The back of your client's head is resting on your stomach or chest. Place your first 3 fingers of both hands across the forehead with the ring fingers at the root of the nose (where the nose meets the forehead). Pull back for 3 minutes as your client breathes slowly, powerfully, and deeply on both the inhale and the exhale (Fig. 5-24).

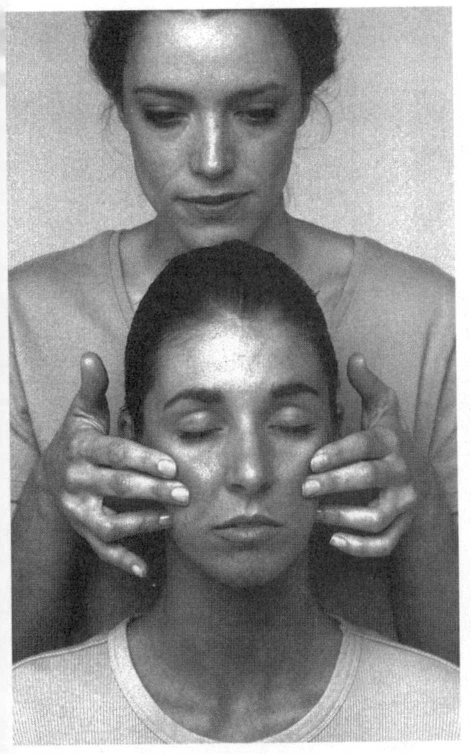

Fig 5-22

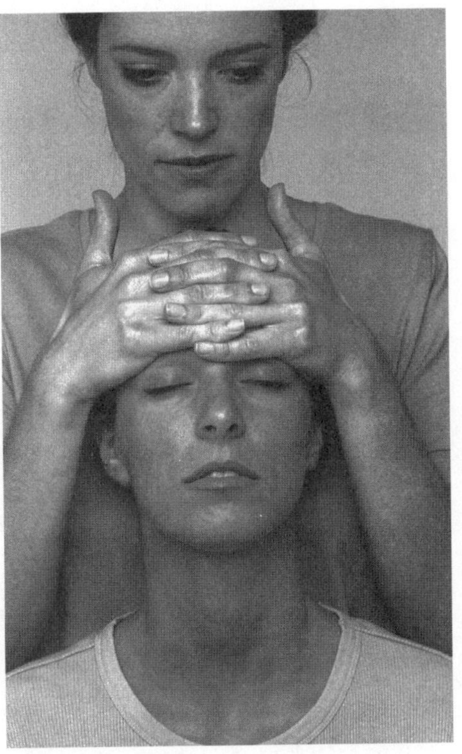

Fig 5-23

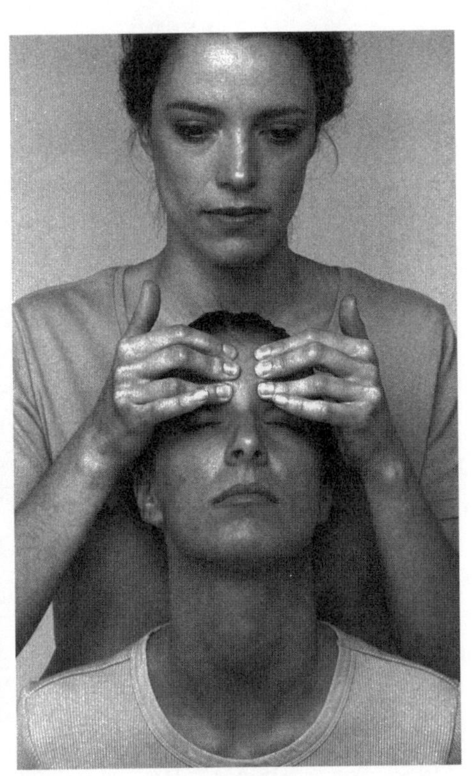

Fig 5-24

4. Place your index fingers on top of the closed eyes, with the fingertips touching the side of the nose. Apply softly increasing pressure straight into the eye socket (Fig. 5-25); then draw the fingers across the eyes to the temples. Total time: 10 seconds.

5. Place the middle fingers just outside and above the corners of the mouth (Fig. 5-26). Pull back using strong pressure for 10 seconds or more.

6. Cup both hands under the chin, pul the head back into your stomach and chest for 10 seconds (Fig. 5-27). The head will rotate back.

7. The client is still seated.

a. Have your client roll the tongue up to the hard palate and inhale through the open mouth (Fig. 5-28), exhaling through the nose, for 5 minutes. Urge the client to take the deepest possible breath on the inhale.

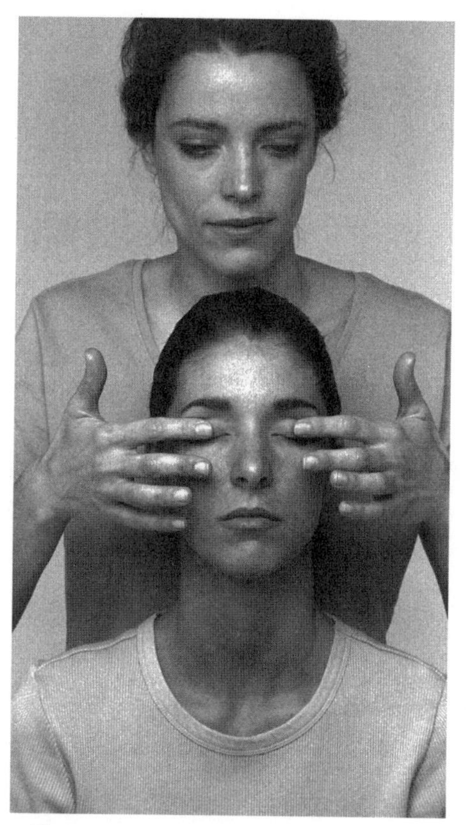

Fig 5-25

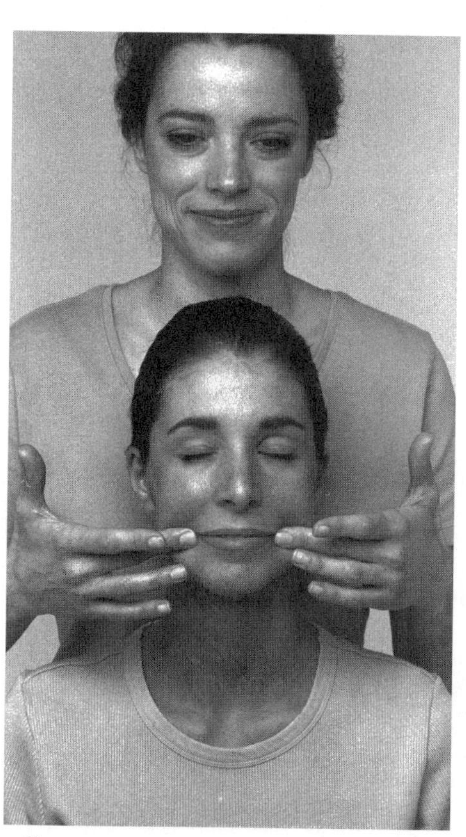

Fig 5-26

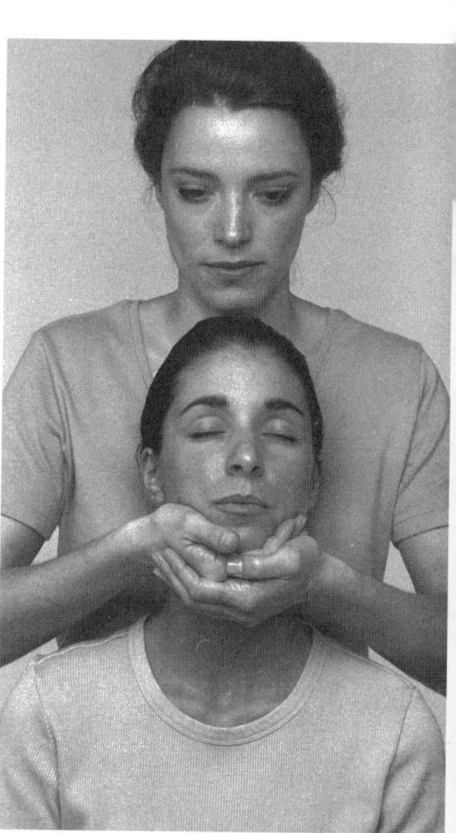

Fig 5-27

With the tongue rolled up to the hard palate, the nerve pathways to the pituitary and hypothalamus are stimulated. This combination of tongue placement and breath will lead your client into an altered state.

If the client gets dizzy or light-headed encourage a long, deep inhale and exhale through the nose until composure has returned. Then encourage your client to finish the entire 5 minutes.

b. At the end of the 5 minutes, the client inhales deeply and holds the breath in, while pressing the tongue firmly into the hard palate. While the breath is being held, ask the client to visualize energy traveling from the sacrum all the way up the spine to the brain. If it is easier, you may ask the client to visualize light or electricity flowing. When unable to hold the breath any more, the client exhales like a cannon firing. Repeat two more times. Time: 1-2 minutes.

c. The client places the tongue behind the front teeth, pressing forward. The client breathes long and deeply for 3 minutes.

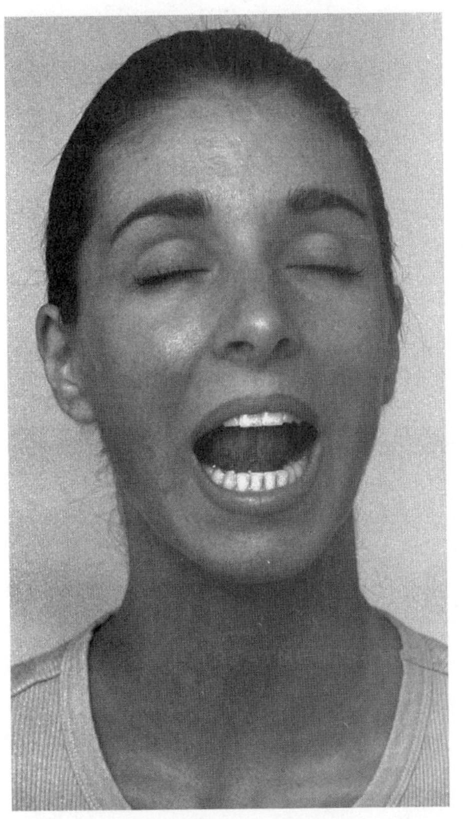

Fig 5-28

Releasing Fear and Grief

(20 minutes)

IN THIS TREATMENT YOU WILL HELP YOUR CLIENT REACH A DEEP STATE OF BODY REST AND HEAL DEEP EMOTIONAL SCARS.

Before beginning, explain to your client that you will be asking a few questions during the treatment, and you both need to agree on a sign for "yes" and "no" that is easy for the client to use. It might be: a verbal "yes" or "no," a nod of the head "yes," or a shake of the head "no"; a small right-hand movement for "yes," a small left-hand movement for "no." Make sure you both agree to the signals in advance. This subtle communication will be used in Step 3.

1. Have your client relax on the back. Standing to the left side, place your hands side-by-side, palms-down across the chest. The heels of your hands are on the sternum (Fig. 5-29). Lean down gently to press into the chest and sternum with part of your body weight. Move your hands simultaneously back-and-forth, rocking the person gently, and dragging the skin a few inches as you go for about 1 minute.

As you do step 1 above, begin a guided relaxation by talking to your client in a kind and gentle manner. Keep this up throughout the whole procedure. You may begin with something like: "We are here together to rest and relax.... Take a deep breath, a big one ... and let it go.... That was good. Please take another life-giving

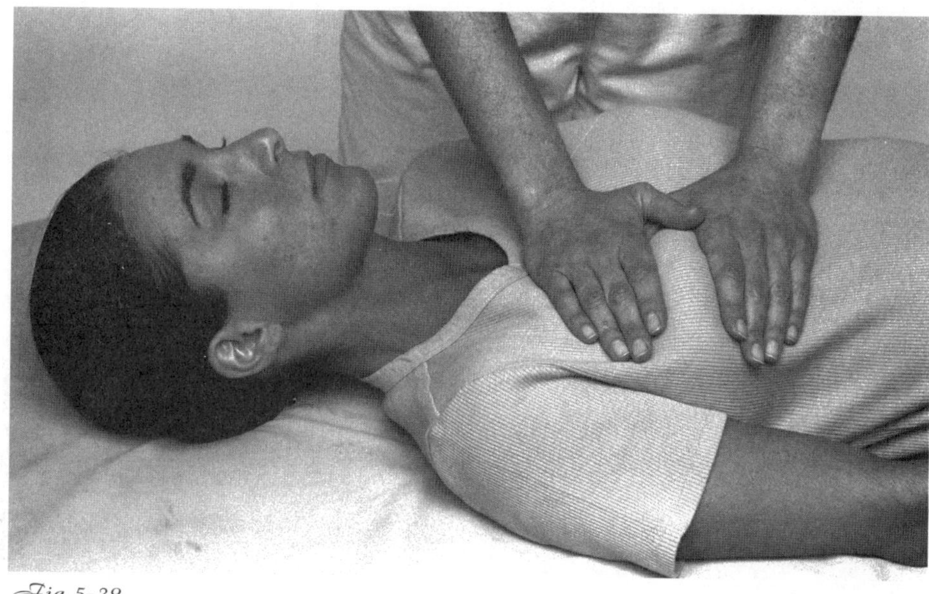

Fig 5-29

breath ... letting go with ease and comfort ... breathing deeply when it helps you to rest.... Feel the pressure of the table supporting you.... Rest deeper.... Listen to the music which helps you relax more.... With your eyes closed see yourself as secure, protected, and safe...."

2. Move the right palm to the left upper chest. Place the left palm on the right upper chest (Fig. 5-30).

Rock back and forth softly sending prana through your hands to the client for approximately 2 minutes. Continue to talk with the client:

"The muscles of your buttocks relax and spread.... Your leg muscles become like warm butter, soft ... warm, very soft.... It's not even necessary to listen to the sound of my voice as you become calm.... Still, enjoying the hand contact ... with a sense of rest and protection, I want you to go to your fear.... Access an emotional scar that you have, a deep scar from your life or ... your long-ago past.... It may be a fear; it can be a forgotten experience.... It might be a car accident (earthquake, tornado, divorce, etc.), or ... something from your long-ago past.... Whatever it is, recall it now."

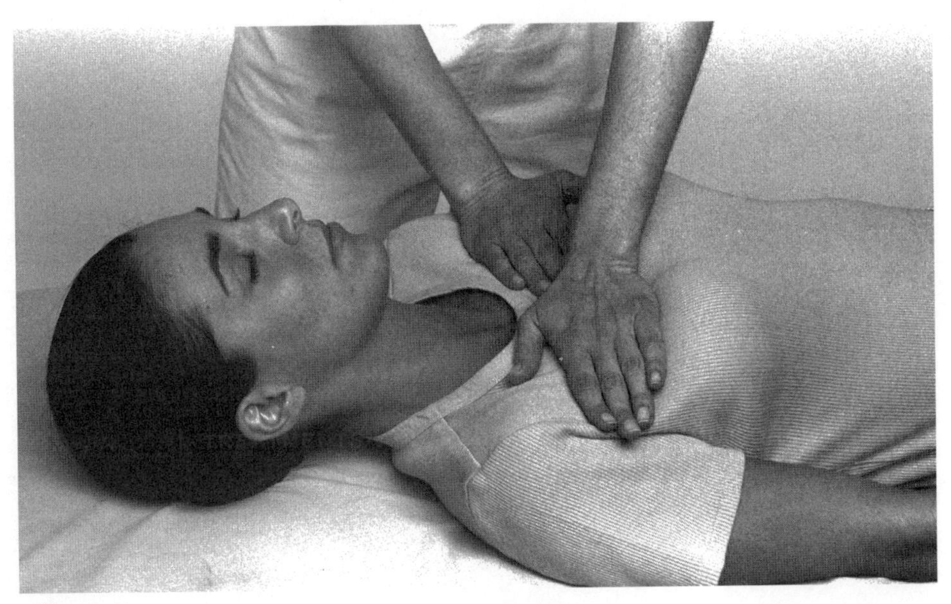

Fig 5-30

Now, moving the left hand to the upper chest on the left side, do the same kind of massage for about two minutes.

3. Place your left hand on the right upper chest. Have the client close her eyes. Then place your right hand over her eyes and forehead (Fig. 5-31). Stay in position for about 2 minutes.

Use the subtle communication that you both agreed on as you ask "yes" or "no" questions. "Have you found a memory or an incident?... [Watch for response.] ... the feelings and the pictures ... hearing the conversations in and all around you.... Now pass through the fear.... We have all dropped a fork onto the kitchen floor before.... Let it go free.... Go to sleep...."

4. Keep the right hand covering the forehead and eyes. Curl the fingers back to the palm on your left hand.

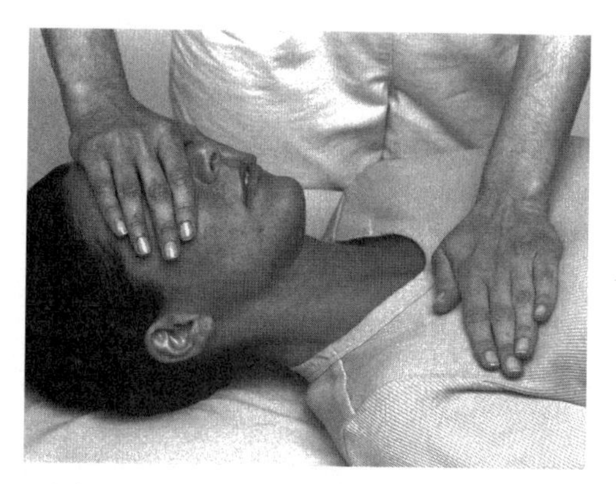

Fig 5-31

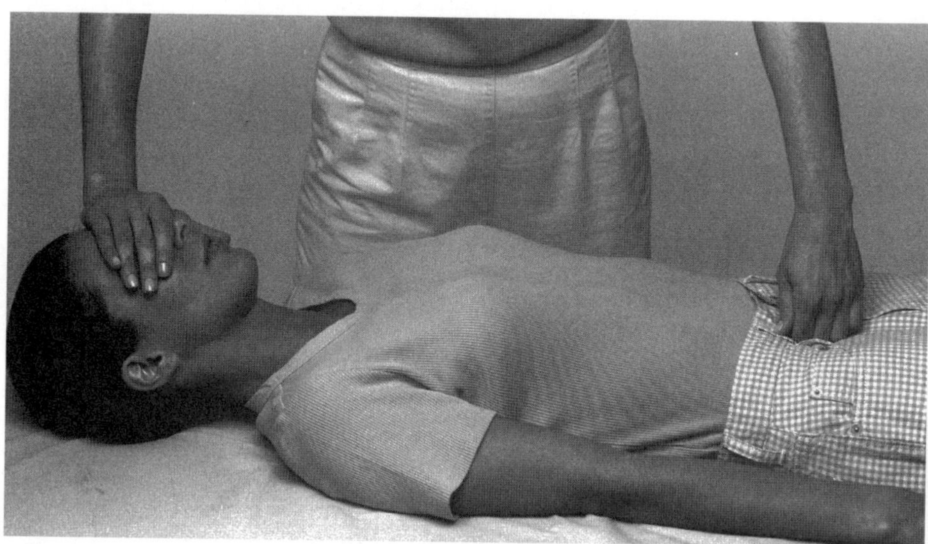

Fig 5-32

Then use the knuckles and your thumb to push deep into the abdominal tissue around the belly button for about 2 minutes (Fig. 5-32).

Continue to talk in rhythm with the client's exhale, pausing as the inhale occurs. "Go through to the other side of this stress.... Walk on through to the other side.... Take a nap now.... Go to sleep like you do in your own bed.... Find the void of sleep, that big, open black empty space ... that you visit each night, when you drift to sleep.... Look to a faraway horizon that you can start to focus on now....

5. Keep the right hand over the eyes as in Step 4. Move the left hand back to the right upper chest (refer to Fig. 5-31). Maintain the position for about 1 minute.

Continue to talk: "Float high; go up to the mountain top.... Be on top of your mountain ... standing there ... looking to the endless horizon before you.... Meditate like that ... go away, far far away.... Meditate now; concentrate on the endless blue horizon, and don't come back until I call you...."

Then wait for a minute or more in silence and, as you remove your hands, say: "All is great; all is vast. There are no limits.... As the vast sky and the great earth know each other ... so do you know your farthest reaches.... Begin to nap.... Go to sleep ... watching the vista, watching ... watching ... looking, seeing those images ... viewing the pictures before you.... Keep enjoying what you see ... the view from there is magnificent.... Enjoy the sights; meditate more; meditate on the picture...."
Allow your client to rest in silence for 5 more minutes.

6. This step has three parts.

a. Give the bottom of each foot a firm massage for about 1 minute each (Fig. 5-33). Use a variety of strokes. You can use long ones from the heel to the toes. You can place your thumbs on any tight spots you find and use continuous circles as the main stroke.

b. Pull each toe (Fig. 5-34). Total time: about 30 seconds.

c. Place the ankle in traction by bending the foot towards the shin wit your hands wrapped around the foot. Then pull the foot with about 10 pounds of pressure (Fig. 5-35) for 30 seconds. Do both feet.

This is like pulling a person's leg because the whole leg moves a little as well. It helps bring your client back from the meditation, letting her know it's over.

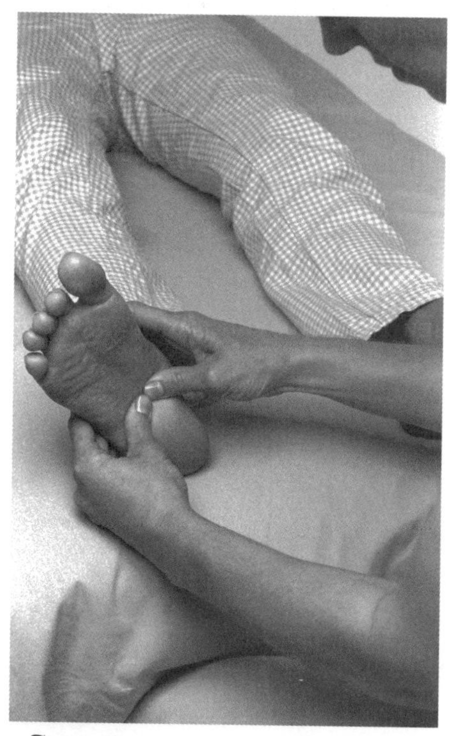

Fig 5-33

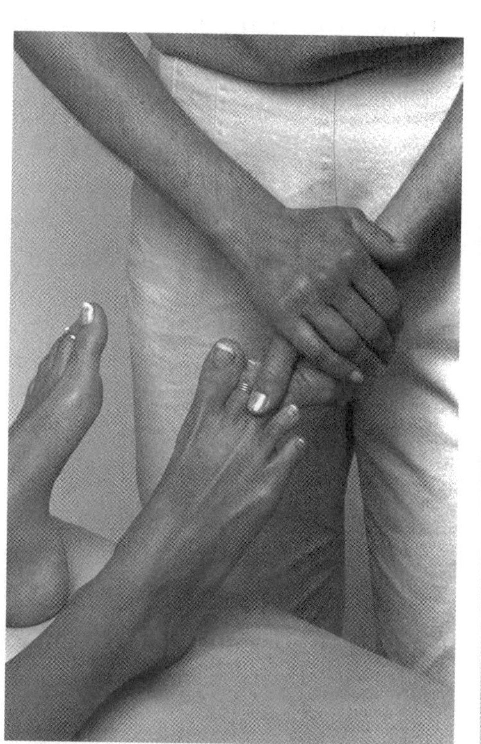

Fig 5-34

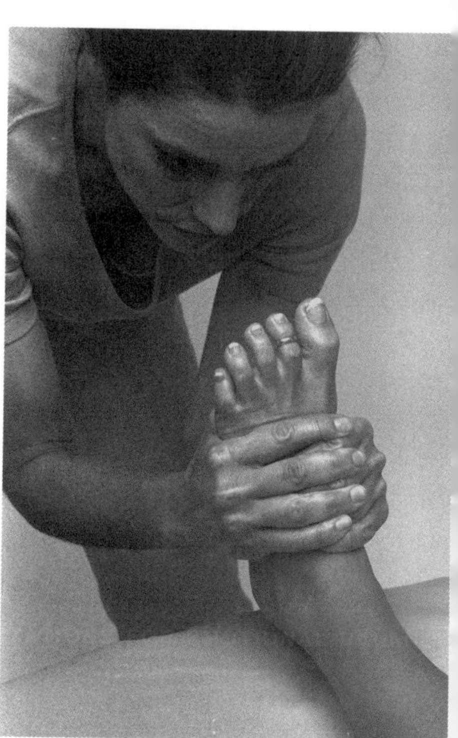

Fig 5-35

Two Meditations for Emotional Balance

"You must understand; your life is based on the capacity of the energy inside of you, not outside of you. Therefore, meditation to keep your mind clear so that your spirit can come through is not a joke. It's essential."

—Yogi Bhajan[6]

Both these meditations stimulate the third eye. The third eye or brow point is the point at the center of the forehead between the eyebrows, associated with the pituitary gland and mid-brain. It is known in Sanskrit as *ajna* **chakra**, the sixth energy center, and it has a relationship with the spinal cord, the bone marrow, and the higher brain areas. Placing three fingers at the brow point activates the *ajna* chakra.

The third eye is a place of focus for the physical eyes during meditation. And focusing there for a few minutes creates brain-wave changes. Rolling the physical eyes up stretches the optic nerve bundles. The nasal half of the right optic nerve bundle connects to the left mid-brain, while the nasal half of the left optic nerve bundle connects to the right mid-brain. They cross each other at the optic chiasma, situated above the pituitary gland.

The pituitary gland or master gland is one of the ancient landmarks of the sixth chakra—used in meditation for calming the mind. Mastery of this chakra brings knowledge of the past, present, and future.

Meditation to Center a Person

(9 to 11 minutes)

THIS MEDITATION CALMS THE MIND AND CAN CENTER A PERSON. THE PRESSURE YOU APPLY AND THE RESISTANCE YOUR PARTNER SUPPLIES HELP BLOOD AND PRANA FLOW THROUGH THE SHOULDER AND NECK JUNCTION.

THIS IS A GOOD MEDITATION FOR BEGINNERS.

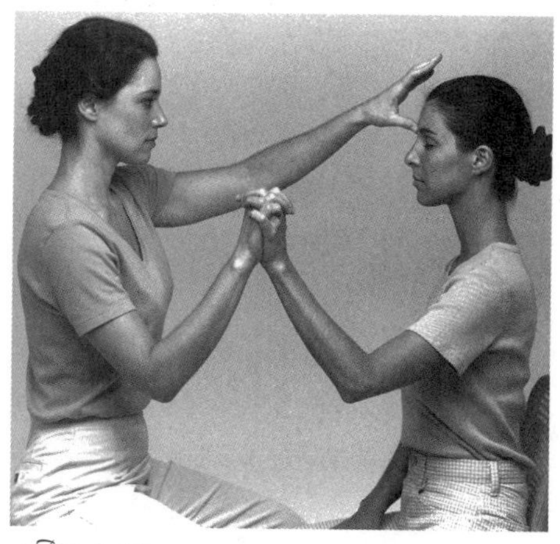

Fig 5-36

If you are new to meditation take courage and do this with a friend first. Develop confidence, and then do it with your clients. It is a **Venus kriya**—you and your client meditate together. It is fun and gives pleasure.

1. Sit in a chair or on a high stool. Your partner is seated on a lower chair facing you. You should be seated about 2-4 inches higher than your partner in this meditation (Fig. 5-36).

2. Ask your partner to interlace the fingers of her left hand with the fingers of your right hand. (With a male partner reverse the hands. Interlace your left hand with his right hand.) You can say something like: "Close your eyes and lock your fingers with mine.... Pull my hand towards you ... harder.... Do your best ... harder." Time: 30 seconds.

3. Place your left thumb on the center of your partner's forehead above the bridge of the nose, fingers above the head. Send **pranic energy** through your thumb and fingertips to the client for the entire meditation. Time: 45 seconds.

4. Keep your left thumb in place on your partner's forehead. Now push on her forehead strongly 6 times. At the same time ask her to resist your pressure with equal force so that you do not push her over. Take 10 to 20 seconds for each push.

Work together. Have her keep her spine straight, without leaning forward to overcome your thumb pressure.

5. Have your partner sit still for 5 minutes, focusing on the third-eye point. Ask her to keep her eyes on the third-eye point as she continues to meditate for 2 more minutes.

Advanced Practice
(9 to 11 minutes)

1. Push on the forehead contact with steady, strong pressure as your partner resists with equal pressure. Time: 3-5 minutes.

2. Push harder on the forehead, then slowly back off—over and over again for 3 minutes. Work with your partner; make sure she resists your pushing with equal force.

3. Have your partner sit still, continuing to meditate for 3 more minutes. After you release the forehead contact, she will experience tranquility.

Meditation to Open the Third Eye
(3 minutes)

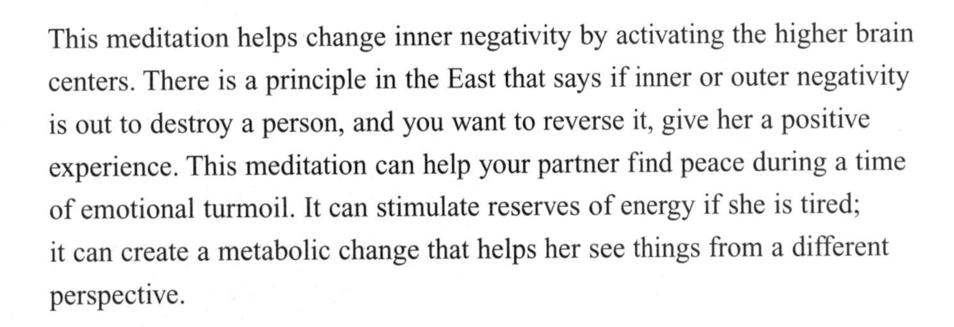

This meditation helps change inner negativity by activating the higher brain centers. There is a principle in the East that says if inner or outer negativity is out to destroy a person, and you want to reverse it, give her a positive experience. This meditation can help your partner find peace during a time of emotional turmoil. It can stimulate reserves of energy if she is tired; it can create a metabolic change that helps her see things from a different perspective.

It does not take long for results to blossom in meditation, and when two people meditate together the effects are multiplied.

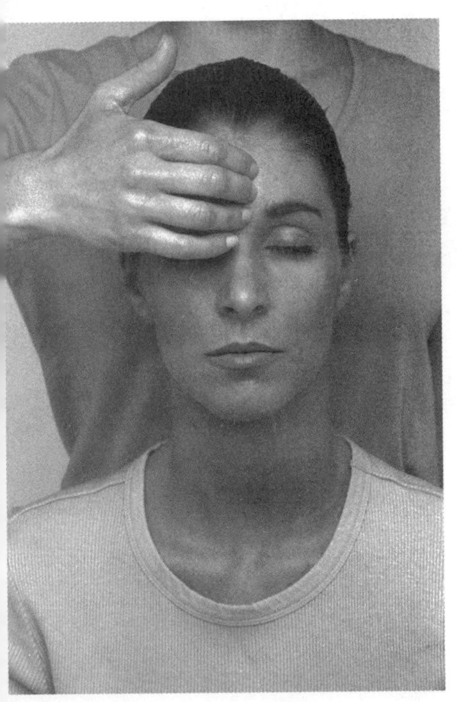

Fig 5-37

1. Your partner sits on a chair or a stool with the spine straight. Her eyes are closed and rolled up at a 45-degree angle, looking at the center of her forehead.

2. You can stand behind your partner or sit to one side. Lightly touch your partner with three fingers: your ring finger on the bridge of the nose; your middle and index fingers on the forehead (Fig. 5-37).

Hold the position for 3 minutes as you send **pranic energy** to your partner.

Comment
A doctor at the Khalsa Chiropractic Association meetings described for us his experience with this meditation: "The overall experience stunned me; I opened my eyes and I was kind of surprised you were all still here. I was aware of what was going on, but I was taken to a whole different place. And I was surprised that I was still here when I opened my eyes."

Yogi Bhajan replied: "Life has many surprises. You can, with the touch of your hand, give somebody an experience of infinity. That's what he's talking about. He's shy about saying it because he's Western. He has no training about it. He has no aspect of it. He has no detail of it. Then an experience happens. When we touch infinity we do not know what to say."

Healing Hands

Healing hands are the projection booth. Healing hands have heart. Healing hands reshape deformed tissues, restructure what is disorganized, and nurture without words. They are the two antennae of prayer for the person who has placed himself under those hands.

It may seem improbable but healing hands make health possible.
Healing hands warm the cold, dry, and prematurely aged tissues.
Healing hands radiate the light of the invisible, making health visible.
Healing hands take care of unruly tissue and out-of-control symptoms.
Healing hands hold life together when all of life is falling in pieces.
Healing hands organize what is chaos.
Healing hands also make chaos of that which is too structured.
Healing hands come from the soul, represent the soul, and make the soul known.
Healing hands bless the person they touch.
Healing hands begin in silence, treat in silence, and return to silence.
Healing hands express the love that cannot be known by words.
Healing hands give shape to the formless,
Healing hands do each day what God never does.
Blessed is the person's life who has a chance to be touched by the soul
with hands that heal.
Healing hands are not taught,
Healing hands treat the most obnoxious human being,
Healing hands treat the untreatable,
Healing hands are the healing.

Treatments to Strengthen the Body and Immune System

The treatments in this chapter are for the exploration of the physical body. They help the body become strong, and they help restore normal function to the entire structure. They can connect areas of the body-mind landscape that have been out of adjustment. Also, they reveal the way human touch changes the basic metabolism of someone that you care about, for many hours. These treatments take 30 minutes or more, so you will invest time on your client. There are excellent sources for more information about mind-body connections[1].

To me, these long treatments cook the body. As the hands work on the muscles the temperature below the surface goes up. And when your hands are warm from the first step they add more heat to the skin, muscles, nerves, and channels below the surface—like sliced apples inside a pie crust sitting in a 425-degree-F oven. After 45 minutes, soft apples come out; far different from the fresh-cut crisp ones that went in.

Longer treatments provide time for clients to rest, relax, and give themselves the nourishment they need. Longer treatments allow you to build strength, to get to know the body you are touching, and to use your intuition. When there's no hurry you are receptive to images that can influence what you say during the treatment. The entire landscape of the body is emotional territory. Therefore, the greater the time you have, the greater the opportunity to affect the client's body and mind positively. The more you live what you are doing and the more you love the client, the better your treatment shall be.

Royal Body Treatment

(about 32 minutes)

THE ROYAL BODY TREATMENT COMPLETELY CONDITIONS THE BODY. IT IS MAGNIFICENT; AND WHEN YOU FINISH, EXPECT THAT THE CLIENT WILL FEEL NOBLE, ACT ROYAL, AND LOOK AT THE WORLD THROUGH SOVEREIGN EYES. YOGI BHAJAN SAYS THIS TREATMENT WAS ORIGINALLY DEVELOPED FOR THE ROYAL FAMILY IN EGYPT MANY CENTURIES AGO.

It is fun to touch, massage, and caress the variety of places on the body. Most strokes that you will use are short, strong, and soothing. Use a small amount of massage oil on each area to help make the experience comforting and calming. Where there is no specific direction use your thumb, fingertips, or palm to do the massage strokes below.

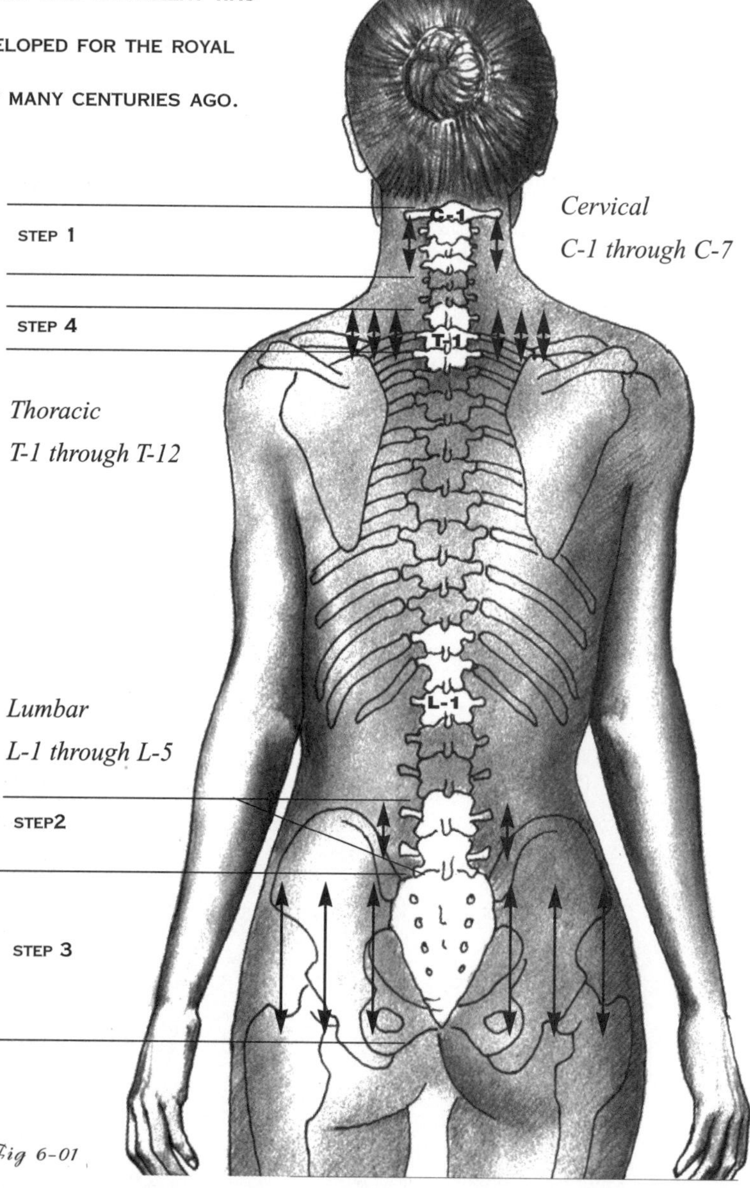

Fig 6-01

1. Have your client lie face down. Massage the upper 2 inches of muscle in the back of the neck (the base of the skull with all of its lumps). Massage the entire area from underneath the ears to the midline of the neck for 2 minutes (Fig. 6-01).

2. Massage the muscles at the L-5 level. Press down with your thumbs on either side of the lower back and stroke up the spine 2 inches. Then slide down to your starting position. Repeat the stroke for 1 minute.

3. Move to your client's buttocks muscles. The buttocks are one of the three largest muscle groups in the body. Everyone that I have treated has at least one and usually two to seven tight spots. To me, they feel like round isolated clumps of tense muscle. When these thick clumps are pressed with deep pressure by warm hands the tissue loosens, stretches, and lengthens.

The buttocks muscles will take more pressure than smaller muscles, so use some strength. You need a blunt instrument such as the thumb, that can penetrate the thick buttocks tissue. Or use the heel of your hand; or use your fists. If you are smaller than your client you can massage one side of the buttocks at a time, placing both thumbs side-by-side.

Use as many angles of massage as you can create. Be thorough and massage deep into the muscles beside the tailbone and sacrum. There can be enough tightness that you could massage for hours. But, in this step of this treatment, massage for 2 minutes.

Here are 5 variations:
a. Begin by using your thumbs to stroke from the sacrum across the hip muscles to the side of the body. Work on both sides at once.

b. Press straight down into the buttocks muscles, perpendicular to the floor, using the fingertips (Fig. 6-02). Slide from the sacrum across the buttocks muscles to the side of the hip.

c. Press into the buttocks muscles at a 45-degree angle.

d. Using the heel of the hand or the fists, press in at an angle perpendicular to the curve of the body.

e. Stand close to your client's shoulder, face the feet, and press at an angle most comfortable for your height and weight. If you are standing up, keep your feet on the floor, or if you work on a futon, keep your knees on the floor.

If you are not satisfied with these angles then choose one for yourself. It might be going straight-in parallel to the floor. Try an unusual angle.

Or, you can also use your elbow. The buttocks muscles are large, flat, and capable of taking heavier pressure (more pounds per square inch), than your thumbs can provide. There's more penetrating power with the elbow, for shaping connective tissue that has jelled.

There can be sore spots in these muscles, so use the pain tolerance of the client to guide the depth of your pressure.

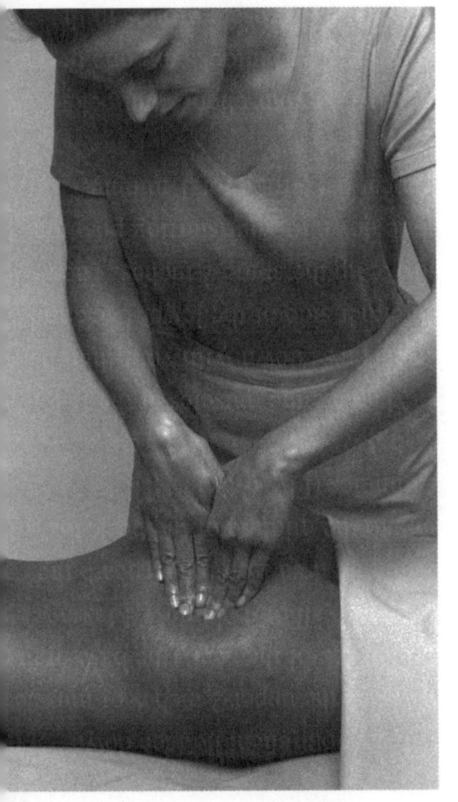

Fig 6-02

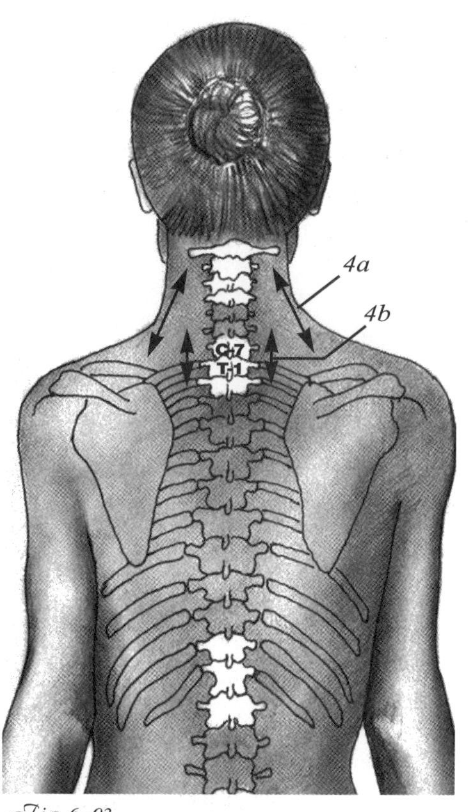

Fig 6-03

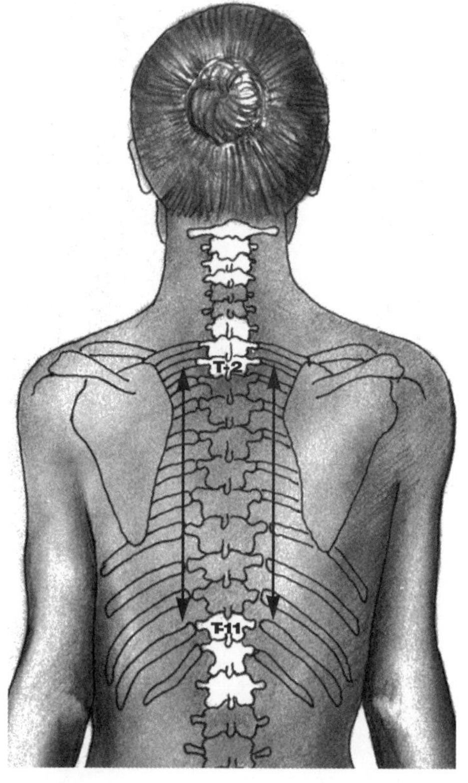

Fig 6-04

4. Move to the shoulder muscles where they curve into the neck. Massage the lower neck (C-7 to T-1) and the top of the upper back (Fig. 6-03 and 6-01).

a. Stand at the head of the table. Place your thumbs on either side of the spine, an inch lower than the large bony process at the base of the neck (Fig. 6-03). Press down with a soft touch, building to your maximum pressure for 5 seconds. Move your thumbs up a thumb-width, and press down in slow motion to your maximum pressure for another 5 seconds.

b. Move to one side of your client. Stroke from the shoulder up the neck with your thumbs, returning to your starting position with your fingertips (refer to Fig. 6-03). Thumbs slide up; fingertips pull down. Then do the other side. Total time: 2 minutes.

5. The client is still face down. Place your fingertips on either side of the spine. Massage the entire middle back from T-2 to T-11 (Fig. 6-04). Begin with a soft massage. Starting at T-2, use your fingertips to slide 2 inches down, then 2 inches up, for about 10 seconds. Then push deeper into the muscles with your thumbs on either side of the spine and repeat one more time. Move your hands farther down the spine repeating the strokes with the fingertips, then the thumbs. Finish at T-11 a minute later.

6. You will treat a large area in a short time in Step 6 (and Step 7), since it's 11 to 14 inches from the upper back to the kidney region. So massage with strong pressure right from the start, and work fast enough to cover this part of the torso.

a. The client remains face down. Place your thumbs on each side of the bony processes at T-2, and stroke towards the sides of the body. Follow the line of the ribs. Use your fingertips alternating with the thumbs. Proceed down the back 14 more inches on both sides from T-2 to T-11 (Fig. 6-05). Total time: 2 minutes.

b. Massage the muscles on either side of the spine between T-11 and L-1. Place your thumbs on either side of the spine in the muscles, stroking from T-11 about 3 inches down to L-1, then slide back up to T-11 (Fig. 6-06). Repeat this movement for a total time of 1 minute.

7. The client is face down. With your fingertips massage the small areas between the spinous processes at the midline for 2 minutes. Start below C-7 and end between L-4 and L-5 (refer to Fig. 6-06).

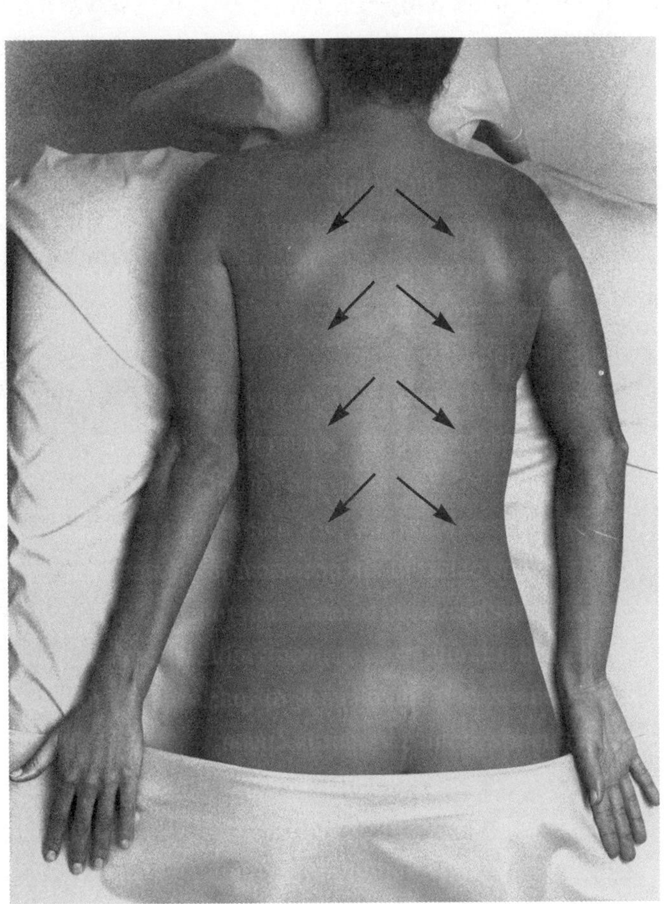

Fig 6-05

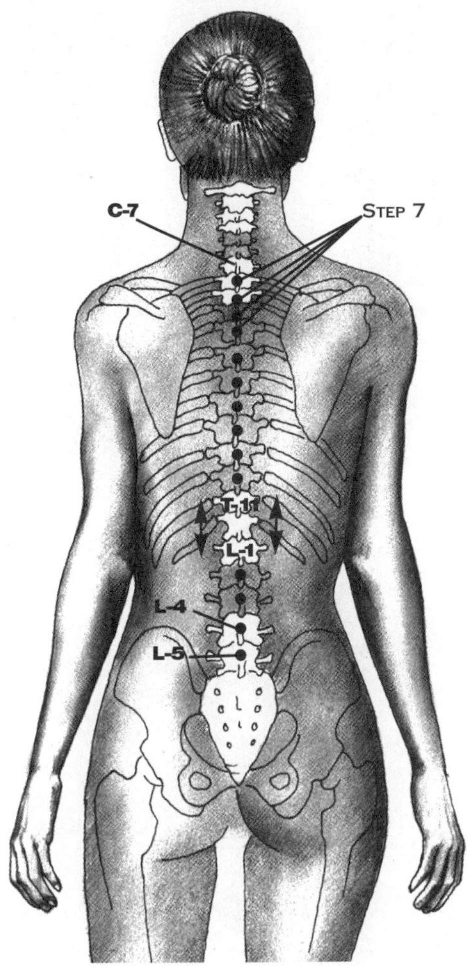

Fig 6-06

8. Have the client turn face-up.
Place your palms on the hip bones that protrude in the front. Use gentle pressure as if to stretch them apart (Fig. 6-07). Use several motions: the first is a seesaw movement rocking the pelvis to the right, then to the left, and back again; the second motion is a seesawing back and forth at an angle. For the last movement go up and out with your right hand, then down and out with the left, and repeat two more times. Total time: 1 minute.

9. Massage the outside of the thigh from the hip all the way down to the knee, either one leg at a time or both at the same time (Fig. 6-08). Use either your fingers and fingertips or the heels of your hands. These muscles can take deep pressure, although they can be sore and painful. Total time: 1 minute.

10. Massage the knees.
a. Place both hands above one knee. Your thumbs are above the knee cap, the fingers are behind (Fig. 6-09). Stroke up and down (about 2 inches in length) a few times, then rotate your hands toward the outside of the thighs, repeating. Rotate your hands farther to the outside, repeating again. Then rotate the other way covering as much of the muscle regions above the knee as you can.

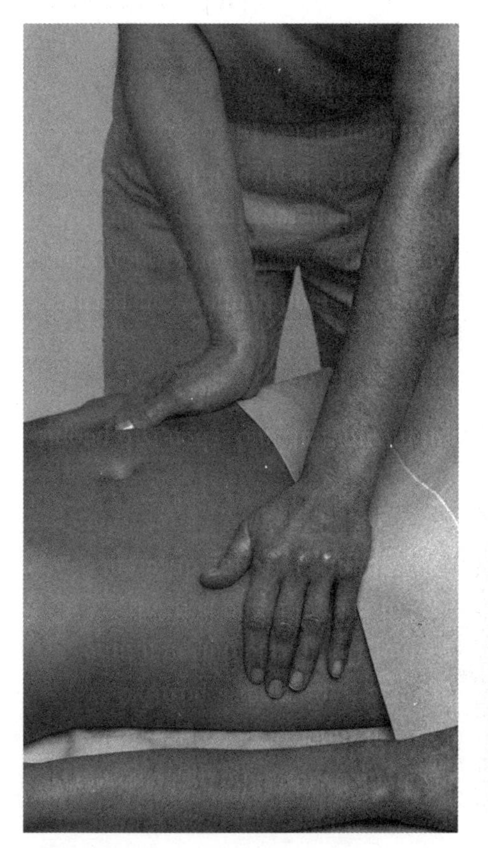

Fig 6-07

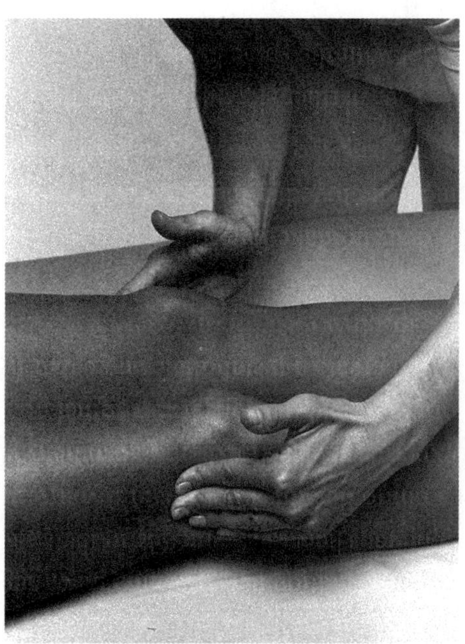

Fig 6-08

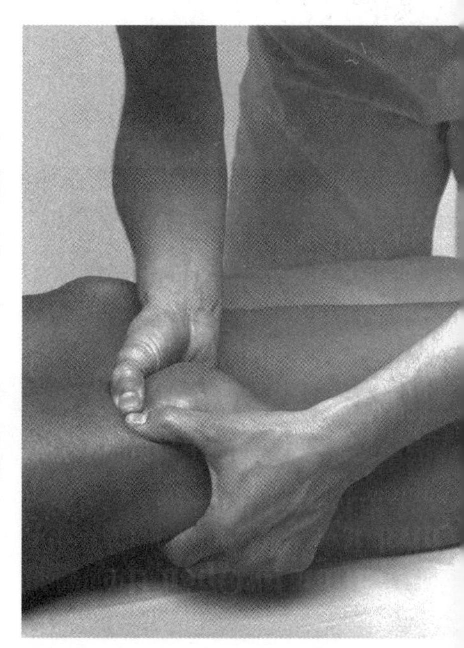

Fig 6-09

Then grasp below the knee with both hands, your fingers behind, thumbs in front. Starting at the inside of the leg, put your thumbs side-by-side and repeat the sliding strokes you did above the knee. Cover as much of the muscle and bony tissues below the knee as you can. Then perform this knee massage on the other leg. Total time for both legs: 2 minutes.

b. Place your hands above the knees with the thumbs on the inside, fingers on the outside. Slide the hands a few inches above the knees then back down (Fig. 6-10). Then rotate the hands clockwise and counterclockwise above the knee. Repeat the same strokes below the knee. Total time: 1 minute.

c. Hold one knee with both hands. Place your thumbs in front and the fingers behind the knee (refer to Fig. 6-09). Use your thumbs to massage the knee cap, making small circles around it. Repeat on the other knee. Total time: 1 minute.

11. Have your client turn face-down. Massage both calves at the same time using circular strokes. Use either the heels of your hands, the fingers, or your thumbs (Fig. 6-11). As you make circles, first move up-and-down, then move side-to-side. Total time: 1 minute.

12. Hang your client's feet over the end of the table, or prop up the lower legs with a pillow.

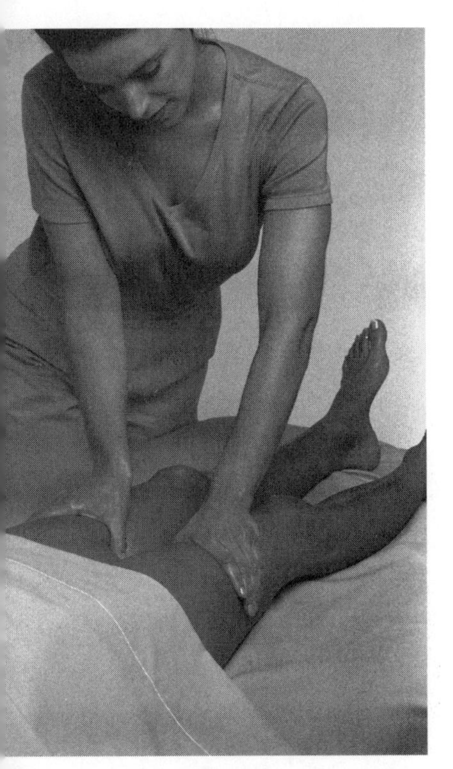

Fig 6-10

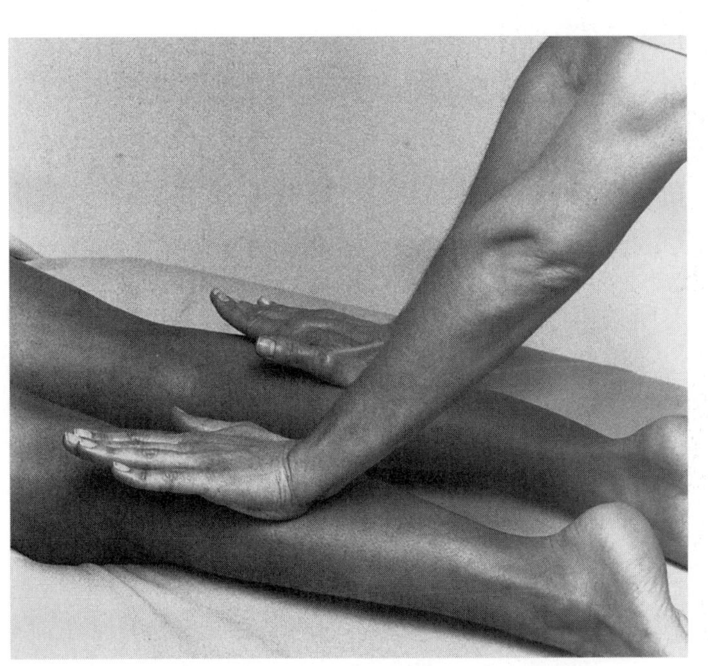

Fig 6-11

a. Massage the Achilles tendon with strong pressure (Fig. 6-12). First push the tendon down with your thumbs, and slide from the heel 5 inches up towards the calf muscle. Then squeeze the soft tissue underneath the tendon (thumb on one side, first finger on the other side), and again slide up from the heel region 5 inches towards the calf (Fig. 6-13). Do this for 1 1/2 minutes on each side.

b. With your thumbs, stretch the tendon by pushing it across towards the other ankle. Then pull it the other way going back-and-forth for 1 minute.

13. Have your client turn over facing up. Place your thumb on top of the big toe, and bend the last joint down toward the floor. Pull the big toe straight outward taking out the "slack," then quickly pull it farther, which may produce a popping sound. Do the other toes in a similar manner (Fig. 6-14). Total time: 30 seconds.

I find it useful to use both hands. One hand holds the client's toe while the other holds your wrist. Then, both hands in concert move quickly to lengthen the toe.

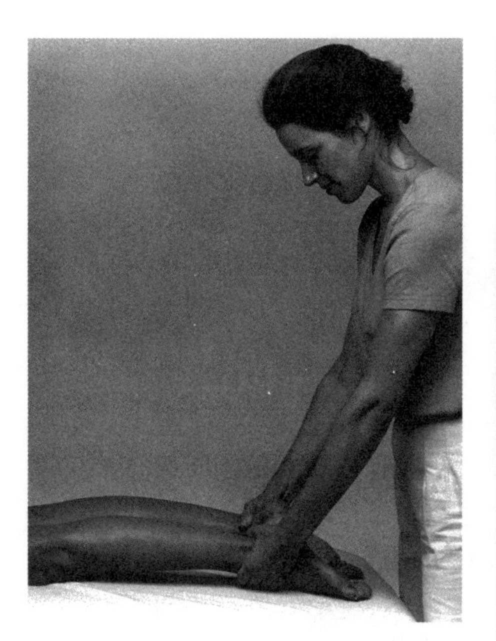

Fig 6-12

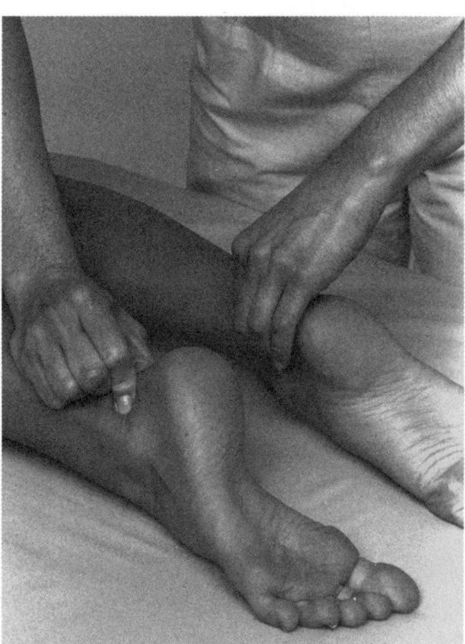

Fig 6-13

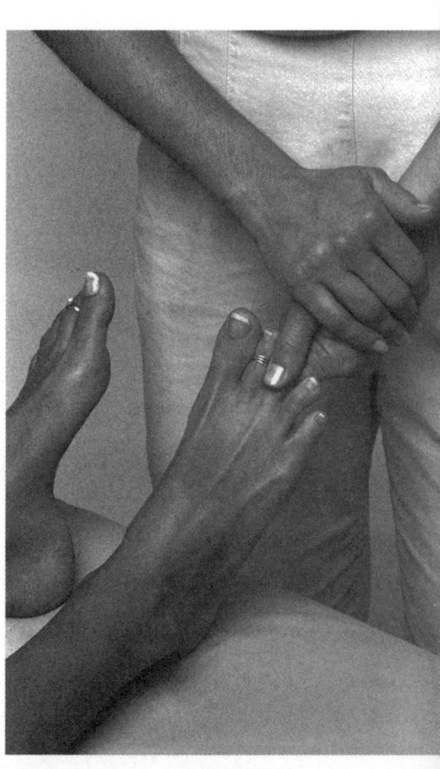

Fig 6-14

14. Sit by the client's head. Strongly massage the facial bones and underneath the cheekbones, from the nose to the jaw near the ear (Fig. 6-15).

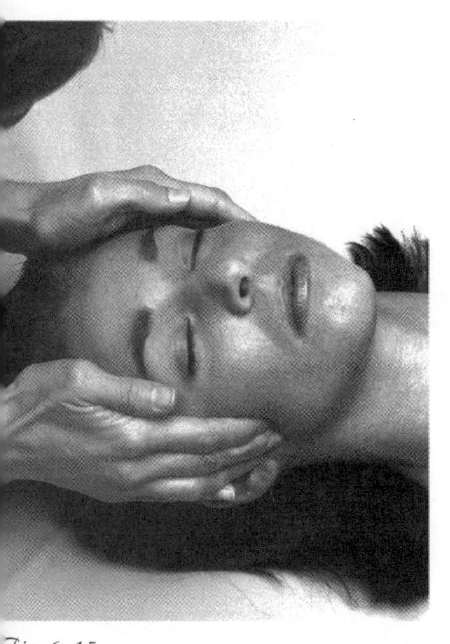
Fig 6-15

Then use your fingertips to massage the scalp all around the ears (Fig. 6-16). Be sure to spend time on the areas of tension that you find. You may find a ridge of scalp muscle near the ear that is very tight. It can feel like bone. Also, stay on the muscles where your client says there is tightness or pain. Total time: 1 minute.

15. Go to your strong side. Place both hands on the client—fingers to the temples and thumbs on the front neck muscles (Fig. 6-17). Massage in continuous circles for 30 seconds, maintaining contact on both areas. Use light pressure on the front neck muscles.

16. Stand or sit at the side of the table. Squeeze the lower half of the client's nose. Bend, stretch, and twist the cartilage there for 1 minute (Fig. 6-18). Then stroke up and down on the remainder of the nose for 1 more minute.

17. Massage the tissue between the upper lip and the nose, from one corner of the mouth to the other. Use the tips of the first 3 fingertips of one hand to do this for 30 seconds.

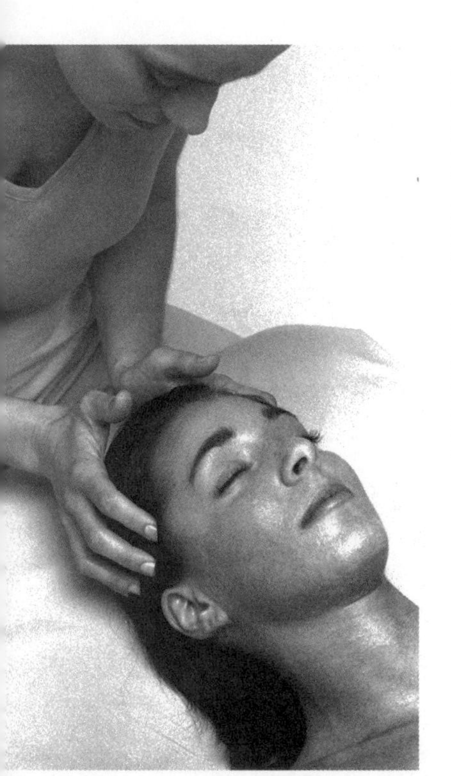
Fig 6-16

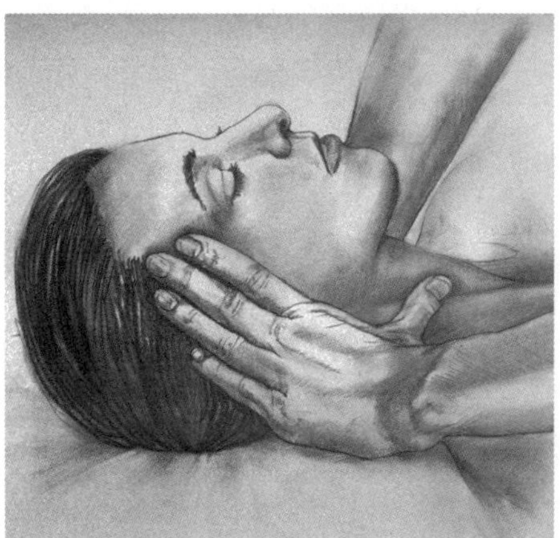
Fig 6-17

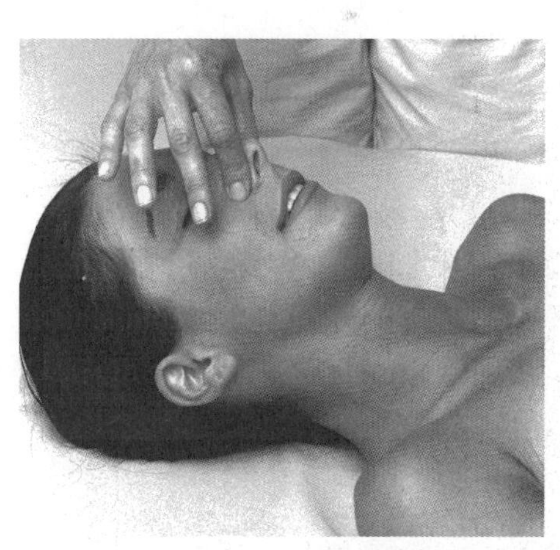
Fig 6-18

Now take the lips between your index fingers and thumbs. Use your index fingers and thumbs like clothespins, and pull the lips upward for 30 seconds (Fig. 6-19).

18. Massage underneath the jawbone for 2 minutes, beginning at the angle of the lower jaw. Probe deeply with your fingertips sliding along the tissu underneath the bone to the chin (Fig. 6-20).

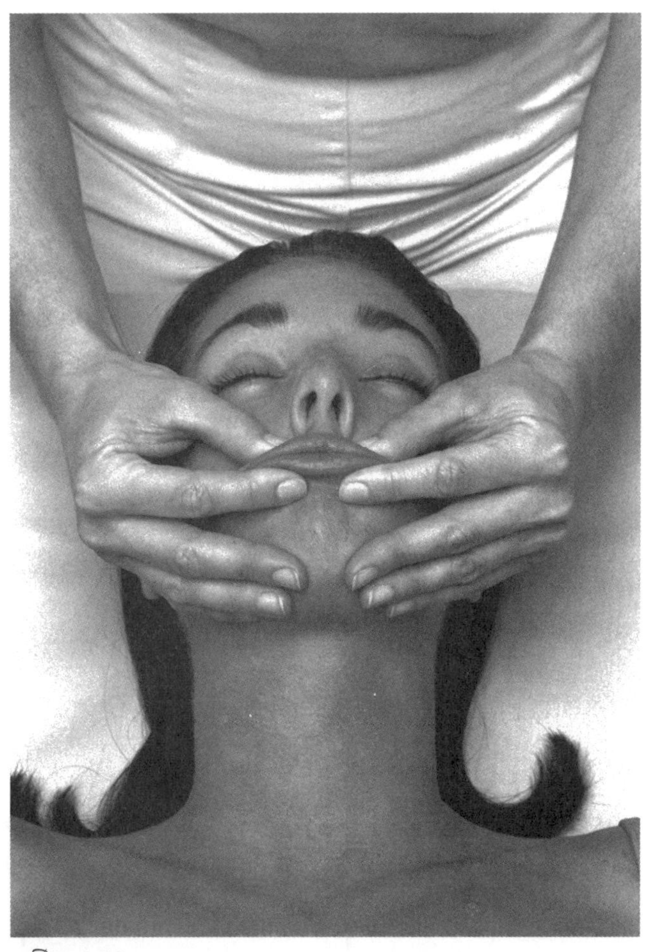

Fig 6-19

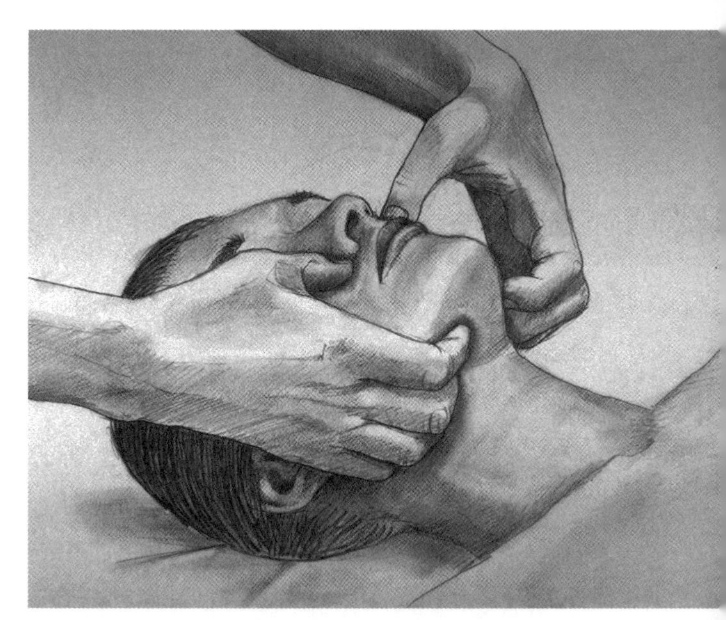

Fig 6-20

Comment

The client can have clothes on for this treatment. However, the treatment is most effective if the client is unclothed, so that you can work directly on the client's skin using small amounts of massage oil.

Stay with the order of steps in this treatment and enjoy the results. Many patients comment about what a boost it is to have the neck massaged like it is in Step 1. When you help the client to relax in the upper neck, the brain rests. Some of the endless mental chatter stops, and tensions that surround the throat center (5th chakra) begin to dissolve. The throat center corresponds to the voice, to talking, both with the inner self and the outer world. Any tensions in this area can reflect either communication difficulties or inner conflicts about self-image.

In Step 2, the lower back muscles correspond to the lower centers (1st and 2nd chakras). Here tensions concerning basic survival and sexuality are stored.

Pressing the buttocks muscles in Step 3 increases the local blood supply, and the arteries carry more blood to the area of treatment. Then the tight bands of muscle and connective tissue become more like jello and less like calcified lumps.

In Steps 5 and 6a, the T-2 through T-11 musculature corresponds to the heart center (4th chakra) and the navel center (3rd chakra). The heart center is the seat of compassion—the ability to love and give. The navel center is associated with power drives, deep emotions, and self-identification. Yogi Bhajan comments: "There are eight vertebrae between T-2 and T-11. These vertebrae are the eight that control longevity, long life, and health[2].

In Step 6b, the 2 inches of muscle along the spine between T-11 and L-1 musculature connect to the 3rd center.

In Step 8, you rock the client's front pelvis region by pressing the bones apart. Then probe and massage the lower abdominal muscles along the inside of the "bowl" formed by these bones. Releasing tensions here alleviates emotional problems associated with the 1st and 2nd chakras.

Steps 9 to 12 ground the client. Massaging the legs, knees, calves, and Achilles tendon intensifies contact with the physical world. The legs and knees connect us to the earth. Legs are for standing up in life, for propelling forward into growth and expansion. Yogi Bhajan comments on the effect of massaging the Achilles tendon: "This will put pressure on the frontal lobe of the brain, and the stimulation from the massage will relax the brain of your client. The neurons will start balancing, and the gray matter will start adjusting itself, and the spinal serum will start flowing upward without your doing anything at the top[3]."

In Step 14, you help relax and bring fresh blood to the face. The scalp muscles around the ear are very thin muscles; they assist the jaw muscles to close the mouth. There are tensions that build in people from clenching the jaws, or grinding the teeth at night, or from holding extra tightness in the jaw during daily activities.

In Step 15, you release hidden neck tensions by working the front neck muscles. The temples are the most sensitive part of the face, an essential region to stimulate. They are like miniature satellite dishes that receive cosmic and solar energy. The temples are also called the cradle of the pituitary (king of the glands).

In Step 16, the nose is an extension of the front brain and a gateway for the breath. It is also a part of sensory intuition: "sniffing out opportunities" or "smelling a rat."

Massaging the upper lip (Step 17) helps clear the mind, brings blood to the front part of the brain, and sends **pranic energy** from the lower back all the way up the spine to the top of the head.

When you grasp both lips together you help mix the pranic with the **apanic energy** and balance the blood. Pinching the lips can relieve muscle cramps in the arms, feet, legs, and back. Lip pinching works wonders for someone with calf cramps, a charley horse, or muscle spasms anywhere along the spine. Coaches, dancers, athletes, and parents can use this technique.

In Step 18, you are relieving lymphatic congestion and unresolved tension from the throat center (self-expression).

Diamond Treatment

(about 23 minutes)

THIS TREATMENT TAKES ITS NAME FROM THE DIAMOND, THE MOST DURABLE AND PRECIOUS OF ALL GEMSTONES. THE DIAMOND IS FORMED UNDER TREMENDOUS PRESSURE AND AT EXTREME TEMPERATURES OVER A LONG PERIOD OF TIME.

The Diamond Treatment helps strengthen the practitioner's hands, forearms, and shoulders. You must have strong hands to do this treatment effectively. Some pressure points are held for 2 1/2 minutes at the maximum tolerance level of your client. It takes concentration, strength, and stamina. If you are new to bodywork the first 3 steps will test your physical and mental persistence. Conserve your stamina while doing these steps by leaning into the points using your body weight. Using just your arm and hand muscles will tire you out. Use body English with a slight bend in your elbows, breathing deeply as you do so.

1. Have the client lie face-down on the table. Use your thumbs to press the upper back, 2 inches out from the spine and 3 inches down from the base of the neck at T-2 (Figs. 6-21 and 6-22). Use maximum body weight on the thumbs for 2 1/2 minutes. Breathe deeply and from the stomach to help your stamina. Climb up on the table if necessary.

2. Use body leverage as in Step 1, and lean into the points that are in the middle of the lower back (at the level of L-2), 2 inches out from the bony bumps in the midline. Use deep pressure for 2 1/2 minutes (refer to Fig. 6-22).

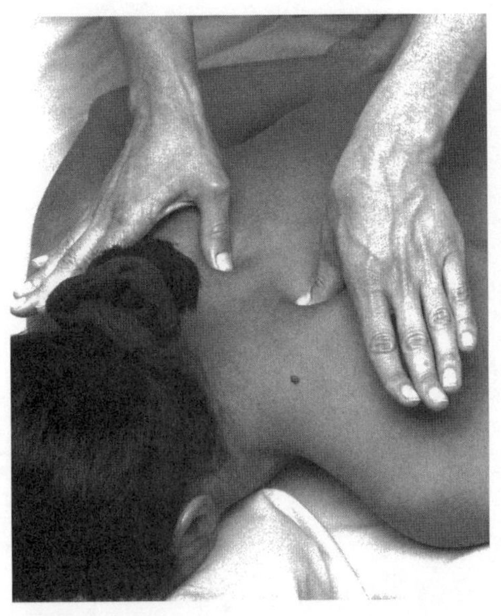

Fig 6-21

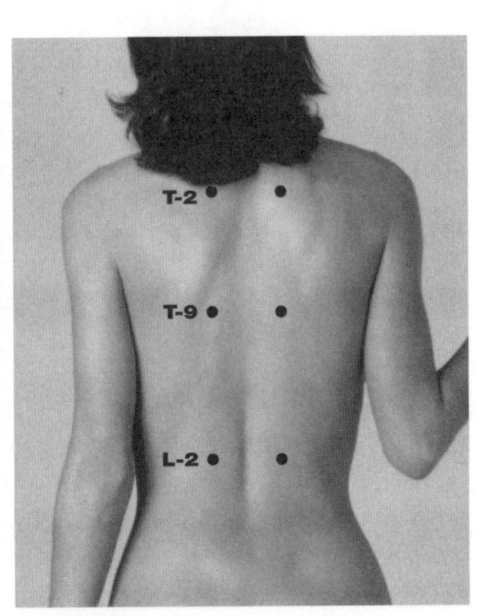

Fig 6-22

3. Lean into the muscles adjacent to T-9. That is a half inch lower than the line that you draw connecting the bottom edge of the shoulder blades (refer to Fig. 6-22). Use your maximum pressure for 2 1/2 minutes. Conserve energy and use leverage as in the other steps.

4. Have the client lie down on the right side, with the client's left arm above the head, so you can massage into the armpit (Fig. 6-23). Stand behind your client.

Place both palms down, one on top of the other. Use your fingers to stroke with firm, circular movements, from the armpit to the waistline for 1 minute and 15 seconds (Fig. 6-24). Switch sides and repeat. Both sides together take 2 1/2 minutes.

5. The client is lying on the stomach. Use the heel of your hands on the junction of the buttocks and thighs. Push toward the head then release; repeating the movement over and over for 15 seconds (Fig. 6-25). Then turn

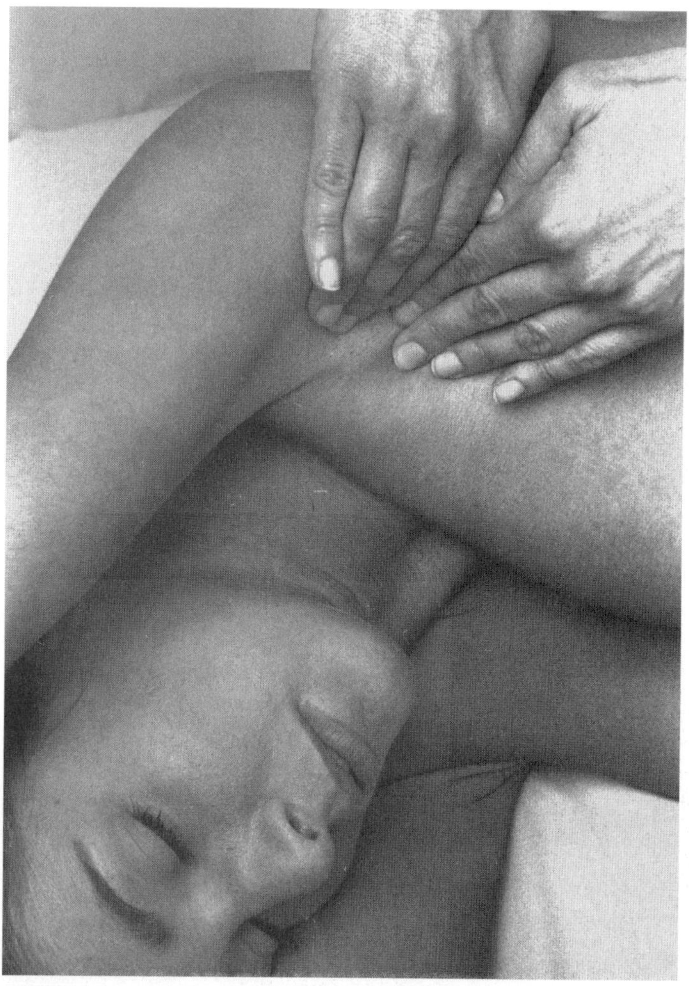

Fig 6-23

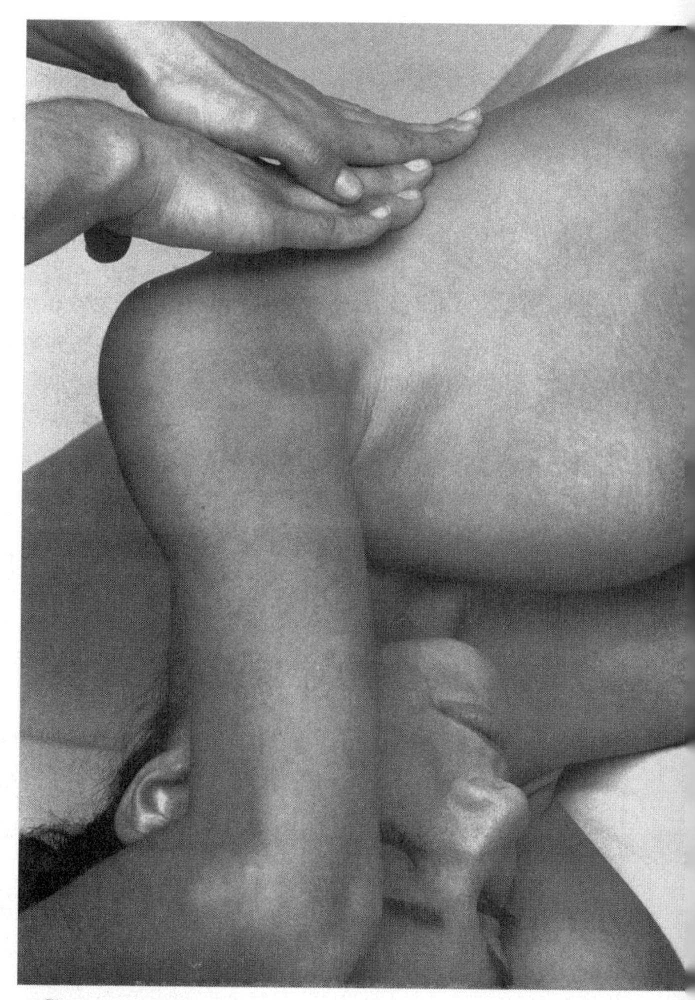

Fig 6-24

to face the client's feet, and push straight down toward the floor (and towards the feet), then release the pressure. Repeat the motion for 15 seconds.

6. Use the heel of your hands to knead behind the knees in a circular motion for 30 seconds. Do both sides at once (Fig. 6-26).

7. Have the client's feet over the end of the table or propped up with a pillow. Use the thumb web of the hands to push the Achilles tendons down towards the floor for 30 seconds. Do both sides at once (Fig. 6-27). You can apply strong pressure.

8. Pull the toes so they release—"pop" them. This is done by holding the end of the toe and pulling with a quick motion away from the foot (Fig. 6-28). At least stretch them; the noise is not necessary. Total time: 30 seconds.

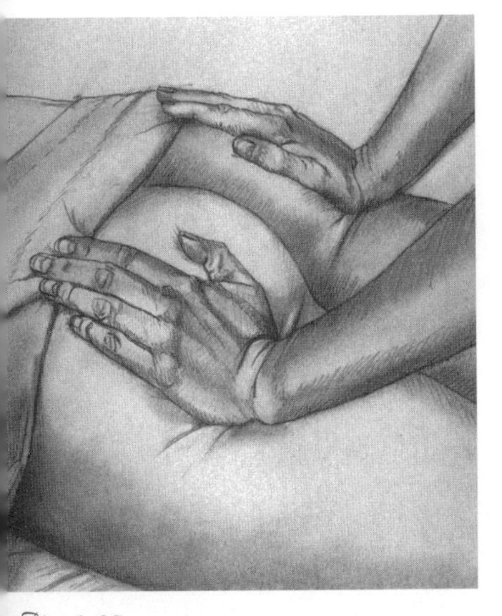

Fig 6-25

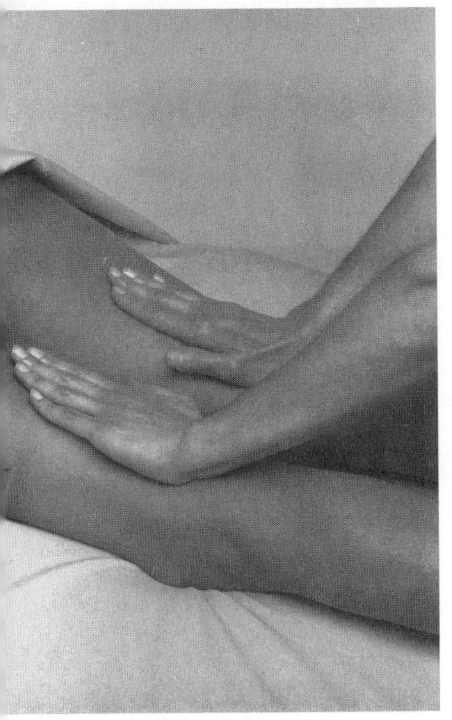

Fig 6-26

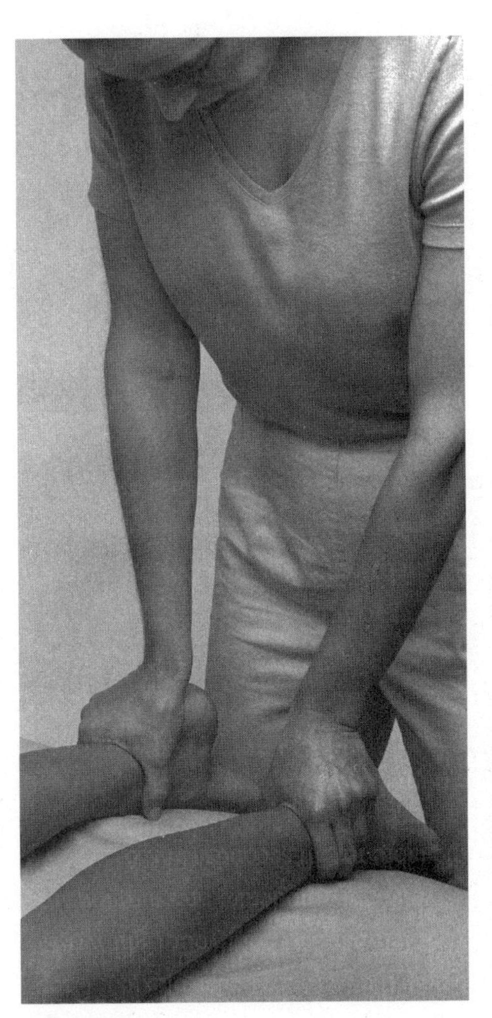

Fig 6-27

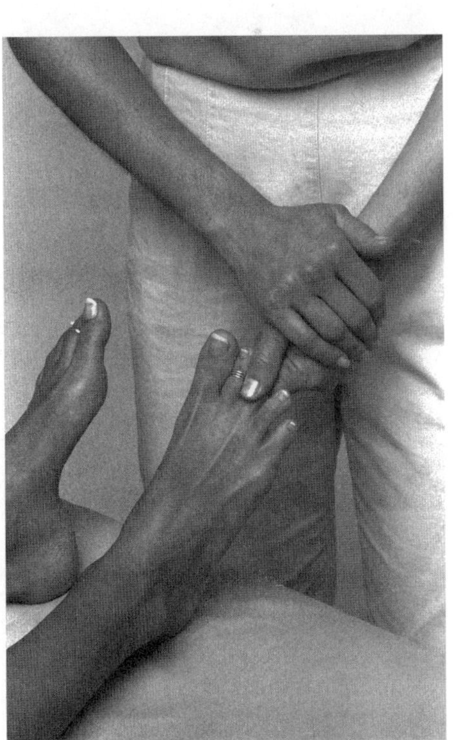

Fig 6-28

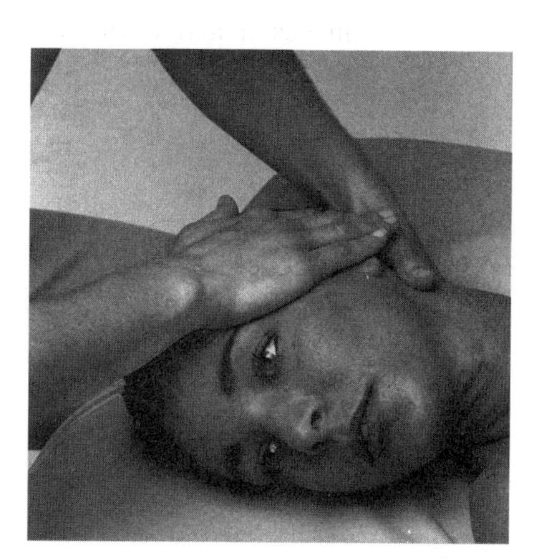

Fig 6-29

9. The client lies face up. Sit or stand at the head. Place your right hand on the temple, and place your left hand behind and supporting the neck. Turn her head in slow motion to the right, taking 30 seconds (Fig. 6-29). Stay at the maximum point for 10-15 seconds. Then go back the other way. Repeat, turning her head to the left. Total time: 2 minutes.

10. Go to the client's left side, placing your right thumb in the center of the forehead above the nose. The right index finger touches the top center of the skull. Place the left hand in **jacket mudra** at the middle sternum (Fig. 6-30). Bear down with firm pressure. Hold for 2 minutes.

11. Gently massage both temples at once using the first 3 fingers of each hand to make circles (Fig. 6-31). Total time: 2 1/2 minutes.

12. Squeeze the client's nose with your thumb and forefinger (or use the jacket mudra). Now pull the nose away from the face (towards the ceiling) for 5 seconds. Pull on the soft, loose, bendable part of the nose (Fig. 6-32).

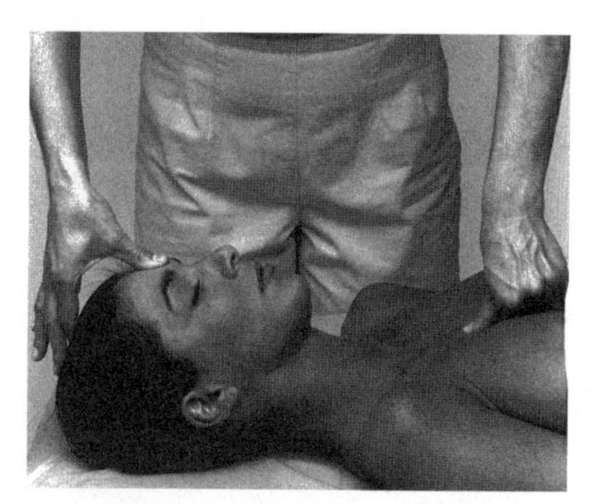

Fig 6-30

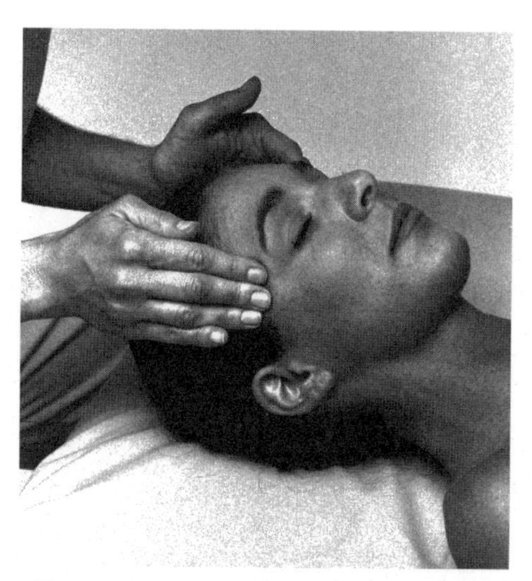

Fig 6-31

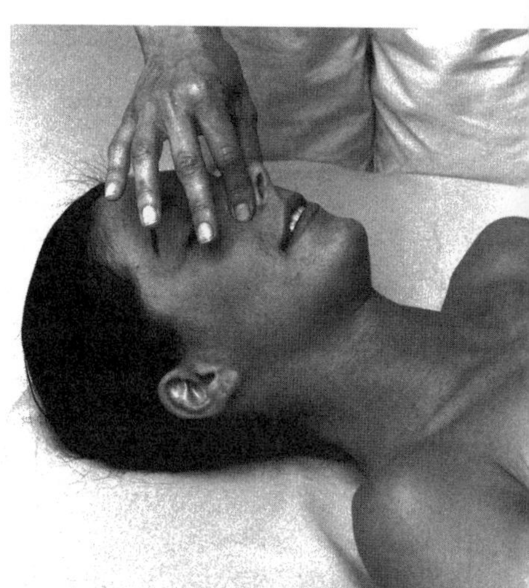

Fig 6-32

13. To seal what you have done, place one palm down covering the navel and press down for a count of 108 (about 2 minutes) (Fig. 6-33).

14. Use massage oil in this step. Spread your thumbs and index fingers. The web of the thumb presses into the thigh muscles 6 inches above the knees. Squeeze, push down, and slide about 6 inches up and down for 30 seconds (Fig. 6-34).

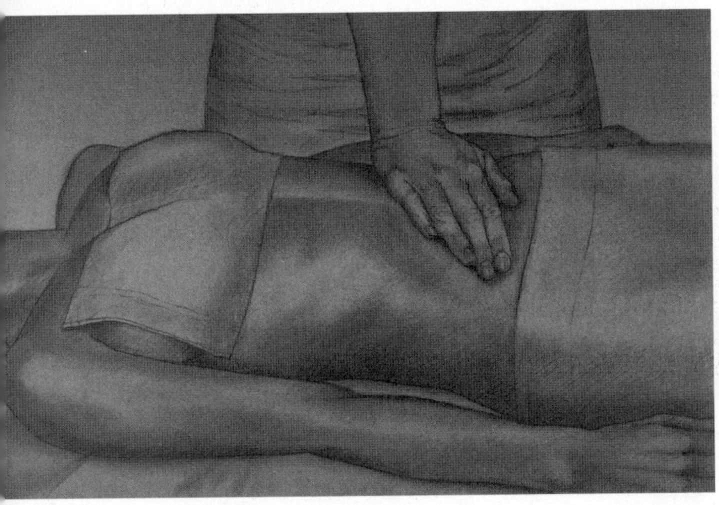

Fig 6-33

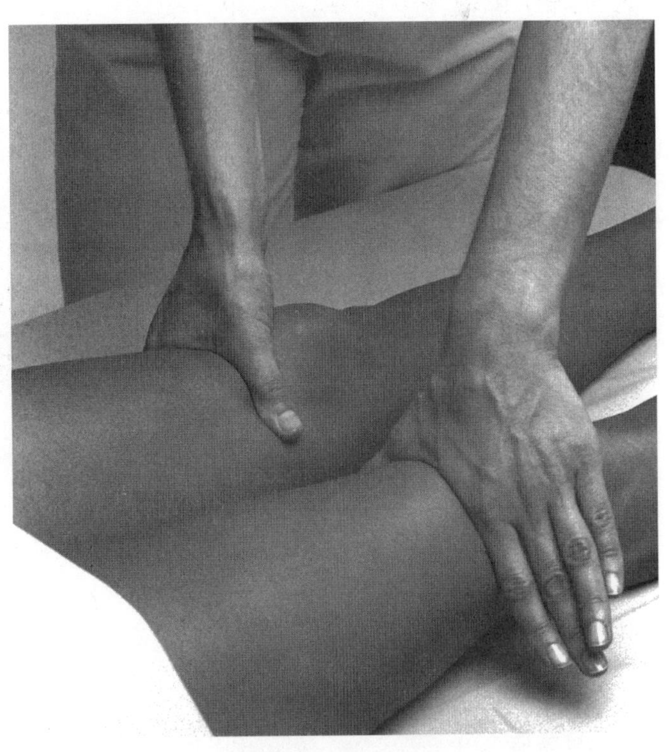

Fig 6-34

15. Steps 15 to 18 can bring heat back to the spine and stimulate the flow of spinal fluid.

Have the client turn face down, and stand to her right side. Place your right hand palm-down, straight across the spine at the T-8 level. Place the left hand palm-down across the sacrum (Fig. 6-35). Lean down on the hands straight toward the table for 30 seconds.

16. Stand to the client's right side. Rest your right palm on the right shoulder blade. Place your left hand in jacket mudra, with knuckles on the top portion of the left buttock muscle (Fig. 6-36). Lean down on both hands for 30 seconds.

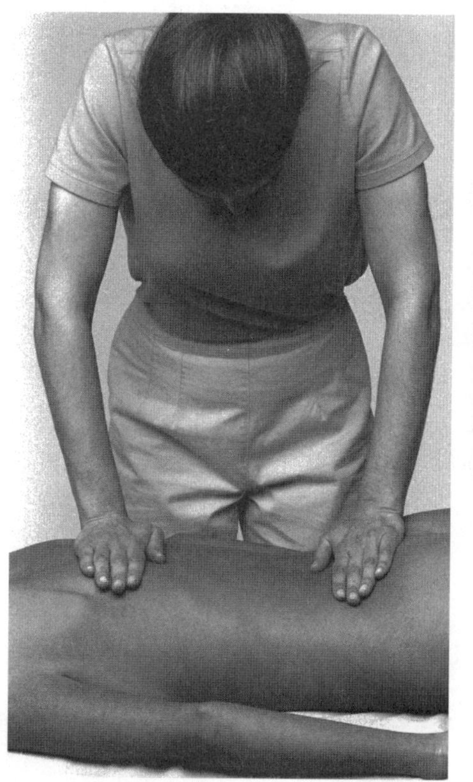

Fig 6-35

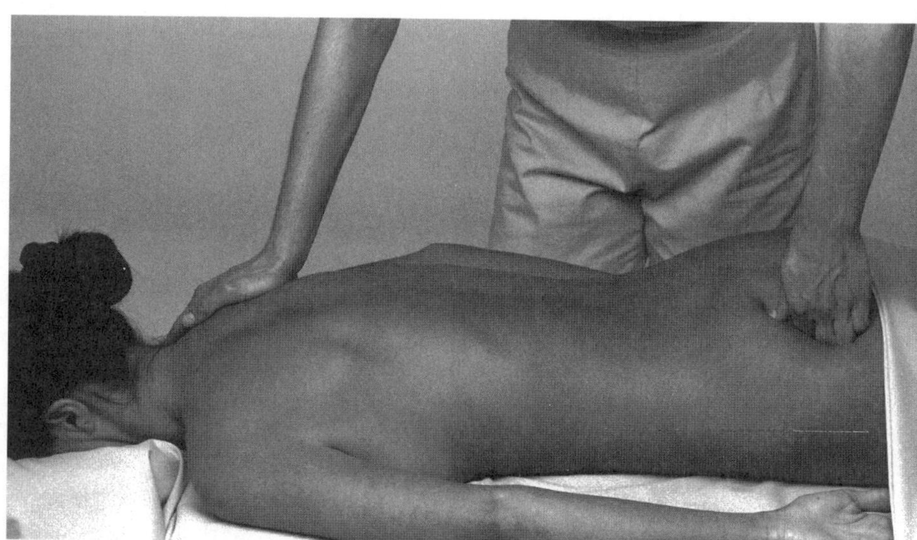

Fig 6-36

17. Switch the hand positions to the opposite sides of the client's body, using the heels of both hands instead of the previous hand positions (Fig. 6-37). Lean down on the hands for 30 seconds.

18. Place your palms down on the midline of the spine: right hand to the upper back (fingertips toward the head); your left hand on the sacrum (fingertips toward the tailbone). Rock back and forth in a seesaw motion for 30 seconds (Fig. 6-38). Use your body weight to accentuate the rhythmic motion.

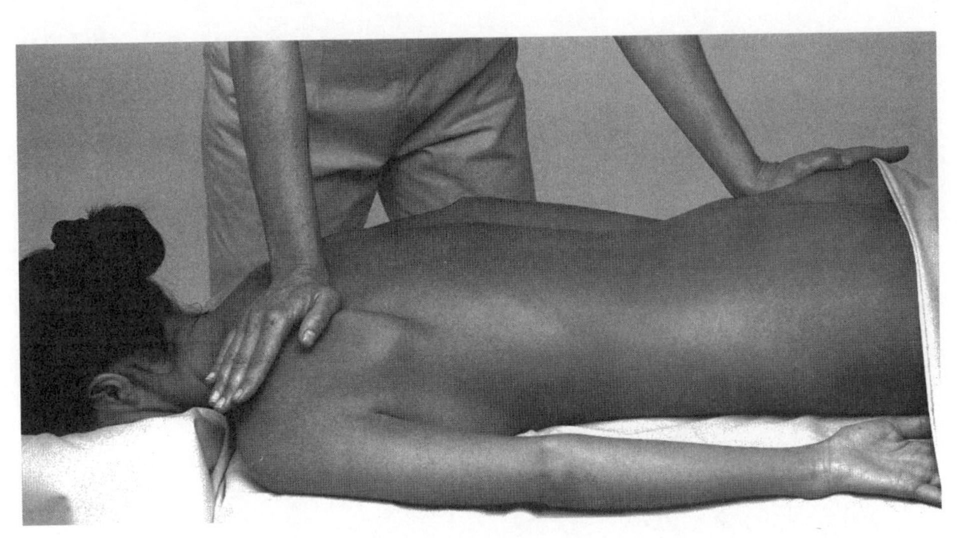

Fig 6-37

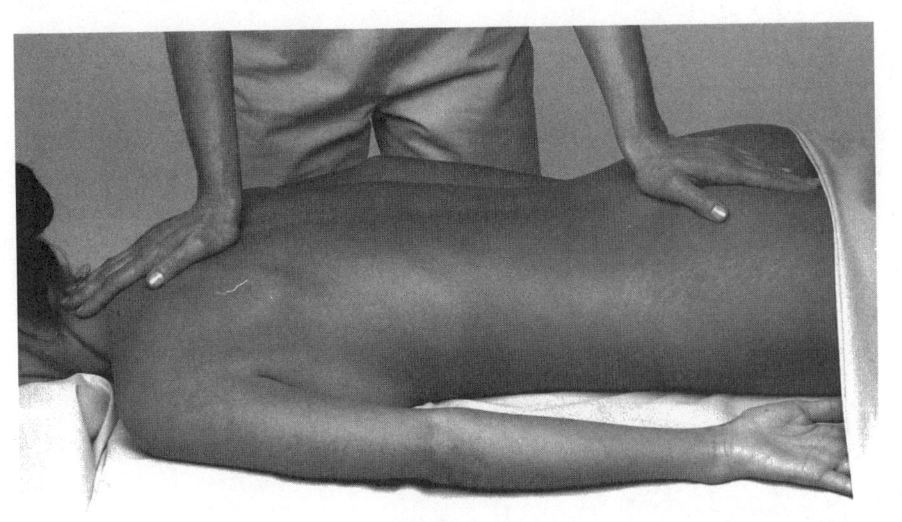

Fig 6-38

Comment

This treatment balances and restores the flow of pranic energy.

The first part of this treatment is like acupressure. The principle in acupressure is that constant pressure on special points helps the body produce change. For example, an area that needs more energy due to tiredness and sluggish circulation gets a boost. The opposite is also true—an overactive area that is irritated or "hyper" relaxes and calms down.

The pressure points in Step 1 coincide with lung points. For people who are experiencing lung problems, the possible psychological correspondences include deep old hurts stored and festering in the muscles. They may have a lot of guilt from blaming and being blamed, without forgiveness of self or others. People with this problem usually lack the ability to laugh, to have fun, or feel joy in their lives.

The pressure applied on the points in Step 2 helps overcome indigestion, diarrhea, swollen abdomen, and noisy intestines. It also helps alleviate pain and stiffness in the lower back.

The pressure applied in Step 4 balances your client's cerebral hemispheres. It also helps release some of the tension and fear of abandonment that can be stored in this body-mind region.

In Step 5, the pressure applied with the heel of the hand connects the lower half of the body to the upper half and grounds the client in the first chakra.

In Steps 6, 7, and 8, the grounding and distribution of energy that started in Step 5 is completed.

In Steps 9 and 10, the treatment at the higher centers in the neck and head region is completed.

In Step 10, your pressure consciously connects two points of vitality: the brow point and the pituitary gland (both associated with the third eye).

Chakra Balancing Treatment

(about 16 minutes)

The principle in all bodywork is to help another person feel better. The interacting that takes place is one in which the practitioner injects the receiver with personal nourishing energy. The truth is that a client in pain needs a charge of positive energy in order to recoup. A client needs strength in facing the day, and for changing with life.

If you have played cards you know that in draw poker you are dealt a hand, and you look at the cards before you to decide which ones to keep and which ones to discard. You discard and the dealer asks you, "How many?" "Give me three," you say. Your hand reaches for the new cards and you stop breathing for a moment as you turn the new cards face-up. The game continues when you decide whether to fold or how much to bet to stay in the game. Even if you fold, the next hand will come soon.

The relationship between a bodyworker and the client is similar. The client comes in with the hand that she has been dealt and is ready to discard part of it. You are the dealer ready to give what the client needs. And what she needs is a hit, a recharge. The client wants to feel nourished. So, this treatment is practice for you to give life energy to your client.

In the first part of this treatment you stimulate three major areas of the body-mind landscape: pubic bone, navel point, and heart center.

Procedure

Have the client wear a bathing suit or shorts for this treatment.

1. The client is lying face-up. You are standing to the right side, with the fingers and thumb of your right hand spread apart. Place the index and middle fingers on the mid-sternum. Your thumb goes on the soft tissue right below the sternum (solar plexus). Use your left hand to hold your right wrist as you apply moderate pressure toward the table for 30 seconds (Fig. 6-39).

2. Place your left fingers on the sternum and the left thumb at the solar plexus. Move your right hand to the pubic bone, fingers on the left side, thumb on the right. Grasp the pubic bone and press down firmly on both hands for 20 seconds (Fig. 6-40).

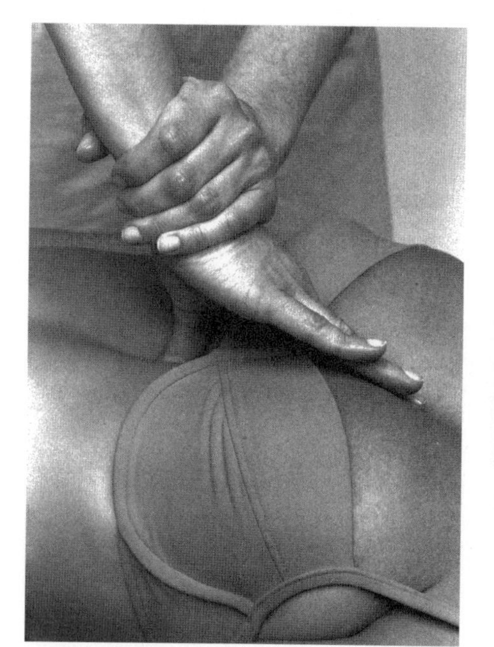

Fig 6-39

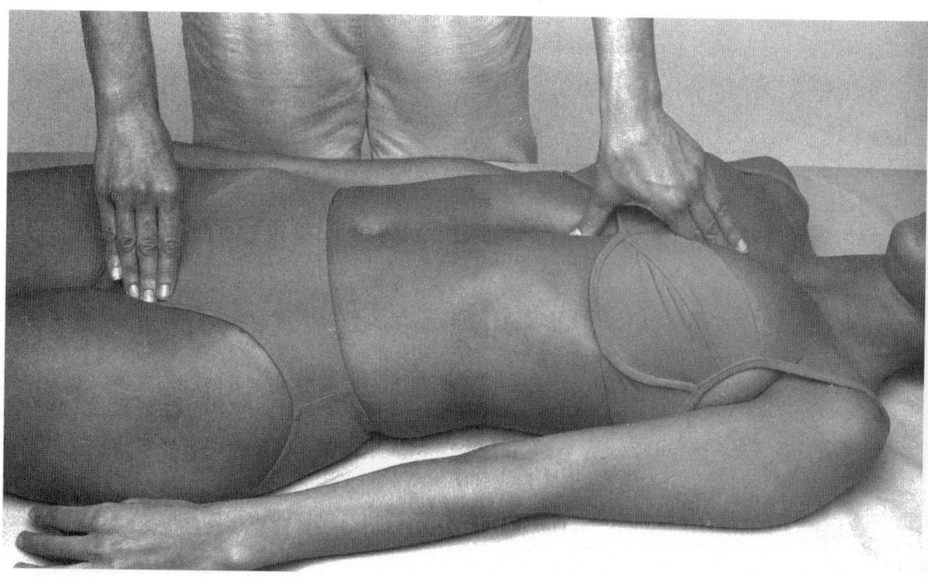

Fig 6-40

3. Make a fist of the right hand, and place it at the client's navel. Hold your right wrist with the left hand. Now press down into the abdominal tissue as deep as you can for 25 seconds (Fig. 6-41). Use client tolerance to determine how deep you go.

4. Make **cone mudra** with one of your hands, and push directly and firmly down into the navel for 10 seconds (Fig. 6-42).

5. Straddle the client's legs, or stand to one side of the table. Use your thumbs to press deeply into the inner thigh muscles (Fig. 6-43). Start on the tendons about 3 inches from the groin. (These tendons feel like cables or small ropes.) Press down firmly for 10 seconds then move a thumb width farther up the leg pressing down again. Total time 1 1/2 minutes.

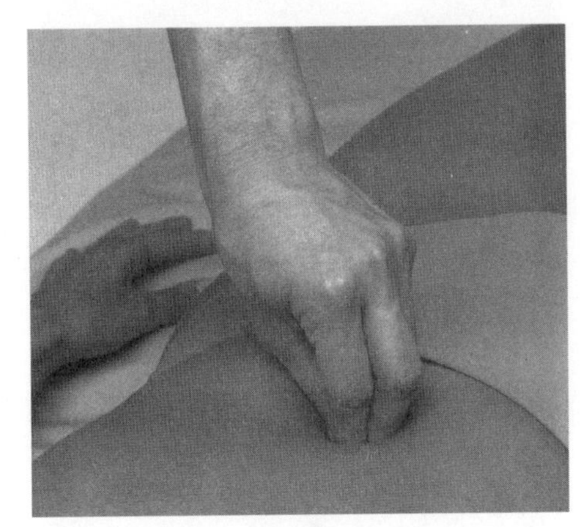

Fig 6-42

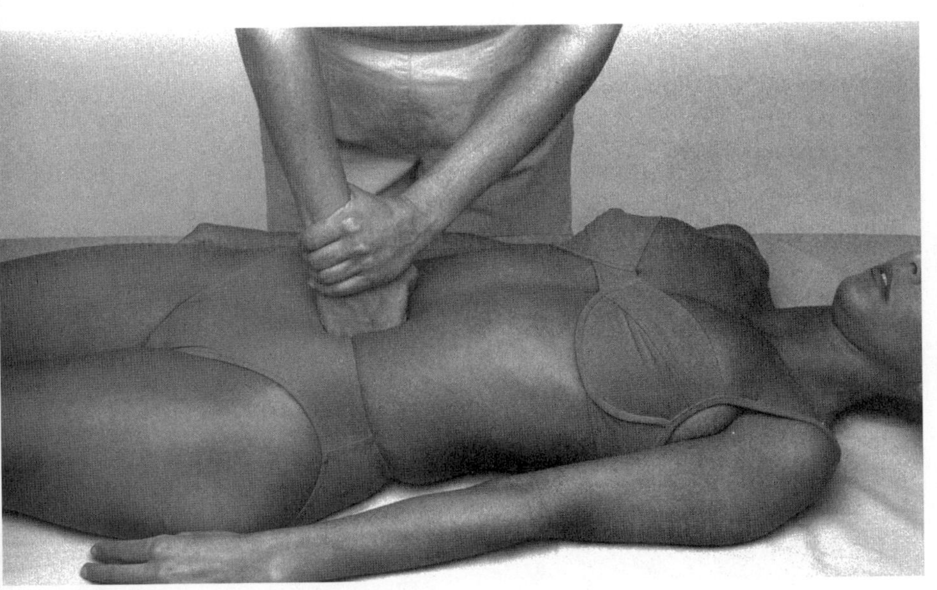

Fig 6-41

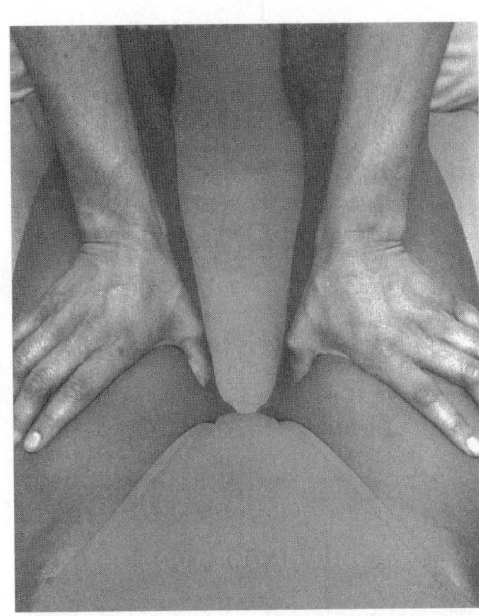

Fig 6-43

6. Grasp above each knee, with thumbs to the inside, fingers to the outside (Fig. 6-44). Lean down with some of your body weight and squeeze with deep pressure for 10 seconds. Do both sides at once.

7. Stand at the feet and use similar hand positions as in Step 6: thumbs on the inside of the lower leg, fingers to the outside. Press the thumbs into the inside of the calf muscles, at a point 2 finger-widths below the kneecap, just adjacent to the shin. Your thumbs will touch muscle adjacent to the shinbone (tibia); the fingers will be on the outside of the calf muscle (Fig. 6-45). Do both legs at once, using a strong pressure for 15 seconds.

8. Move the thumbs down the leg to 4 finger-widths above the ankle bone. Using the thumbs, press firmly into the muscle adjacent to the shinbone for 10 seconds (Fig. 6-46).

9. Move the hands back up to the point in Step 7, thumbs on the front of the calf muscles and fingers on the outside calf muscles (refer to Fig. 6-45). Then with the thumbs and fingers squeeze the calf muscles for 5 seconds and release. Then move toward the feet one thumb-width, and squeeze the fingers and thumbs again. Repeat all the way down the leg to about 2 finger-widths above the ankle bone. Do both sides at the same time. Total time: 30 seconds.

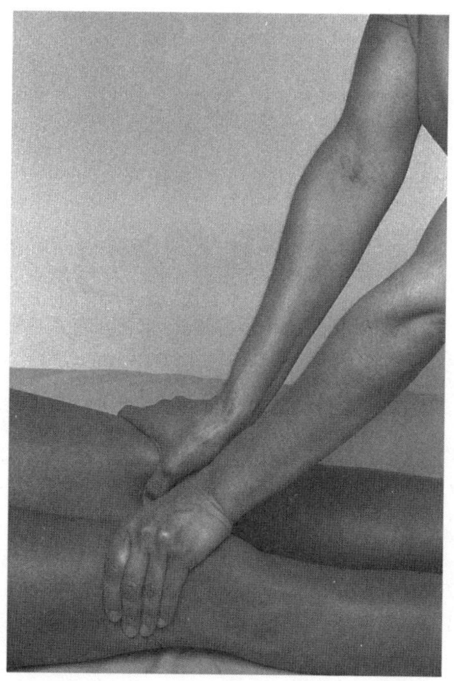

Fig 6-44

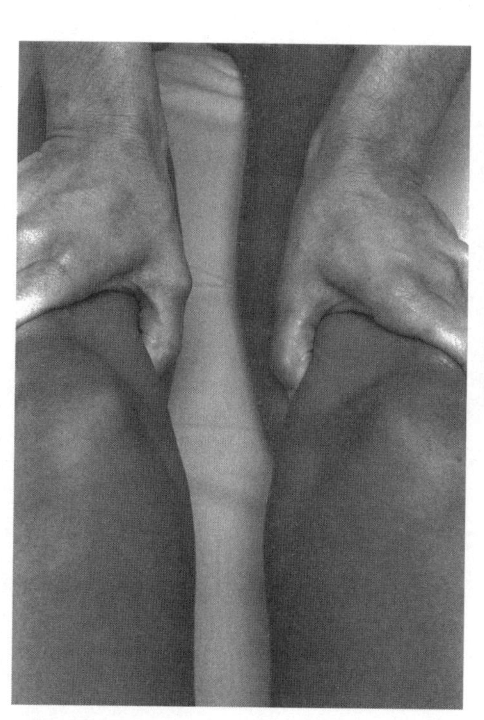

Fig 6-45

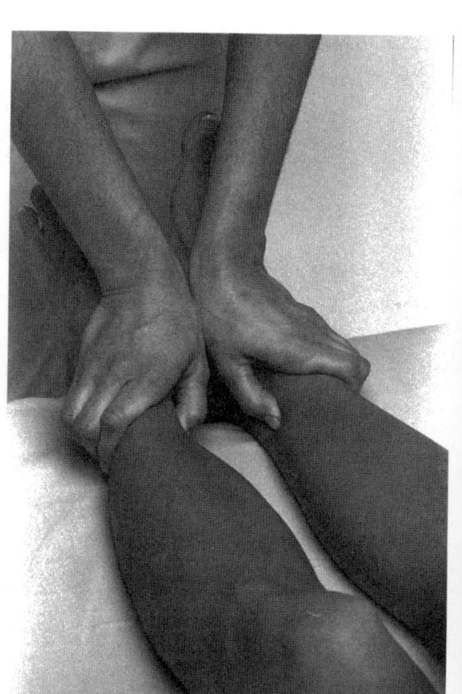

Fig 6-46

If you do not feel strong enough to do both sides at once, do one side with both hands. Place them side-by-side or one on top of the other.

10. Move to the client's left side. Place your left hand on the client's lower right ribs. Make a knife edge of the right hand. Press at a 45-degree angle under the left ribcage with your right hand (Fig. 6-47). Push in and out of the soft tissue going under the ribs. Use as firm a pressure as your client will tolerate. Repeat 15 times. Then switch sides and repeat the sequence. Total time for both sides: about 2 1/2 minutes.

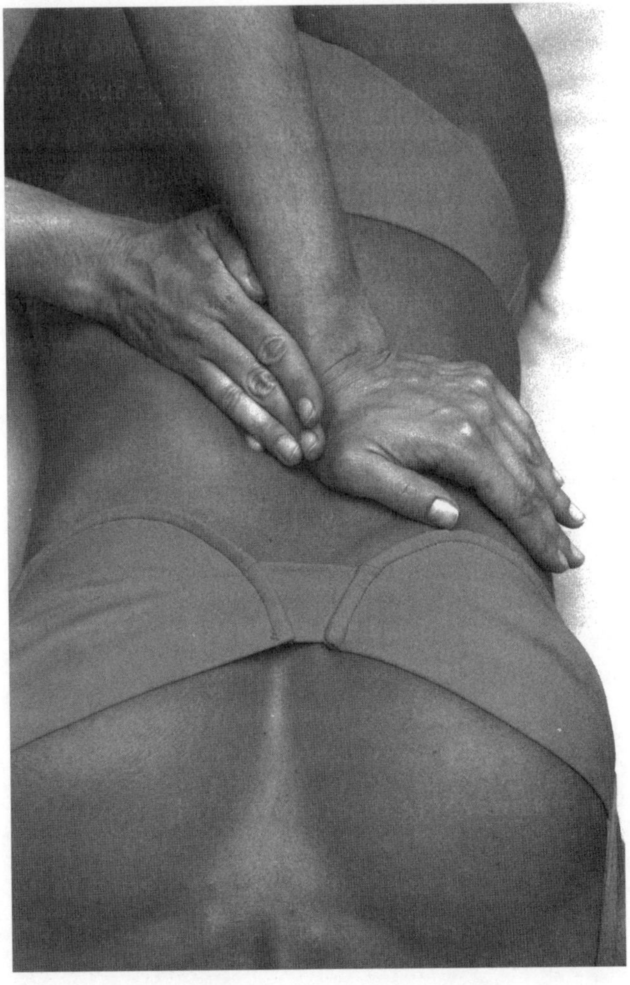

Fig 6-47

11. Place the right hand palm-down on the left lower ribs. Press down and rub the skin by sliding your hand back and forth, an inch forward then an inch back. This movement creates friction and generates heat. Do this stroke until you know there is warmth (Fig. 6-48). Then move your hand farther toward the side of the body, repeating the strokes. Go all the way to the side of the body. Do it for 30 seconds.

Repeat on the right side. Total time: 1 minute.

12. Pinch and lift the skin on either side of the navel between your thumbs and fingers. Hold the skin up for 3 seconds, then release (Fig. 6-49). Do it 4 times.

13. Using your right hand, press deeply into the solar plexus with the thumb; the fingers rest on the sternum. The left hand wraps around the right wrist (Fig. 6-50). Do it for 10 seconds.

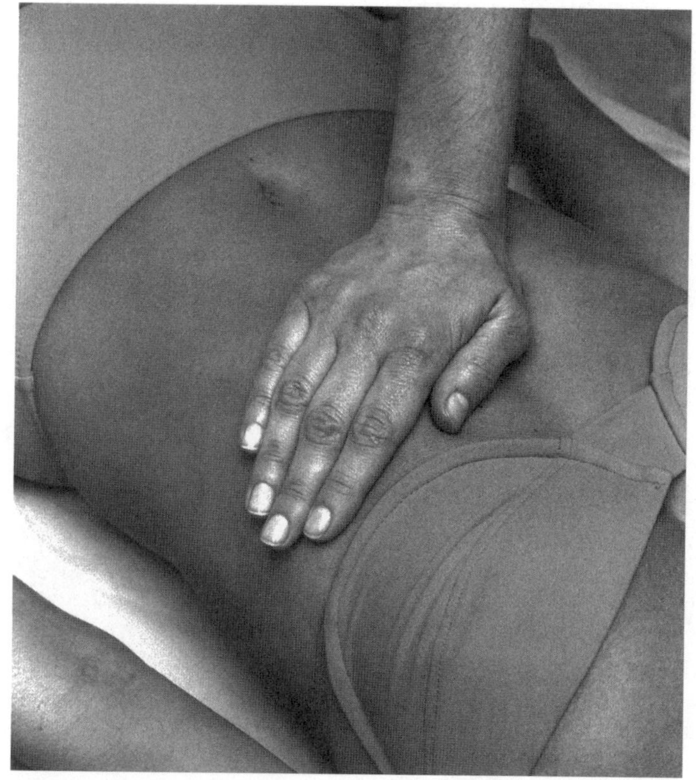

Fig 6-48

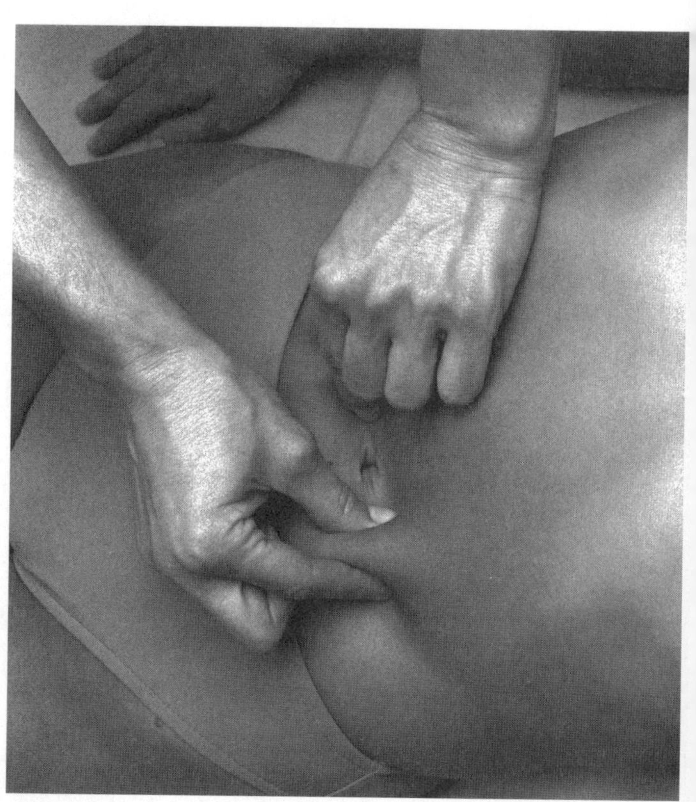

Fig 6-49

14. The client is face-down; you stand to either side. Place your hands side-by-side at the level of the kidneys (T-11), with the fingers pointing up the spine. Bend your elbows slightly. Now make one thrust towards the floor by keeping contact, then pushing down by straightening the elbows. (The tendency is to pick up the hands a little, then drop down when the thrust is made. This makes it a punch when it needs to be a gentle thrust.) Total time: 5 seconds.

15. Start with your hands in the same position as in Step 14. Then twist them, so that all the fingers cross over each other and cross the spine (Fig. 6-51). Now bend your elbows, leaning into the client with your body weight for 20 seconds. If you use a massage table, a better position may be to climb on top of the table and kneel down, straddling your client.

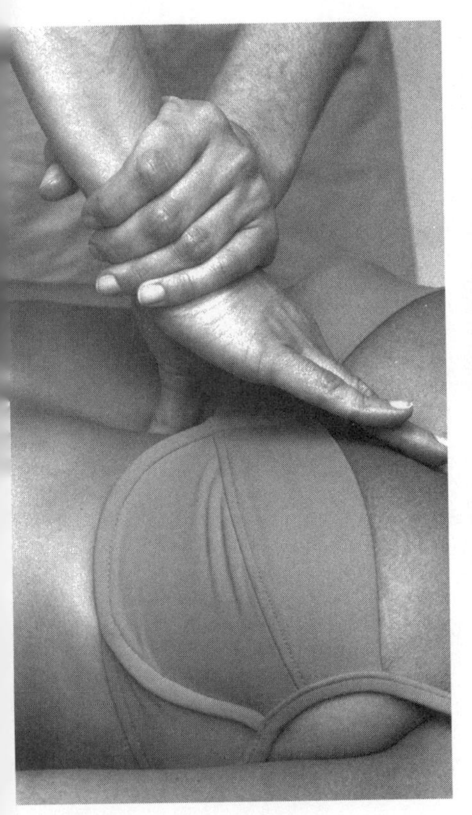

Fig 6-50

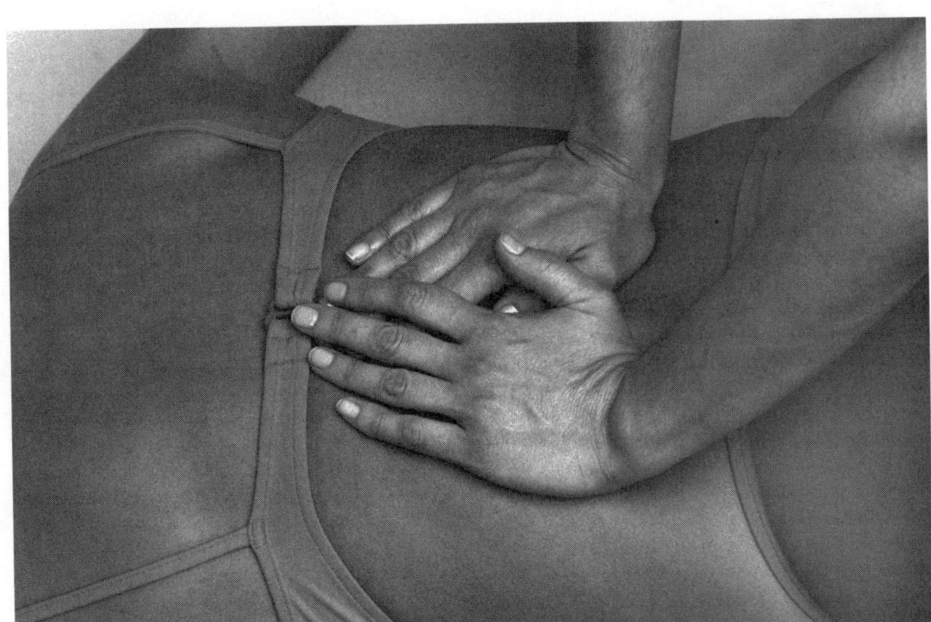

Fig 6-51

16. Move to your client's left side. Your left hand holds your right wrist. Now using your right hand, make 2 or 3 thrusts on the right side of the spine at the same level as in Step 14 (Fig. 6-52). Total time: 10 seconds.

17. Move up to the middle of the right shoulder blade, and place the right hand on the muscles beside the spine, in the same manner as in Fig. 6-52. Do 2 or 3 more gentle thrusts on the right side of the upper back muscles. Direct the thrusts toward the table. Total time: 5 seconds.

18. Put your hands back next to each other in the kidney area, as in Step 14 (refer to Fig. 6-51). With the hands in this position, make 3 to 4 light thrusts towards the table from T-11 to the base of the low back about 5 inches farther down. Total time: 10 seconds.

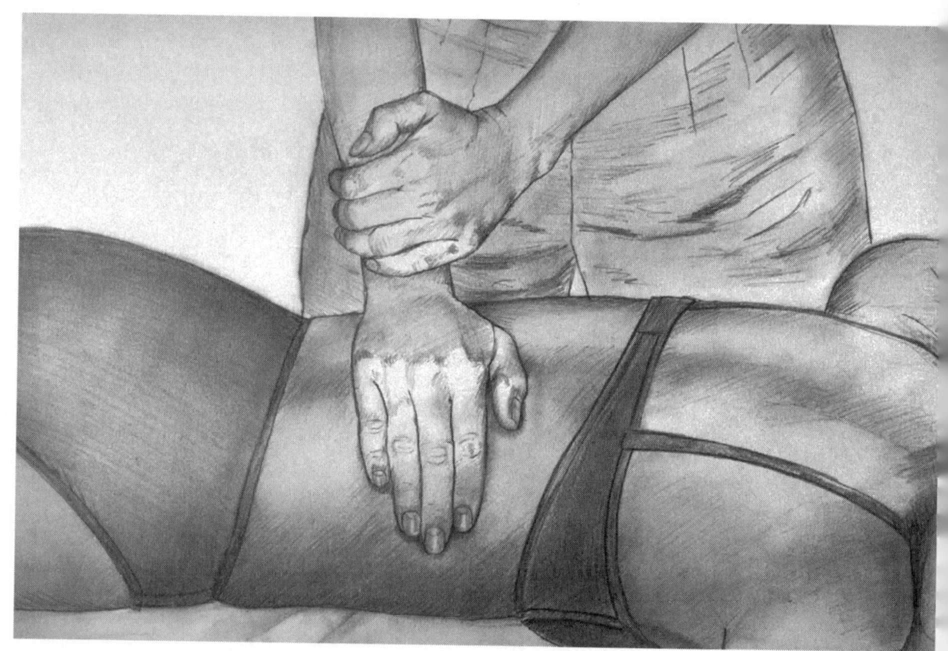

Fig 6-52

19. Stand to the right side, and use both thumbs side-by-side to massage underneath the inside (medial) edge of the left shoulder blade (Fig. 6-53). You may not be able to go underneath the shoulder blade if the person has large muscles or if there are constitutional restrictions between the blade and the spinal column.

(**Constitutional restrictions** are those that are inherited; they're also postural—making the upper back muscles and shoulder blade stick together. With such a person it is nearly impossible to get underneath the blade.)

Use heavy pressure for 5 to 10 seconds, going underneath the blade as far as you can. Start at the superior angle (near the top of the blade), and work your way down to the tip.

Now stand to the left side of the client, and do the same sequence on the right shoulder blade.

This step can calm down a restless mind and help with anxiety and depression. Total time: about 30 seconds.

20. Stand to the right side of the client. Place both hands on the left side of the body. The palms are down and side-by-side, and the fingers are together. Grab as much skin as you can, pulling it away from the ribs and toward you (Fig. 6-54). Repeat it 3 more times. Then change sides and repeat. Total time: 30 seconds.

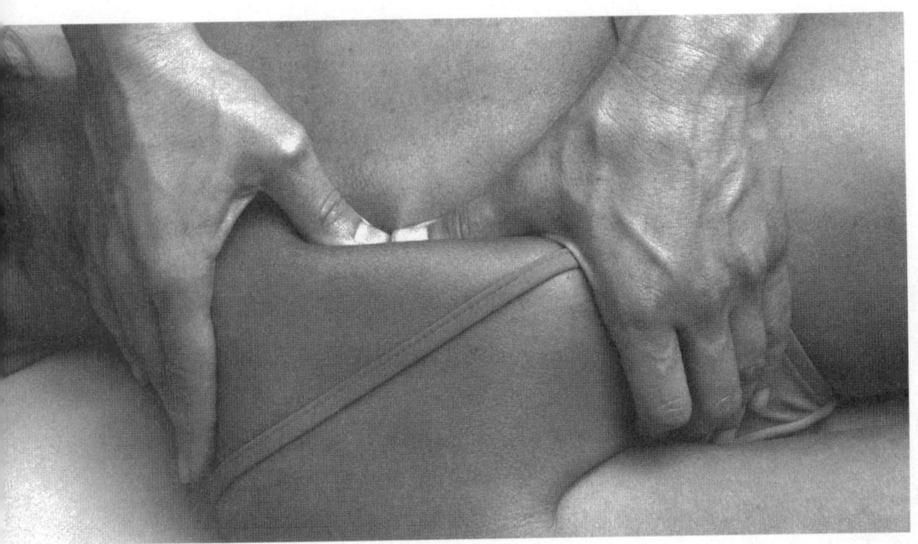

Fig 6-53

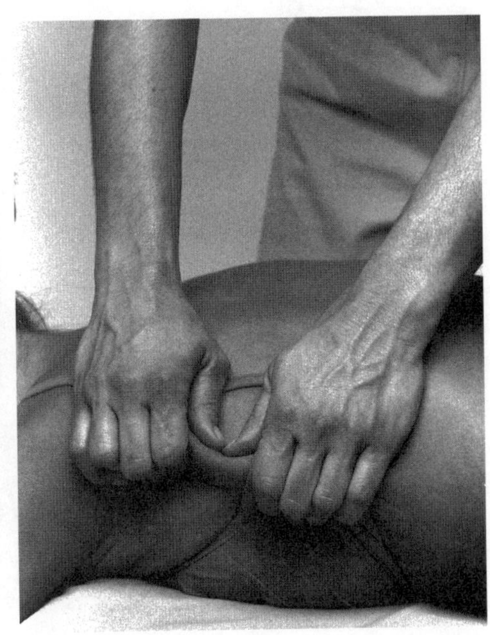

Fig 6-54

21. Still standing to the client's right side, place your right hand palm-down (fingers pointing to the toes) on the sacrum. Stabilize and add pressure by putting the left hand across the right at a 90-degree angle (Fig. 6-55). Press down towards the table for 10 seconds.

22. Place the heels of both hands into the soft tissue behind the knees and make 2 soft thrusts toward the table. Then push softly again on the right knee and repeat on the left knee (Fig. 6-56). Total time: 10 seconds.

23. Place a small amount of skin moisturizer or massage lotion on your hands and cover the entire back of the leg, especially if your client's skin is dry, or thin, or if there are inflamed patches.

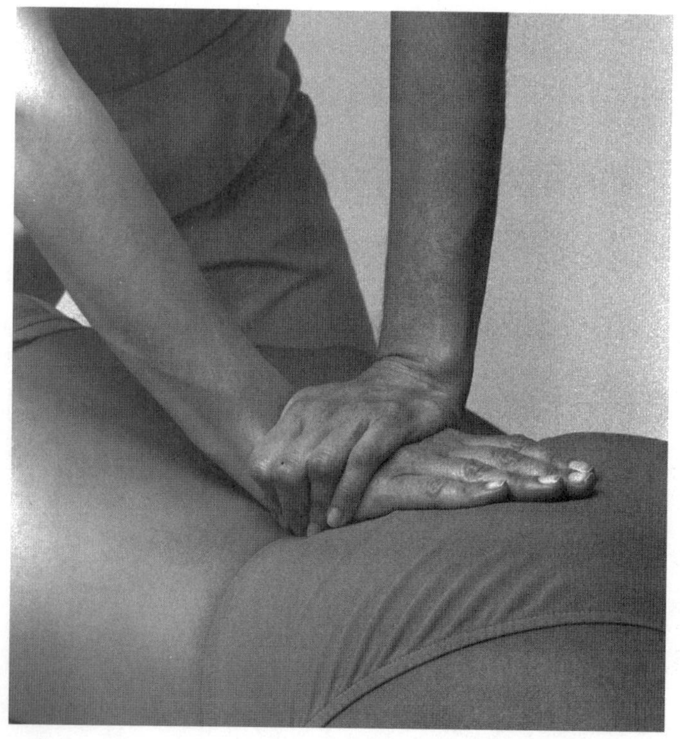

Fig 6-55

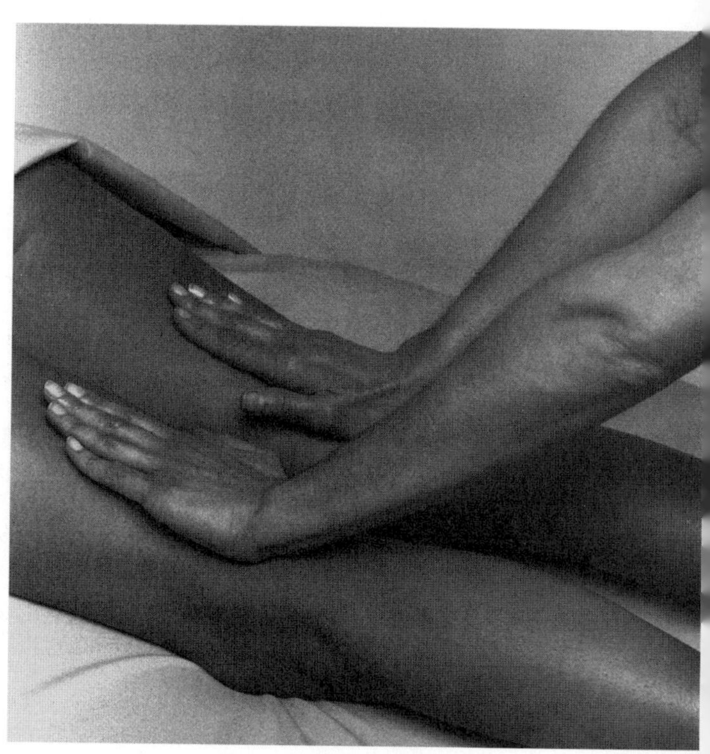

Fig 6-56

Spread the fingers apart, then gently scratch the skin from the Achilles tendon to the buttocks once on each side (Fig. 6-57). Total time: 30 seconds.

24. Hold one of your hands about a foot above the hips, and sweep the hand up the entire spine to above the head 2 times. Total time: 30 seconds.

25. The client is facing up, and you are sitting at the head of the client. Press one thumb down into the episternal notch 2 or 3 times (Fig. 6-58). Press slowly. Total time: 30 seconds.

CAUTION: This movement may trigger a cough reflex. When you press behind the sternum keep your thumb as close to the sternum as you can. Pressing toward the table as you slide behind it can close the windpipe. Be careful. Press slowly; get used to doing this.

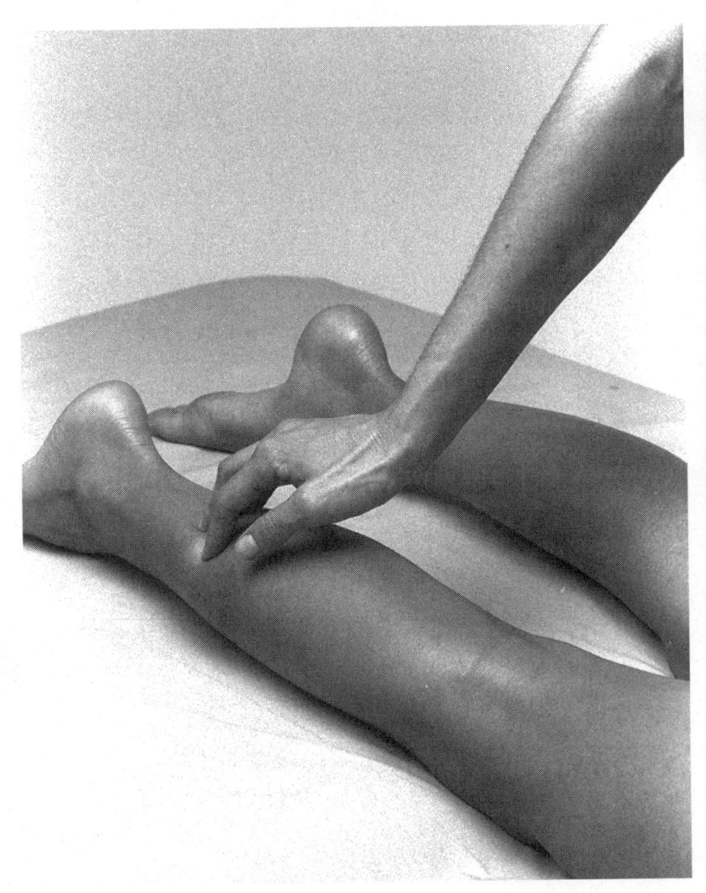

Fig 6-57

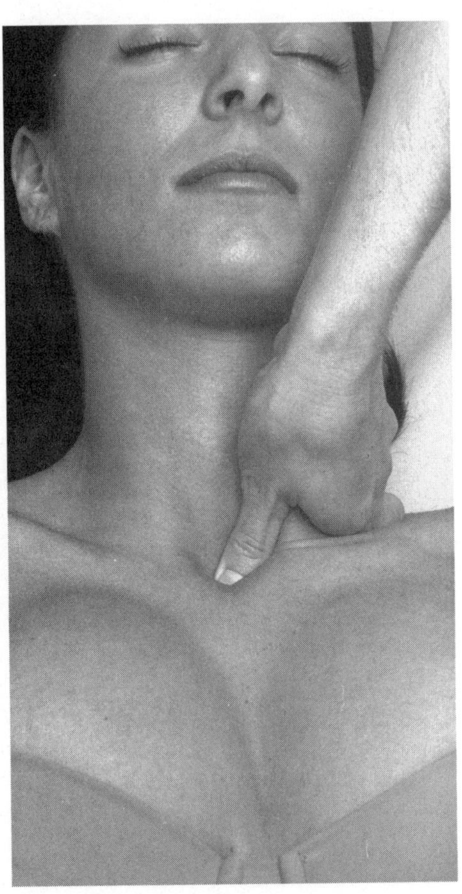

Fig 6-58

26. The client is sitting up. Gently massage the front neck muscles, one side at a time. Use the thumb and curled index fingers to squeeze and slide up and down these muscles (Fig. 6-59). As you are massaging, have the client tilt the head back. This movement opens the throat, clears the head, and sends pranic energy down towards the chest. For the last 10 seconds put traction on the muscle tissue, straight up towards the ceiling. Repeat on the other side. Total time: 1 1/2 minutes.

CAUTION: Have both hands in position, but only massage one side at a time. Stay off the carotid arteries; remain on the front neck muscles.

This is a powerful step. The front neck muscles connect with many distant structures. You can effect changes in the upper chest muscles, the upper arm, and down the forearm to the thumb. The upper back between the shoulder blade and spine will also be affected. Pressure on the front neck muscles in this treatment can be used for problems in the neck and throat, including: laryngitis, sore throat, and thyroid problems.

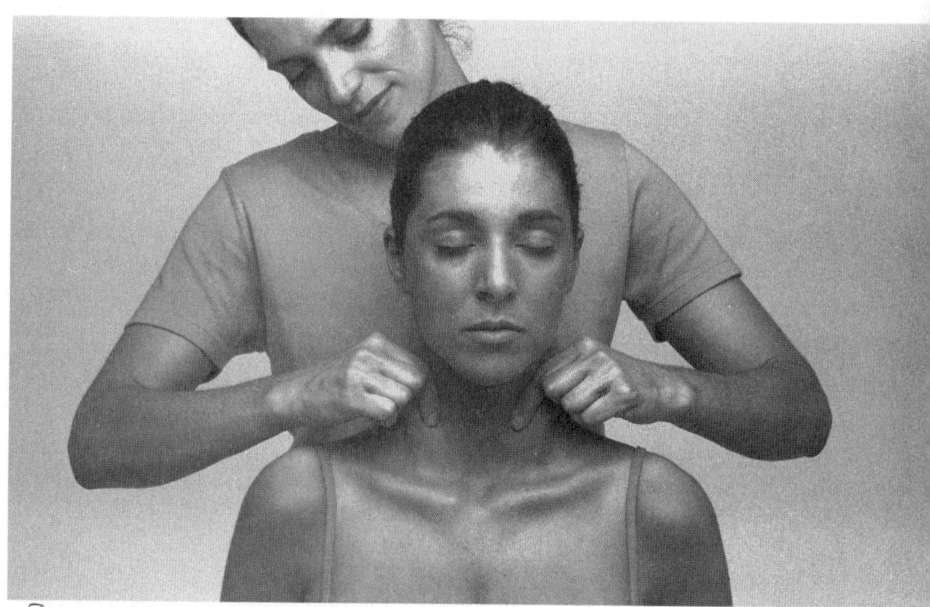

Fig 6-59

27. The client sits with legs over the table. Stand behind the client pressing the upper arm muscles (deltoids) with fingers spread apart and pointing down the arm and thumbs on the shoulder muscles (Fig. 6-60). Push down on the thumbs as you squeeze the deltoids with your fingers for 10 seconds.

28. Hold the upper arm by wrapping all your fingers around the front of the shoulder, and resting the palms on the sides of the upper arms (Fig. 6-61). There is a groove here where your fingers will fit, between the bones of the front shoulder. (It is the bicipital groove for the biceps tendon.) With heavy pressure slide your fingers up and down in this space between the bones for 40 seconds. This space can be sensitive and sore. Do both sides at the same time.

29. The client can sit on a stool or you can kneel on the table. Rest the back of your client's head on your stomach. Some practitioners find that resting the head on the lower sternum works better.

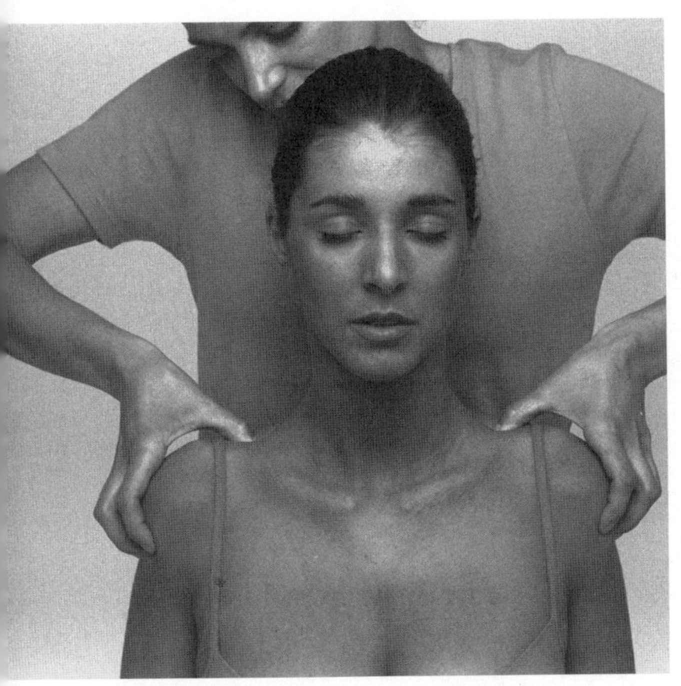

Fig 6-60

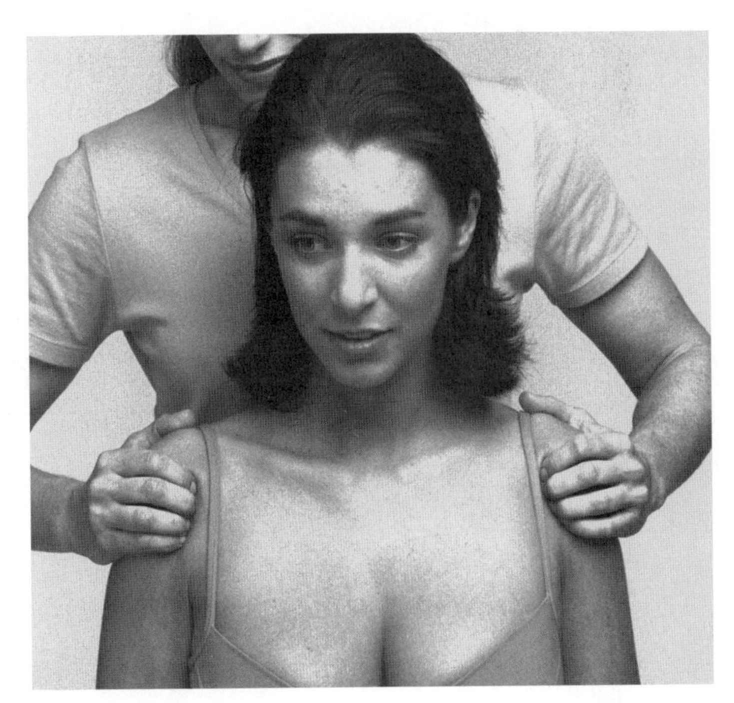

Fig 6-61

Place your left middle finger across the bridge of the nose. And place the right middle finger across the skin between the upper lip and the nose. Curl the knuckles of your right index, left ring, and left little fingers under your palm to contact the cheekbones (Fig. 6-62).

With strong pressure on the middle and index fingers pull your client's head straight back towards your chest. Do this for 10 seconds then reverse hands and repeat.

30. The client is lying down, face-up. Put your index fingers on either side of the root of the nose, near the inner corner of the eye. Make sure you are on the bone, as close to the nose as possible (Fig. 6-63). Pull on your finger contacts with firm pressure for 10 seconds.

Finish by sliding your index fingers from the nose contact along the ridge of bone over the eyes to the temples with pressure for 10 seconds.

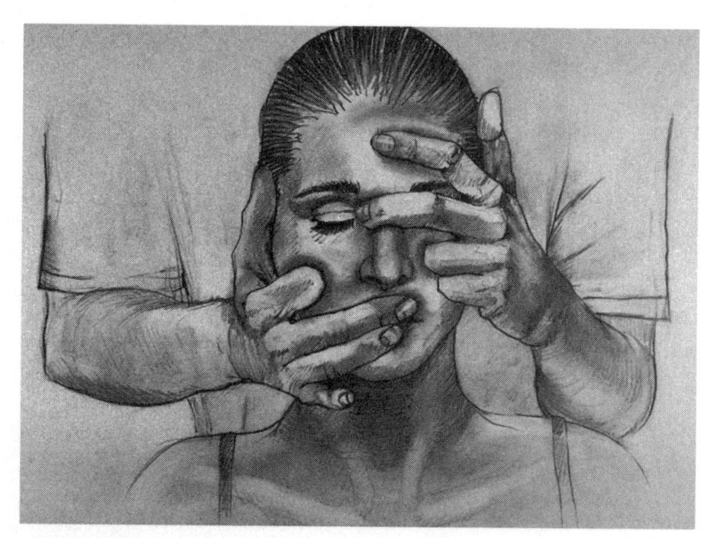

Fig 6-62

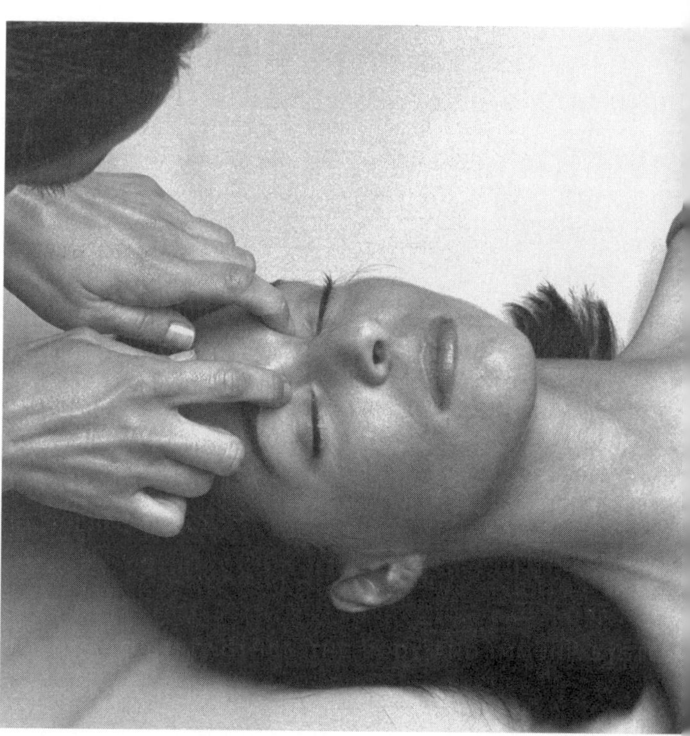

Fig 6-63

Seventh Rib Massage

(21 minutes for both sides)

"HOW CAN YOU TREAT SOMEBODY'S NECK UNTIL YOU'VE RELEASED ALL HIS TENSION IN THE RIBCAGE WHERE HIS PRANAS ARE? WHICH SCHOOL HAS TAUGHT YOU, YOU FOOLS? THE PRANAS ARE IN THE RIBCAGE, PHYSICALLY, MENTALLY, IN A SUBTLE WAY, AND YOU DON'T EVEN RELEASE THEM? AND THEN YOU WANT TO GO AND TREAT A PERSON EVERYWHERE ELSE IN THE BODY, AND YOU THINK YOU ARE GOING TO CURE THAT PERSON? YOU MUST BE LUCKY."

—YOGI BHAJAN[4]

Seven—the most mystic and magical of all the numbers, endowed with occult, religious, and cultural symbolism. Ingrained in our very conception of life, seven is the number of periodicity; the rhythm of each week—the seven days of Creation according to the Bible. Do you pause on your seventh day to meditate on the six days past? Do you plan the next seven?

What is it about this number that attracts us so? There are seven ancient planets in our solar system: Mercury, Venus, Mars, Jupiter, Saturn, Uranus, and Neptune. Seven come eleven, what is it that controls us so?

What are the ribs? They are bony landmarks in the upper body that can be seen and felt. The ribs are elastic, like rubbery bones. They move with the breath; they jerk when we sneeze; they flatten when we sleep. The ribs can be felt at the sternum, on the sides of the body, and in the back, even though they are covered with muscles and skin and connected by cartilage.

There are 12 ribs that embrace the upper body. They are attached to the vertebrae and arch around to the front where most attach to the sternum. The first rib is buried underneath the collar bone and the muscles just above the second rib. The first rib that you can actually feel is the second.

The seven true ribs surround the chest, attaching to the top seven upper back vertebrae, and they all grasp the sternum forming the ribcage. So the true ribs make up the barrel that protects the heart, lungs, windpipe, and gullet. The ribcage carries the pranic energy that moves through the lungs with breathing. The ribcage is a vessel that will expand as much as you want it to. It contracts too, depending on your use of the breath, your exercise, your constitution, and your sense of self-esteem which is revealed in your posture.The ribcage also creates a protective boundary for the heart.

This treatment concerns the last rib in the set called the true ribs, the magic number seven rib.

Procedure

The seventh-rib massage works best on bare skin, although it is possible to do it on a person wearing clothes. Have massage lotion or oil ready. Have your client strip to the waist.

1. How to locate the 7th rib: Have the client lie on the stomach on top of a sheet. Draw an imaginary line across the middle back that connects the lower edge of both shoulder blades. This line crosses the 8th thoracic vertebra. The 7th rib starts 2 inches above the intersection of this line with the spine and 1 1/2 inches out from the bony processes in the spine midline. Remember, this is only an approximation. Search around and you will find it.

The 7th rib continues out to the sides of the body at an acute angle. It drops down from your starting point, passing under the lower edge of the shoulder blade on its way to your client's side (Fig. 6-64). The 7th rib is about 6 inches lower than the armpit, when the arm is extended straight out from the side of the body.

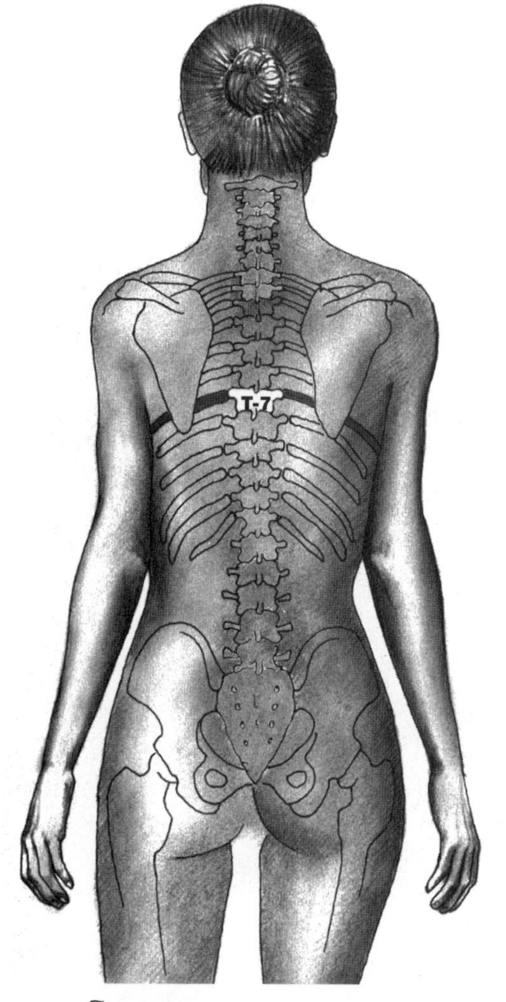

Fig 6-64

2. The client lies face down. Work on one side of the body at a time. With both hands massage the 7th rib from its junction with the spine (1 1/2 inches from the spinous processes), working around towards the side of the body. Concentrate on massaging the rib itself by grasping it with your thumbs and forefingers together, stroking along the rib in two directions (Fig. 6-65). You may go into the spaces between the 6th and 7th ribs or between the 7th and 8th ribs. Slide underneath the blade if you need to. Be thorough. Cover every square inch of the 7th rib. When you finish the back portion of the rib, have the client turn on the side while you keep stroking along the rib, back and forth (Fig. 6-66). Then the client rests on the back, as you slide along the rib }all the way to the sternum.

Turn the client onto the stomach again, and begin working on the other 7th rib. Total time for both ribs: 13 minutes.

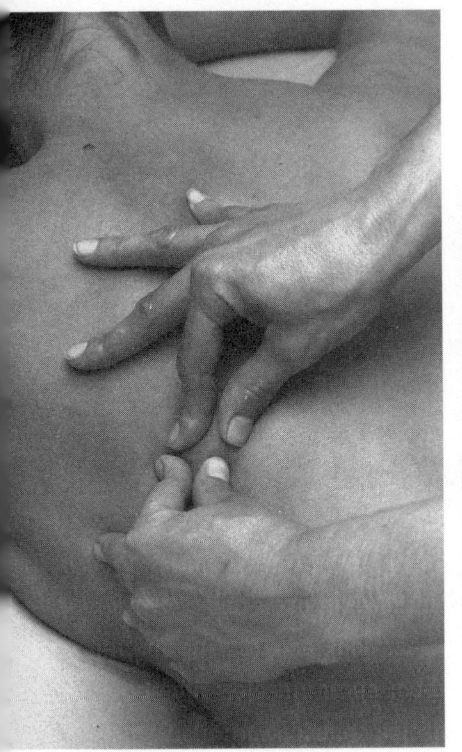

Fig 6-65

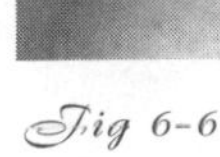

Fig 6-66

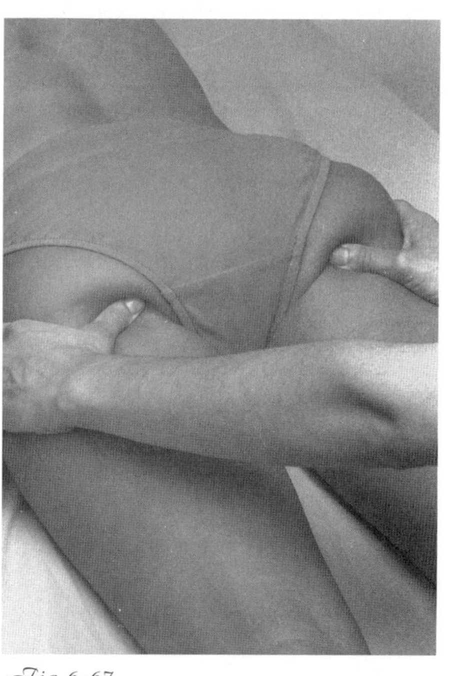

Fig 6-67

3. The client lies face down. Massage the thighs and buttocks creases with your thumbs (Fig. 6-67). Following the crease, push into the tissue with your thumbs, using different strokes. Push straight down towards the table; push in towards the inner thigh muscles; and push towards the outer thighs. Slide back and forth each time you change directions. Time: 2 minutes.

4. Stand to the client's side. Place one hand on the sacrum, the other on the lower back. Fingers point to the side of the body (Fig. 6-68). Use body English to lean on your right hand first; then lean on the left. Using a seesaw action, rock back-and-forth for 2 minutes.

5. Push deep into both armpits using the fingertips of both hands (Fig. 6-69). Massage using circular strokes. Use both hands together on one side if your client is larger than you. Massage for 1 minute on each side.

6. Hold the left foot off the table with your left hand while you hit the arch of the foot with the fist of your right hand (Fig. 6-70). Begin in the area where the arch joins the heel; travel up toward the big toe; and then return back down, back and forth. Do the entire bottom of the foot except the heel. Switch sides and repeat. Percuss for 1 minute on each foot.

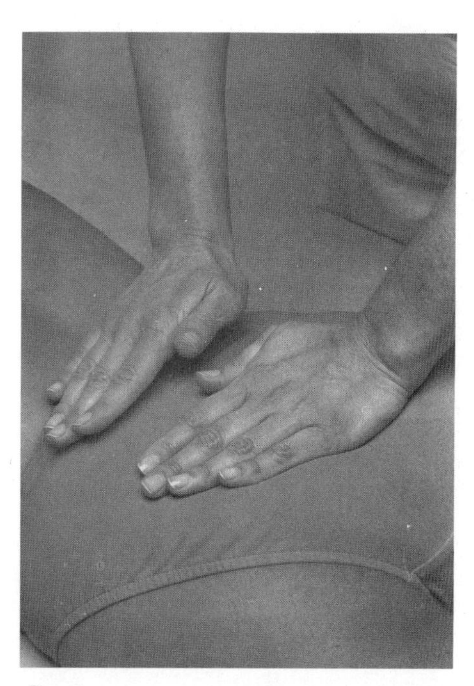

Fig 6-68

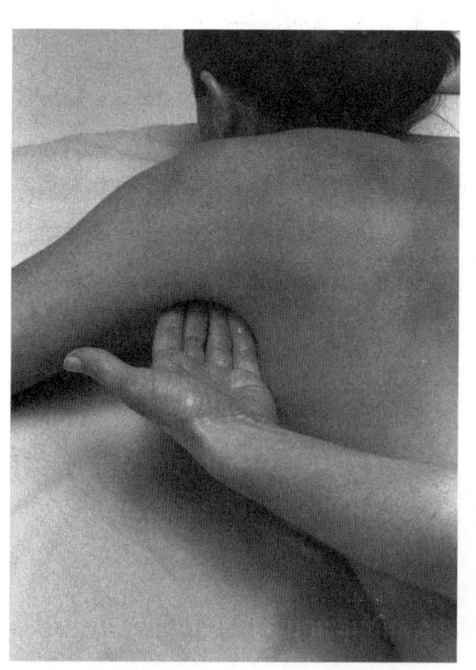

Fig 6-69

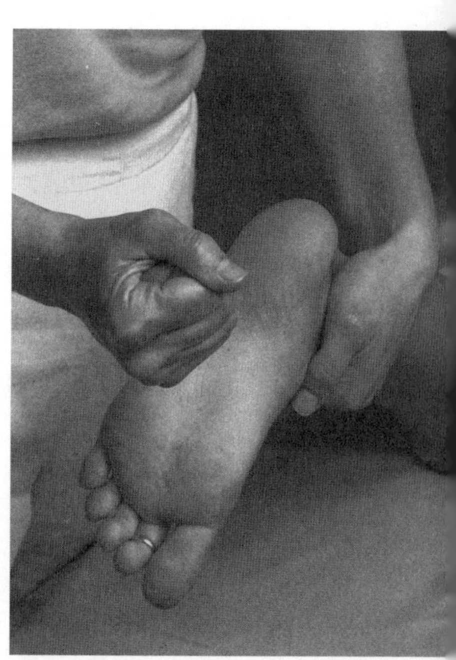

Fig 6-70

Comment

The seventh rib attaches to the spine at the seventh thoracic vertebra. Here in the muscles adjacent to the spine are important pressure points for the diaphragm. These points help many problems. For example, they can be used to help relieve feelings of stuffiness and pain in the chest. They are helpful in overcoming belching, hiccoughs, and nausea. Linger on these **pressure points** as you start this treatment, to create an energy arc for the entire spinal column and the front of the body.

Mountain Above, Thunder Below

(about 16 minutes)

For me the visual image of the practitioner and client in Mountain Above, Thunder Below, is like a hexagram in the *I Ching,* an ancient oracle from China. The hexagram is named Providing Nourishment, something that many healers do for the clients they see. Providing Nourishment has two parts (two trigrams): mountain and thunder, i.e. the practitioner keeping still like a mountain with the client below like thunder. Thunder is something sudden, it has dynamic energy, and it implies progressing quickly.

The first time I did this treatment on Susan, a massage therapist who works with me, something unusual happened. Susan always has cold hands. When I asked her about them she said, “My mom has cold hands too.” After the treatment her neck and shoulders were very warm; she was red in the face, and her ears were beet red. Later that afternoon she saw patients, and I spoke to her 3 hours later before she went home. She said, “My hands have been hot the whole afternoon. I just finished the last massage, washed my hands in cold water, and they are still warm.” This was in Los Angeles in January when the tap water is in the mid-50s Fahrenheit.

Procedure

The following 5-step treatment is to help cure what is ailing people. The first two steps lead clients into performing Steps 3 and 4 well, that is overcoming the limitations that clients would feel doing it alone. Have your clients reach for powerful breaths through the nose (both inhale and exhale). Inspire them to keep going, and I guarantee they will have an enjoyable experience in Step 5.

1. Have your client lie face down. Then kneel down on top of the table or on the floor straddling the client. Sit on the buttocks, facing the upper body (Fig. 6-71). (If this position is not comfortable for your client, turn around and face the feet.) Arrange yourself so your client is comfortable. Sit for 5 minutes.

2. After 5 minutes, climb off, and have your client turn on to one side pulling the knees to the chest, stretching the lower back. Then have the client roll over on the other side repeating the stretch. Time: 30 seconds.

3. Your client is on the stomach. Have the client reach back with both hands touching the lower back, palms-down. Next, the client arches the upper body and legs off the table for 30 seconds.

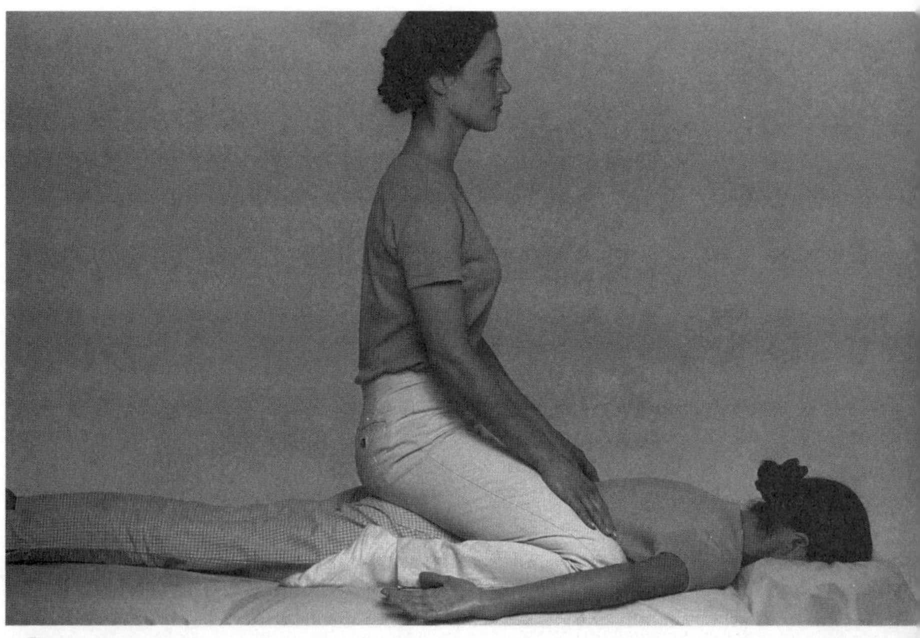

Fig 6-71

If your client is in good shape try it for 3 minutes (Fig. 6-72). Otherwise, do the exercise in 30-second segments, alternating with short rest periods until 3 minutes are completed.

4. Still face-down have your client spread the legs wide, bend the knees, and reach back to hold the ankles (Fig. 6-73). (Some large people have difficulty reaching their ankles. Use two belts, placed around the ankles to assist them arching up. Bath towels, ties, or ropes can also be used.)

Have your client rock the pelvis forward, arching the lower back as much as possible. The chest and thighs stay in contact with the table. Encourage your client to arch with tension and to breathe deeply the entire time.

A client in good shape may do this for 2 minutes. Inspire that client to persist for the full 2 minutes. If your client is in less than good shape, hold the position for 30 seconds at a time with 30 second rests. However, if the client has a pain, an injury, or hurts after a few seconds, have the client come out of the position and relax.

5. The client turns over, face-up, and relaxes for 5 minutes (Fig. 6-74). You can leave the room and get your client a small glass of water. Return at the end of the 5 minutes.

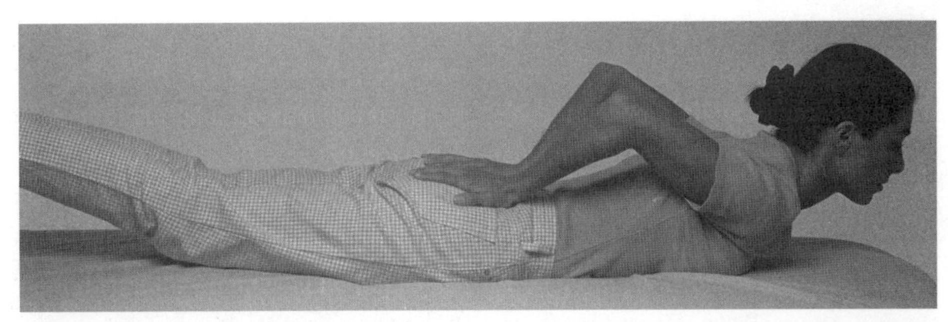

Fig 6-72

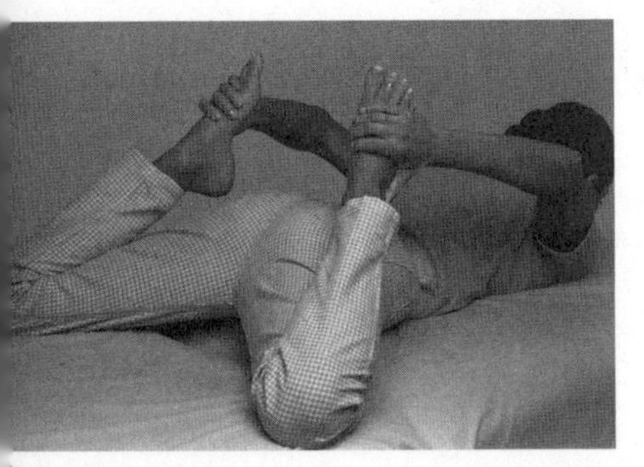

Fig 6-73

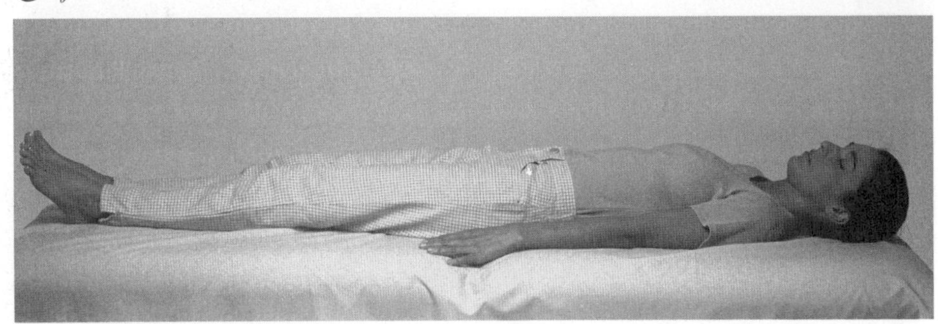

Fig 6-74

Comment

After treatment, one client said: "The first five minutes are hard to go through understand, or relax with. Then I experienced a calm, and a deep relaxation came over me. I felt the centers open up in my spine and energy go down my legs. I can feel waves, starting in my feet, going up to the body. There are sensations in the pelvis and the front of my lower body below the navel."

Then 2 minutes after the treatment finished, she said: "There are chills going down the legs and back up. It's easy to go into a trance now and deeply rest[5]."

Ishnaan, the Science of Hydrotherapy

"Since ancient times, people have prayed for the blessing of *ishnaan*. What is *ishnaan*? *Ishnaan* is the total sum of hydrotherapy.... 'Ish' means disease, weaknesses. 'Naan' means: doesn't exist, taking away. So *ishnaan* means we have no disease and our weaknesses are gone. We don't say we'll take a bath; we never say "bath." *Ishnaan* means going under the cold shower, massaging yourself. It is hydrotherapy, the oldest hydrotherapy method. It is the method of self-healing. *Ishnaan* is when the body by its own virtue creates the temperature change beating off the coldness of the water. *Ishnaan* is the use of water to help the body heal itself of disease. It is very ancient. Early written records describe water therapy long before the Roman or Christian times. *Ishnaan* is not just wetting your body. There is a whole respect to it. There is a whole grace to it.

"Get up from your quilt in the morning and take a long cold shower, going in and out of the water stream five times until you don't feel cold anymore. Open yourself to it. When your capillaries get locked up by forty percent, you are no more a human.

"You have to go under your shower four, five times—you'll not feel the cold at all. Step into the wall of cold and rub your skin with the washcloth. Step back rubbing yourself more and more. Go four or five times into that water. It means your capillaries are open. You made your day. Dry yourself the best you can. And put a big thick blanket around you, and do your *sadhana*. You'll be surprised how light, how young, how intuitive you are now. Because tomorrow can be imagined, by intuition you can know it. One who knows tomorrow rules tomorrow."

—Yogi Bhajan[1]

Just as the sun has been worshiped by various cultures throughout history, so water has been worshiped by people as far back as written records go. The Ganges and the Nile are two rivers that have a long history of being worshiped as givers of life and healing.

Historically, many cultures have used mineral waters for healing. Physicianpriests established temples near hot springs where the sick came for bathing, massage, fasting, and communion with their gods. Daily baths kept citizens healthy in the civilizations of the Mediterranean. In addition, Roman baths were famous as social gathering places. And the Greeks used cold baths to stimulate and refresh their bodies in the gymnasia of the times. Hippocrates gave detailed prescriptions for using cold water in the treatment of many diseases, including gout and pains in the joints.

The Russians, Turks, and Scandinavians have a long history of using sweat baths for healing.

At one time there was hardly any ailment that doctors did not think could be helped by hydrotherapy. Hydrotherapy stimulated the nervous system, fortifying the patient in order to conquer infections. The circulatory, immune, and neuromuscular systems all benefited. In the early part of this century US Veterans hospitals used hydrotherapy in surgery, in treating typhoid fever, and in treating mental illness.

Hydrotherapy disappeared from the practice of medicine following World War I. It was considered time-consuming and antiquated. Prescription drugs were considered to be quicker and easier to use. In 1940, an article in the Journal of the American Medical Association stated: “A curious phenomenon in American medicine is the definite elimination of much reference to hydrotherapy. Similar to the way some parents keep their children ignorant to the facts of life, we appear to protect the medical student from the knowledge of hydrotherapy....[2]”

The disappearance of hydrotherapy was unfortunate because the benefits are transcendent—mind, body, and soul are all blessed by the curative powers of water. Hydrotherapy can relieve chronic complaints such as migraines, insomnia, and constipation and it can help relieve acute conditions such as swelling from injuries.

There are many kinds of hydrotherapy. Treatments exist using varying degrees of water temperature coupled with different kinds of massage. Water temperature ranges are subjective. Use the following table as a guide.

Table of Water Temperatures

	Fahrenheit	*Celsius*
Very cold:	32-56	0-13
Cold:	56-65	13-18
Cool:	65-75	18-24
Tepid:	75-92	24-33
Neutral:	92-98	33-37
Warm to hot:	98-104	37-40
Very hot:	104 and up	40 and up

Here are some general rules for using cold- or hot-water hydrotherapy:

1. The shorter the application and the more extreme the temperature, the more purely excitant will be the effect of the hot or the cold water.

2. For very short periods of time water applications almost anywhere on the body, hands, cheeks, face, legs, or torso are useful to arouse someone from a faint.

Cold water hydrotherapy. Throughout history, cold-water hydrotherapy has been useful in treating shock, fever, cancer, skin diseases, infections (including abcesses, carbuncles, and prostatitis), and hemorrhages, including cerebral hemorrhage. Also, cold water is useful in chronic conditions where body functions are below normal, for example: diabetes, obesity, hypothyroid conditions, and low blood pressure[3].

Cold water acts in several ways. First, a short, cold shower or bath is a tonic. Tonics are stimulants for better health, improved blood circulation, and better muscle tone. Cold water restores, invigorates, and helps build resistance to disease. It stimulates the glandular system, speeds up metabolism, strengthens the entire nervous system. Cold water mobilizes life energy and expands the human aura.

Cold water is also a diuretic and anaesthetic, and it helps to reduce even the highest fever. It relieves pain and constipation, and it aids in the elimination of toxins from the body.

Very cold water applied to the navel point for a short time relieves constipation

In addition, cold water has these other benefits:

- Brings blood to the superficial capillaries.
- Reduces blood pressure on internal organs, thereby flushing internal organs, giving them a new supply of blood.
- Prevents the body from developing an extra layer of fat.
- Contracts the muscles and causes them to eliminate toxins and poisons quickly.
- Increases the body's power of resistance.
- Strengthens the mucous membranes.
- Keeps the skin young and shining.
- Helps the liver function better.
- Revives the body after collapse.
- Helps to reduce nervousness.
- Builds immunity to colds.

CAUTION: If you have a circulatory disease such as Reynaud's syndrome, cold showers or baths are forbidden.

The Cold Sponge Bath

TAKE IT ONCE IN THE MORNING AND ONCE IN THE EVENING.

The easiest and mildest way to introduce cold water, especially for older persons and cold-sensitive individuals, is to take a cold sponge bath.

1. Sit on the edge of the bathtub, dip a sponge under the running water. Instead of a sponge you may use a cotton or wool mitten, a loofah, or a rough cotton washcloth.

2. Keep your pajamas or bathrobe on, and expose one section of yourself at a time.

3. Scrub your arm with the mitten until the skin is red with new blood.

4. When you are finished scrubbing the arm, dry off by rubbing briskly with a towel. There is a double benefit with this technique—the stimulation from the cold *plus* the friction increases circulation and generates very strong heat.

5. Then continue to scrub and rub the skin of your other arm, the legs, torso, back, neck, and head.

6. If you are helping someone who is ill, put the person back to bed immediately with enough blankets to maintain this salutary warmth. This cold sponge bath is invaluable for someone who is weak, bedridden, or very old. It's also a way to train children to get used to cold water.

Cold Showers

"THOSE CAPILLARIES WHICH ARE THINNER THAN A HAIR GET CLOGGED UP. THEY NEED A ROTO-ROOTER ONCE IN A WHILE, AND THAT IS WHAT A COLD SHOWER IS ALL ABOUT."

—YOGI BHAJAN[4]

Special Effects of Cold Showers. Directing the cold water stream with a mobile shower head can bring immediate benefits to parts of the body. For example, you stimulate the entire body if you massage the bottom of your feet with the directed stream. It also relieves cold feet, incontinence (in the elderly), and helps a weak bladder. After you finish with the feet the body will deeply relax.

You can relieve constipation by directing a cold water stream to the abdominal region.

Here are some other specific locations to massage with the hands and water for 1 to 3 minutes while in the shower.

- Massage just below the lower lip. You will become bright and your mind will be very clear.
- Massage between the eyebrows and the upper lip. You will become very energetic.
- Massage the forehead. You will become very sleepy.
- Massage the upper arm from your elbow to just below your shoulder. You will relieve your digestive tract and help your stomach.
- Massage from your elbow to about 2 inches above your wrist to help your digestive tract.
- Massage from 2 inches above the wrist to the beginning of the wrist to help your heart.
- Massage your face, hands, scalp, and the back of the neck. You will boost your brain.
- Massage the fingertips to help your brain.
- Massage the lower third of the sternum and the spine from T-8 (lower shoulder blade) through L-5 (see Chapter 6, Fig. 6-01). Spraying in this area aids the kidneys.
- Massage the mid-back between the shoulder blades. Spraying here helps the stomach.

Cold Showers for the Cold-Sensitive

Cold showers may be difficult for those who are thin or for those who have dry skin, small bone structure, or cold hands and feet. If you are indecisive or have irregular eating and sleeping habits you may be cold-sensitive as well.

If you are cold-sensitive, here are some steps to prepare yourself for a cold shower, and what you can do after the shower:

1. Put the almond oil you are going to use for your pre-shower body massage into a polyethylene or glass bottle. Place the bottle into a small pot filled with an inch and a half of water, and heat it on the stove only long enough to warm the oil. Massaging warm oil on the skin is luxurious in any season. Oil is beneficial for the nervous system.

2. Serve yourself a hot cup of your favorite herbal tea to make you feel warm inside and to increase your blood circulation.

3. Do 26 frogs[5], then run in place for 3 minutes. And next, lie on the back with hands under the hips, and do 90-degree leg lifts for 2 minutes. Then jump into the shower.

4. Afterward: You are dressed. Your body has returned to its normal temperature, and you are energized. Your skin is flushed with blood. Walk briskly, use a treadmill or a trampoline to help re-establish normal circulation and body heat.

Cold Shower for a Woman

"Woman is by nature a water animal. She needs to drink water, be in water, play in water. When she takes a shower, she needs to be sure her skin is soaked enough so that she feels the temperature change. Otherwise, an extra layer of fat will develop.

"Further, any circulation or nerve problems can be prevented by regular cold showers. Cold showers preserve a woman as a woman, they correct imbalanced menses, prevent early menopause, skin problems, and they keep her glow."
—Yogi Bhajan[6]

CAUTION: When menstruating, skip the cold shower; instead, shower with lukewarm water.

1. Begin with a massage of almond or sesame oil. Lightly cover the entire body with the oil, and massage your muscles to stimulate and awaken yourself.

2. Wear cotton bicycle shorts or Bermuda shorts covering about half the thigh while in the shower, because it protects the sex nerve[7] and the large thigh bone from the sudden change in temperature. The thigh bone regulates the production of calcium in the body and is very sensitive to temperature changes[8].

3. Step into the shower and turn the cold water on to a brisk spray. Use water that is as cold as you can stand, and rub your skin vigorously. Stay in the stream for at least 2 or 3 seconds. Standing still is forbidden: Dance! Move! Sing! Breathe deeply!

4. Step out of the water while continuing to rub vigorously.

5. Then step back in; massage the body all over under the water; step out again, and continue this cold water song-and-dance four times.

By the third or fourth time you will have become accustomed to the cold water, because the capillaries will have opened up and brought warm blood to the surface of the skin.

6. Stand under the spray, allowing the breasts to be massaged by the water for a few seconds. Then massage your breasts.

7. When finished, dry yourself briskly with a towel for 3 minutes, and watch the skin flush as the capillaries open.

Cold Shower for a Man

1. Massage the body with almond or sesame oil.

2. Wear underpants to support the testicles during the temperature change and to protect the thigh region. Use cotton bicycle shorts or jockey shorts with long legs.

3. Stay under the water as long as you can, vigorously massaging the skin and breathing deeply. Try 1 full minute. Spray the neck, shoulders, and spine. Shrug your shoulders up and down. Breathe powerfully! Dance a little! Be careful.

Then spray the front of the neck, chest, abdomen, thighs, and feet. Wake up, massage! Do this side for 1 minute also. Total time: 2 minutes.

4. Step out of the shower and dry yourself off briskly. Rub your skin energetically enough to cause the blood to come to the surface—beet red skin. Dry yourself for 5 full minutes, and start your day invigorated.

Cold Bath: the Big Chill

COLD WATER BATH HELPS THE BODY PEED UP ITS GENERAL METABOLIC RATE WO TO FIVE TIMES, AND CAN KEEP THE ODY TEMPERATURE AT HEALTHY, CCEPTABLE LEVELS.

Getting into a bathub full of cold water where the temperature is below 65 degrees F (18 degrees C) is an invigorating experience that generates a feeling of vitality and deep strength[9]. Call it the Big Chill, and be cautious.

CAUTION: Do not use a full cold bath if you are elderly or are seriously ill. Avoid cold baths if you have colitis, high blood pressure, heart disease, or hypothyroidism. If you have poor circulation, a weak immune system, poor kidney function, or hardening of the arteries also avoid cold baths.

Do not take cold baths if you are already cold, excessively fatigued, or menstruating. The following are guidelines only–each person's reaction is very different and in some cases can be difficult to predict.

1. Submerge your body up to the neck from 2 seconds to 2 minutes, depending on your tolerance for the water temperature. Some people start with a 2-second plunge and gradually build up the duration.

How does the body respond to a cold bath? First, there is the shock and the feeling of total chill, inside and out. Then the body adjusts to the water temperature and finds a comfort level. It may even be peaceful. A second chill occurs later.

2. Leave the tub while still enjoying the deep comfort after the initial chill.

Comment

Remember: the primary effect of the cold shower or bath is to stimulate the body as well as the nervous and glandular systems. Also, it invigorates, restores, and tones the body.

Your endurance to cold will increase if you do these procedures daily.

The Hot Bath

ON A BASIC LEVEL, HOT BATHS RELAX AND SOOTHE THE BODY, EASE ACHES AND PAINS, AND HELP THE BODY AND MIND UNWIND.

Hot baths are useful when you need to sweat in order to eliminate toxins, bacteria, or disease from the body. Hot baths also reduce muscle spasms and relieve internal congestion. After exercise, a short bath of up to 2 minutes will eliminate fatigue.

CAUTION: Remember that hot baths deplete energy—which is why they are often recommended before going to bed. Heat is primarily an excitant. Its secondary effects are depression, sedation, and atonia. A long, hot bath is never prescribed for very old, feeble, or anemic people. In addition, those who have a tendency to hemorrhage or those with severe organic diseases should avoid long, hot baths.

1. Fill the bathtub so that the water level is up to your navel.

2. Sit in the bath for *at least* one-half hour, to allow for the circulatory and reproductive systems to adjust.

3. Have a cold washcloth or cold compress ready to apply to your forehead in order to counter the exit of blood from your head.

4. Finish the hot bath with a cold shower. However, those with illnesses and women who are menstruating should finish with a tepid shower.

A hot stream of water directed on the abdomen can alleviate female pelvic pain or bladder and uterine problems.

The Narayan Treatment

(about 45 minutes)

THE NARAYAN TREATMENT INTEGRATES AND UPLIFTS.

It has the skin-on-flesh sensuous feeling of massage, the oil-on-skin satiny feeling that brings warmth. The essential oils penetrate the skin to provide cooling and aroma. And applying towels cooled in ice water is refreshing. The Narayan treatment will transport your client to far away lands.

This treatment takes its name from Narayan oil, which is a blend of mint, eucalyptus, and clove oils. For centuries Narayan oil has been used to cure pain in the muscles, to take care of mild skin problems, and to redress the mismanagement of tissue growth within muscles. It is very effective for tendon problems.

This treatment is cooling, and it can be done in any season of the year. However, in northern latitudes where winters are cold, this treatment is best done in spring and summer.

The Narayan treatment suits those who like cold weather and those who feel warm most of the time—warm hands and feet. Usually anyone with the following characteristics tolerates this treatment well: ruddy complexion; red or blond hair; and red tongue with no coating.

On the other hand, the Narayan treatment done at the warmest times of summer suits the cold-sensitive person, including someone with: a very slow pulse; a thick, white-coated tongue; or a gray, pale, or anemic complexion. In addition, the treatment can be stopped after Step 21.

CAUTION: Do not administer this treatment to those who have heart disease or are in a state of severe fatigue.

Preparing the Site

This treatment can be done anywhere. In the summer, the treatment can be done outdoors in the warm sunshine: on a lawn, in a meadow, or beside a swimmimg pool. Use a futon, an exercise mat, or a massage table. Cover the floor with an exercise mat if you are not using a futon.

1. Place a waterproof tablecloth over the surface you are treating on.

CAUTION: Be careful to avoid putting Narayan oil or water on carpets, upholstery, or hardwood floors. They stain easily.

2. Use one or two sheets to cover the tablecloth and one more to cover the client.

3. Use five to eight 100-percent cotton towels. They're soft, absorb the most water, and the fibers are the best for bringing blood to the skin surface when you dry your client. Use two 20" x 36" towels on each section of the body. (If you use bath towels that are 31" x 50" you will only need one.)

4. Store the wet towels on 1 or 2 flat stainless steel trays with two inch sides (the kind used in restaurants). Keep them soaking in cold water in a refrigerator. Place 6 towels in the water inside the refrigerator for an hour prior to the treatment. The amount of water in the tray is enough to soak the towels by 20 percent. That means the towels soak up the water without being underwater. When you are ready to place a towel on your client, wring out the water leaving the towel damp. To keep your hands warm, wear rubber gloves with thin cloth insulation that you can get at a supermarket[10]. Just slip them on, wring the towel out, and place it on your client. Then take the gloves off while the towels invigorate the client. Cold towels warm up fast on a 98-degree-F body.

One of the other ways to prepare cold towels is to use a new plastic pail. Pour enough cold water and ice into it so that the 6 towels will absorb all the water.

Preparing Your Client

Making your client comfortable with this treatment is important, and it begins with clothing. Ask the client to wear old clothes to the treatment. Although Narayan oil has a natural, pleasant odor it will stain clothing, and the odor will stay in them for more than one washing. Also, make sure the client brings a towel to put over the car seat when leaving the massage. Narayan oil fragrance also lingers on car seats and steering wheels for a long time.

Be prepared for cold-sensitive clients or clients who may feel far colder than they anticipated.

1. Make sure the room is warm enough for the client, regardless of the outside temperature.

2. Offer the client a cup of hot herbal tea before treatment to maintain internal warmth. Otherwise you may have someone shivering on the table, with teeth clattering before you are half way into the treatment.

3. Have several heating pads or moist hot packs available to warm up the client any time during the treatment. If needed, you can place a heating pad on the client's feet for the first half of the treatment.

4. If the client is known to be cold-sensitive, dilute the Narayan Oil to reduce the cooling properties of the alcohol and essential oils by adding 25 to 50 percent more almond oil to the Narayan Oil.

5. Finish the treatment by applying heating pads for 10 minutes.

CAUTION: Do not administer this treatment right before or after your client has had a meal. If the client is overheated, make sure there is a cooling-down period before you begin.

Procedure

The client is undressed, lying on the stomach on a massage table underneath the top sheet. You are standing to the client's left side.

1. Pull the sheet down to the thighs. Squirt a tablespoon of diluted Narayan Oil on one palm. Then rub both hands together, spreading the oil over your palms. Now you are ready to touch the client.

Spread the oil around with your hands over the entire back, the sides of the body, and the buttocks. Rub it in a little while you assess the tension areas, the regions of poor circulation (pale skin), and the lumps and bumps. Remember these places, because you will spend a little more time massaging there. Time: approximately 30 seconds.

2. Using your thumbs on either side of the spine, press deep into the muscles starting at the base of the lower back. Slide slowly up the spine keeping constant pressure all the way to the shoulders (Fig. 7-01). Have your client breathe deeply if it's painful. Repeat the same movement 3 more times. Total time: 30 seconds.

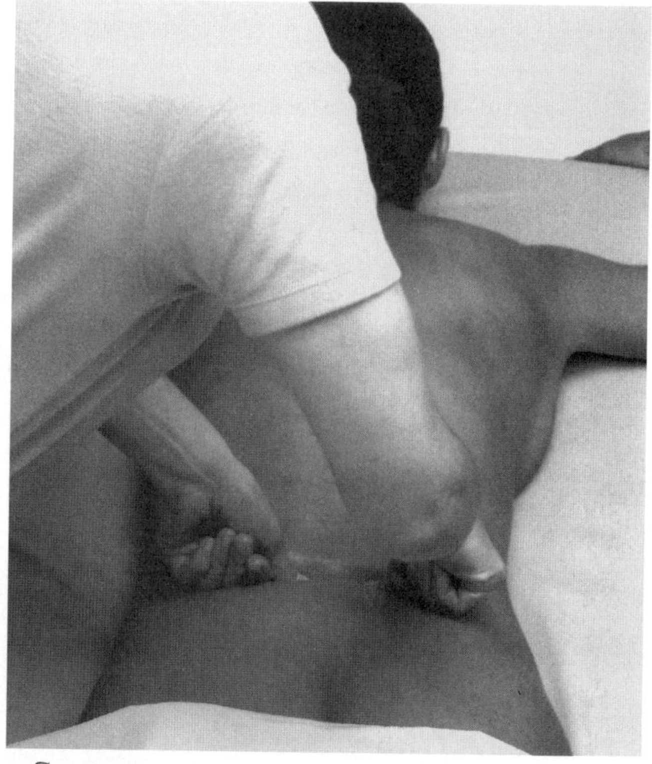

Fig 7-01

3. Place your hands palms-down on the lowest part of the lower back, with the fingers pointing towards the head. Push down gently into the back muscles using the heels of your hands. Move your hands a few inches up the back and repeat the downward push. Continue all the way to the shoulders (Fig. 7-02). Total time: 30 seconds.

CAUTION: If you are treating someone who has brittle bones (osteoporosis) do not do the pushing-down motion. Instead, massage the back by sliding your palms a few inches toward the neck, then a few inches toward your starting place. Then move up 4 inches repeating the motion—the palms sliding up and back. Continue moving up 4 inches at a time, repeating the motions all the way to the shoulders.

4. Hold the client's right wrist. Now pull gently to bring her right arm back close to the body. Use your left hand knife-edge to slide under the right shoulder blade, from the top edge all the way to the bottom (Fig. 7-03). Then push your left hand underneath

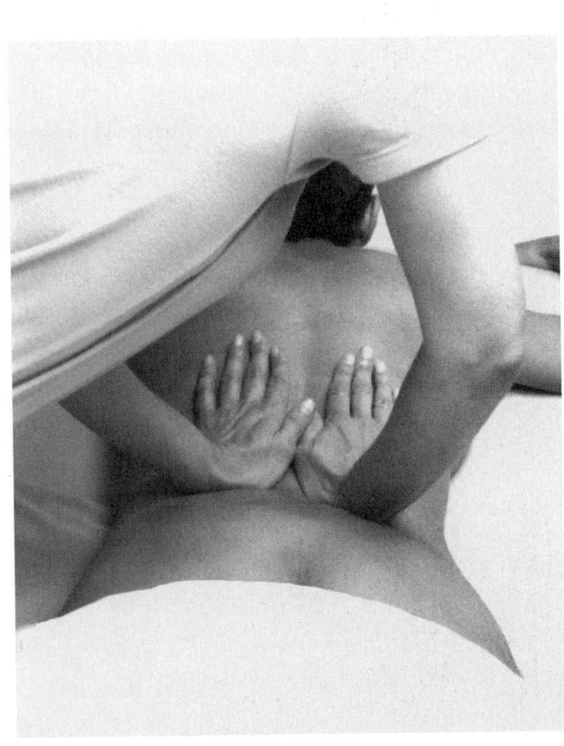

Fig 7-02

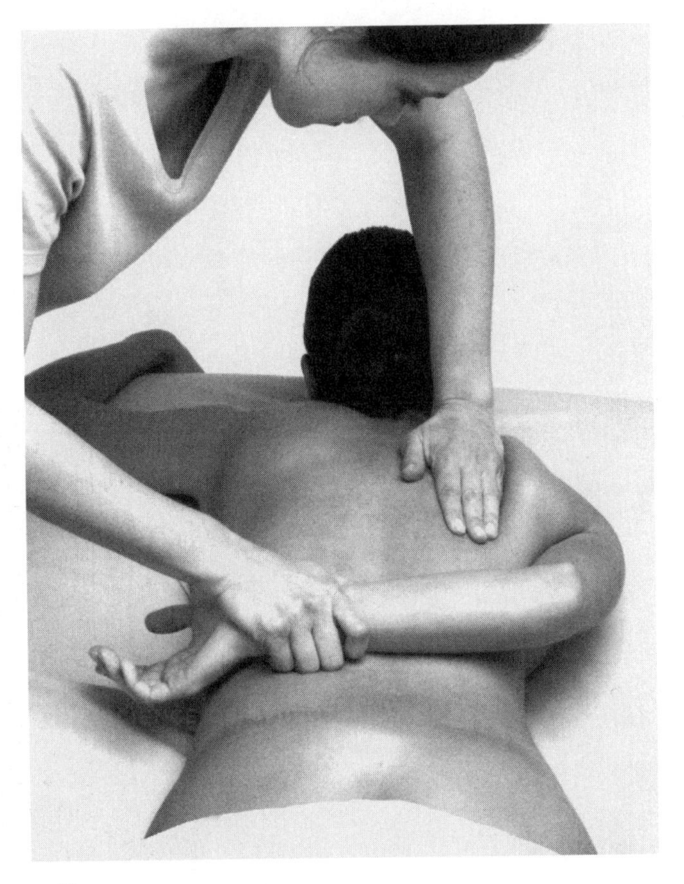

Fig 7-03

the blade with a quick movement, three times. Then switch sides to repeat the same motions. Total time: 30 seconds.

Make the sliding movement quick, remembering that some shoulder blades are easy to go under. Others are glued to the ribs with thick muscles that will not let you enter.

5. Using long up-and-down strokes, slide your thumbs along the middle and upper back muscles for 1 minute (refer to Fig. 7-01).

6. Make fists out of your hands, and use the large knuckles to make long up-and-down strokes along both sides of the spine, from the lower back to the shoulders, and return (Fig. 7-04). Time: 30 seconds.

7. Using your knuckles, stroke from the spine to the sides of the body along the ribs. Follow the contour of the body as you slide from the spine muscles along the ribs to the side of the body (refer to Fig. 7-04). Do both sides. Total time: 30 seconds.

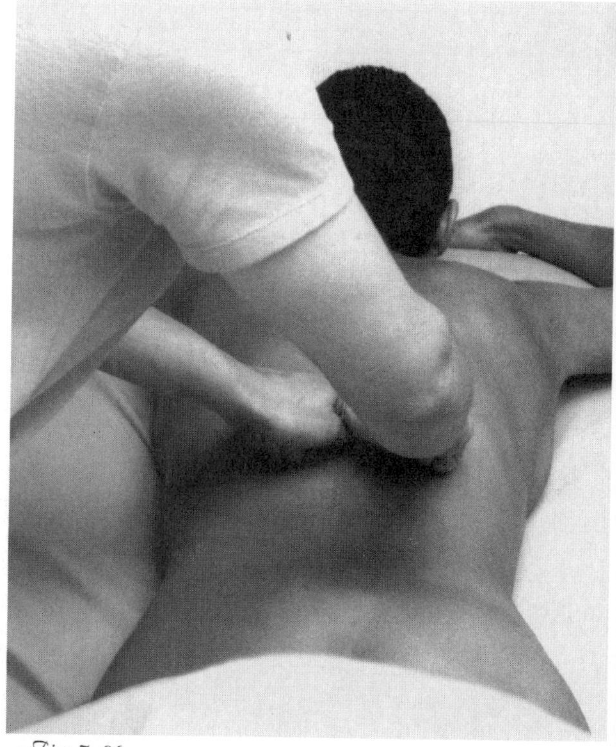

Fig 7-04

Do both sides at once if you are suited to it. But do one side at a time if you are small in stature, or you are working on someone who is larger than you.

8. Continue using your knuckles to stroke on top of the shoulder blades, sliding from the inside to outside (medial to lateral) and back again. Then move your fist an inch lower, and repeat the same strokes. Total time: 30 seconds.

9. Massage the shoulder muscles with the knuckles, from the neck to the shoulder joint and back again. Stay on the muscles. Repeat 2 more times. Total time: 30 seconds.

10. Still using the knuckles, start at the lowest ribs on the side of the body. Now slide up to the armpit and then back again (Fig. 7-05). Do it 3 times. Total time: 30 seconds.

11. Apply more Narayan oil, covering the buttock muscles, if the skin has absorbed your first layer. Stand to your client's right side, placing one hand on top of the other.

Push your fingers deeply into the buttock muscle on the left side. Using your body leverage, press down into the buttock muscle, then slide your fingers from the sacrum to the side of

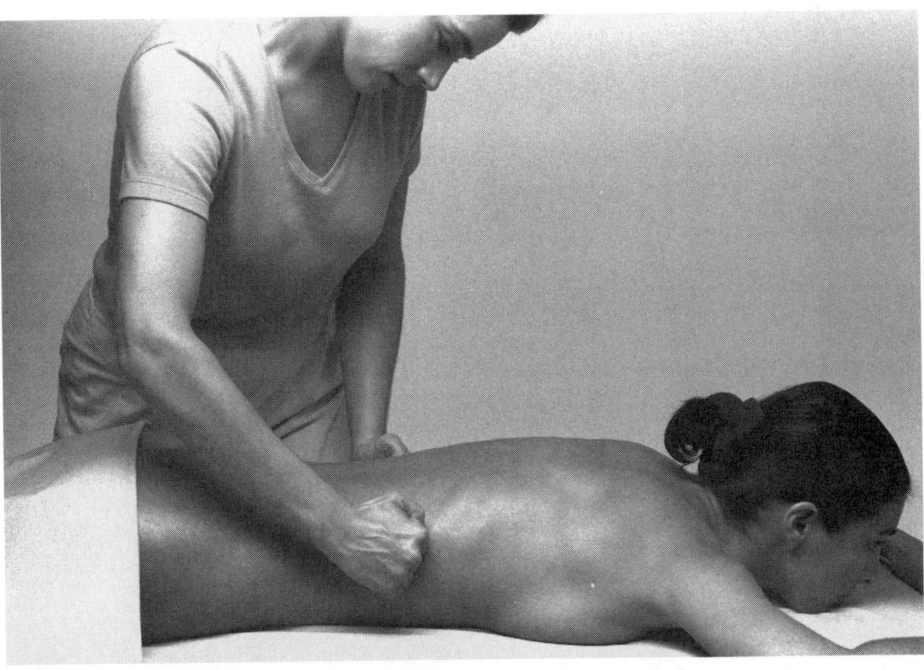

Fig 7-05

the hip (Fig. 7-06). Move your fingers a few inches closer to the tailbone, and repeat the stroke until you cover the whole buttock muscle with these long medial to lateral strokes. Time: 1 minute.

12. Take a cold towel from the tray, ring out the excess water, and place the damp towel over the entire back starting at the shoulders. Use a second towel to cover the buttocks if needed.

The cold from the towels helps to activate the properties of the oil. The client may jump from the shock, so have the client breathe deeply or yell. The body adapts well within a few moments, and the towel becomes comforting.

Have your client place the hands palms-down on the lower back. (The client can locate a problem area or place the palms down in the waistline area of the lower back.) Have the client push and massage that area (Fig. 7-07). Total time: 1 minute.

If there is a shoulder problem that prevents touching the lower back, go to Step 13.

13. Leave the towels on the client and stand to the client's right side.

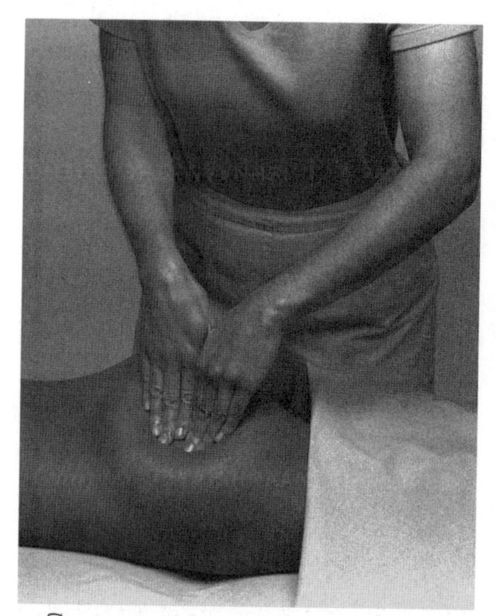

Fig 7-06

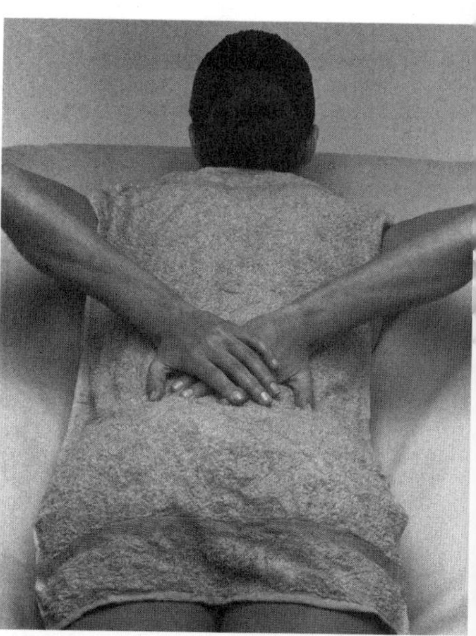

Fig 7-07

CAUTION: Be extra careful if the person has knee problems or a thigh injury.

Hold the toes of the client's right foot with your right hand, and grasp the client's right ankle with your left hand. Now push the right lower leg toward the buttocks. At the same time bend the top of the right foot toward the buttocks with force (Fig. 7-08). Repeat on the left leg. Total time: 30 seconds.

If your client is flexible, you can touch the heel against the buttocks with ease. Push farther and the thigh may rise up off the table.

14. Place your left hand under the right thigh and your right hand on the ankle of the right foot. Lift the right leg off the table as high as it will go (within your client's limits, usually about a foot); move it 18 to 24 inches away from the left leg while pushing the right foot close to the right buttock again (Fig. 7-09). Repeat on the left leg. Total time: 1 1/2 minutes.

15. Take the towels off, and use them to rub the skin from the shoulders to the buttocks. Then use a dry towel to soak up excess water. Rub the skin from the sacrum to the shoulders and from the buttocks up the sides. Pull the sheet up over your client's shoulders. Time: 30 seconds.

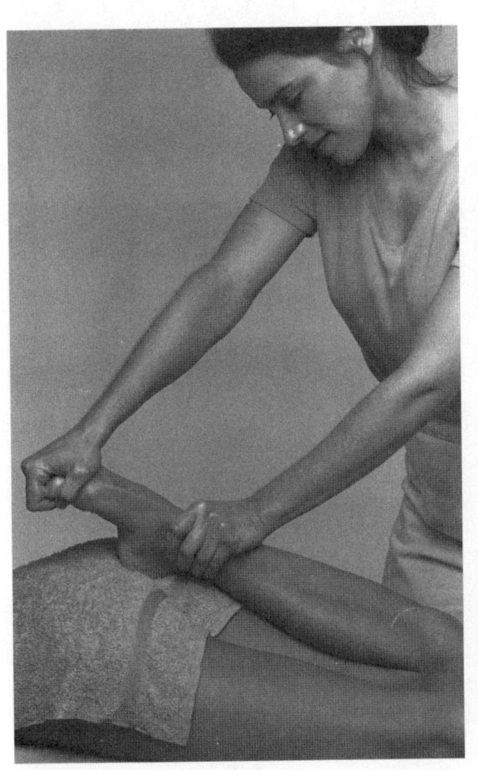

Fig 7-08

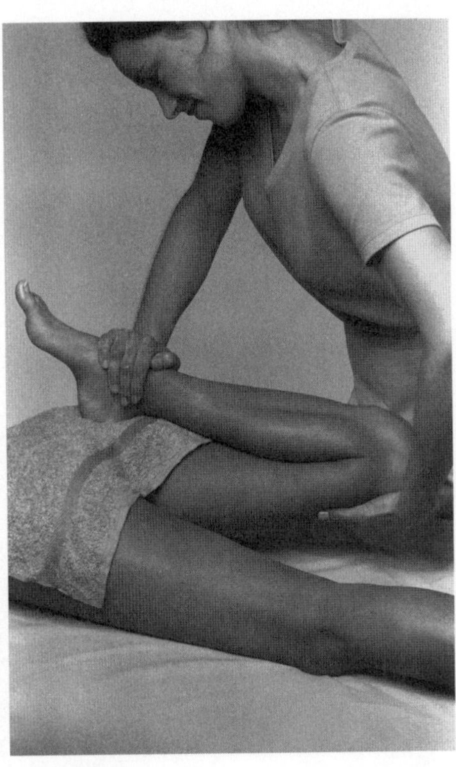

Fig 7-09

16. First uncover the legs by sliding the sheet up to the hips. Place a small amount of Narayan oil on your palms, then spread the oil over the thigh and calf muscles; the back of the knees; the sides of the legs; and the inner thighs. Time: 30 seconds.

17. Massage the muscles in the fold of tissue between the buttocks and thighs with your fingertips, doing both sides at the same time. Using firm pressure push into the muscles, then slide your hands to the right, then to the left, back-and-forth for 30 seconds (Fig. 7-10).

18. Then move both hands to the mid-thighs, halfway between the buttocks and the knees. Massage both sides simultaneously, with your fingertips or thumbs sliding an inch back and forth in slow motion for 15 seconds. Then make small circles at that mid-point for 15 seconds (Fig. 7-11).

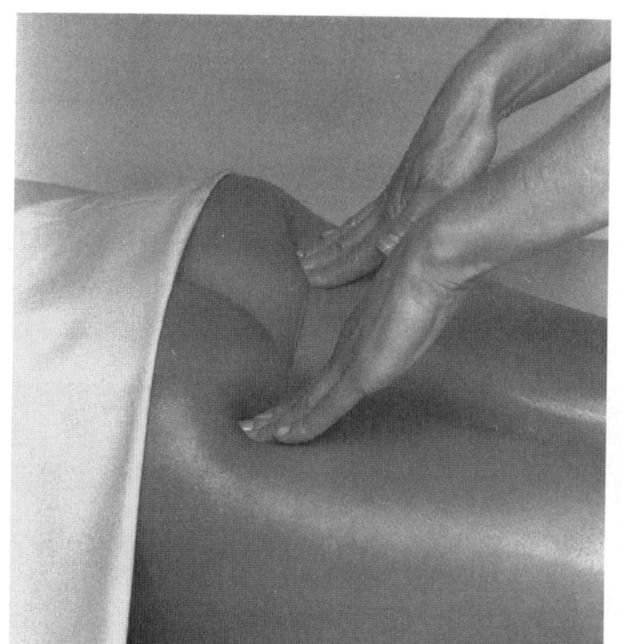

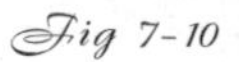

Fig 7-10

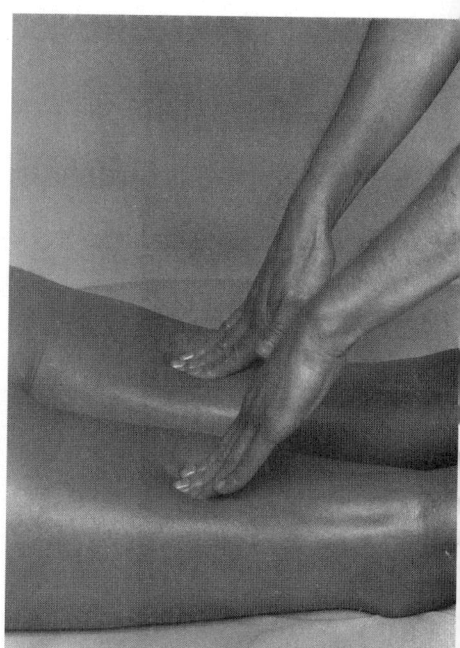

Fig 7-11

19. Move your hands to the center of the soft tissue behind the knees. Now slide your fingertips forward then back for 30 seconds (Fig. 7-12). The soft tissue behind the knees is a neglected area in massage and one that can be sensitive and full of tension.

20. Move down to the middle of the calves. Slide your fingers along both legs simultaneously, stroking down the calves then back for 30 seconds (Fig. 7-13).

21. Place cold towels over the entire surface of both legs, from buttock crease to the ankle for 1 minute (Fig. 7-14). Then take the towels off, and rub the skin with long strokes up and down each leg once or twice for 10 seconds (Fig. 7-15). Now use a dry towel, rubbing the skin with the same strokes, stimulating surface circulation for 10 seconds. Then cover the legs with the sheet. Total time: approximately 2 minutes.

CAUTION: This is a point in the treatment when the client can become cold and shivery. As long as the client feels up to it, and you reassure them that they will be fine, proceed with the treatment. You can place a cotton blanket on top of the sheet if they are feeling cold. Remind them that you will be using heating pads at the end of the treatment to help them return to normal body temperature.

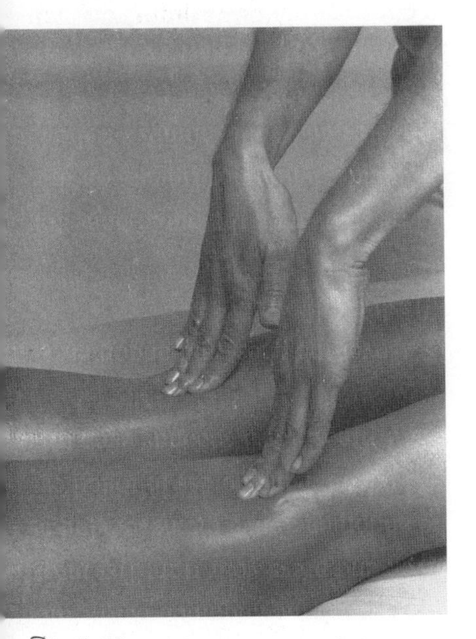

Fig 7-12

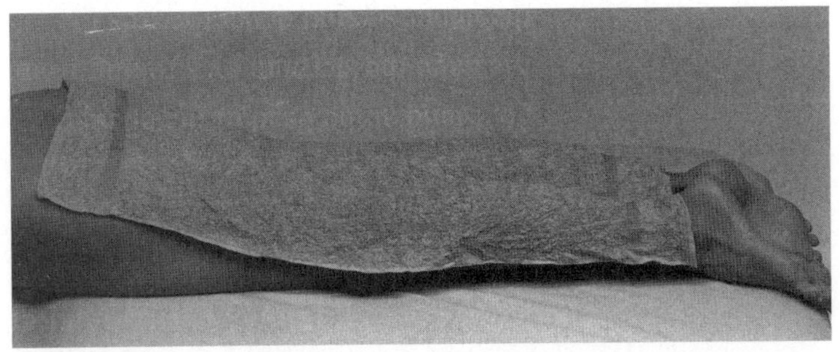

Fig 7-14

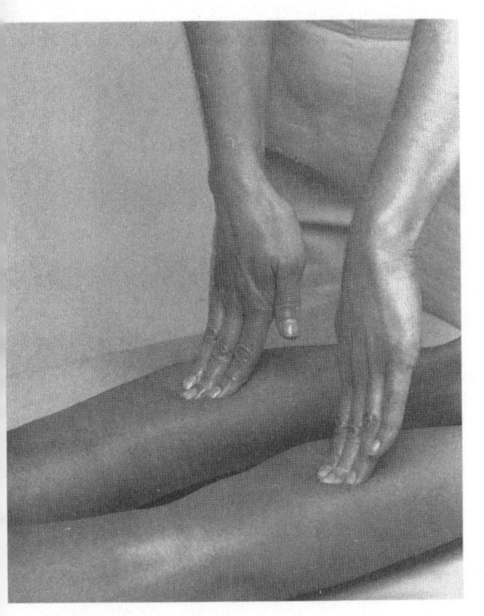

Fig 7-13

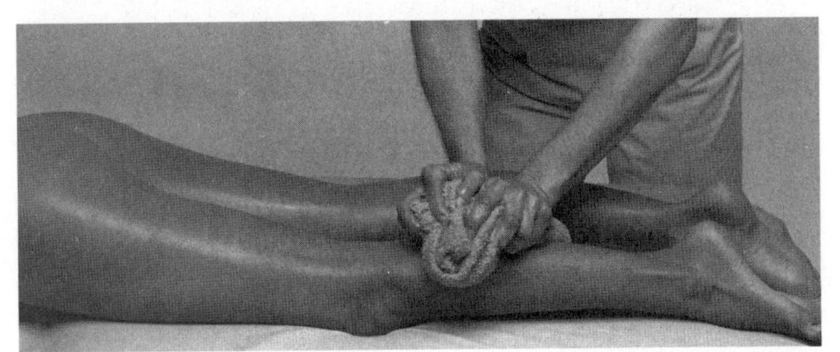

Fig 7-15

In a few cases I have stopped the treatment because the client was too cold. Please talk to the client about how she feels. If she tells you that she is too cold to continue, stop the massage. Give her a dry towel to remove excess oil, and have her get dressed. If she is courageous and wanting to continue, you can use the heating pad on the lower back, feet, abdomen, or chest to help her stay warm.

22. Stand beside your client and reach across the body holding the sheet near each end. Lift the sheet up high, and ask the client to turn over onto the back. Again place the sheet on top of the client. Fold the lower half up, covering the body to just below the genital area. Time: about 15 seconds.

23. Place more Narayan oil on the knees, shins, and front thighs. Be sure to cover all the skin regions that you did not cover earlier on the back sides of the legs.

a. Using the heels of your hands press deep on the upper thighs just below the groin for 15 seconds.

b. Move to the mid-thigh. Use the heels of your hands again with slow motion, and apply deep pressure for 15 seconds (Fig. 7-16).

c. The third position is around the lower thighs (Fig. 7-17). Wrap your hands around the thigh, thumbs to the inside, fingers on the outside, leaning in with your body weight for 5 seconds.

24. Place your thumbs 2 finger-widths below the kneecap, into the front calf muscle, and wrap your fingers around to squeeze the sides of the calf muscle (Fig. 7-18). Your thumbs stroke along the inside of the calf muscle adjacent to the shinbone, while your fingers slide along the outside of the calf muscle. Go from these starting points below the knee all the way to the ankle in stages. Keep constant skin contact, and slide both hands up-and-down a half inch for 3 seconds. Move down the leg an inch—pause for a few seconds at the new spot stroking back and forth; slide down another inch and pause to massage. Continue massaging in this manner towards the ankle. Total time: 45 seconds.

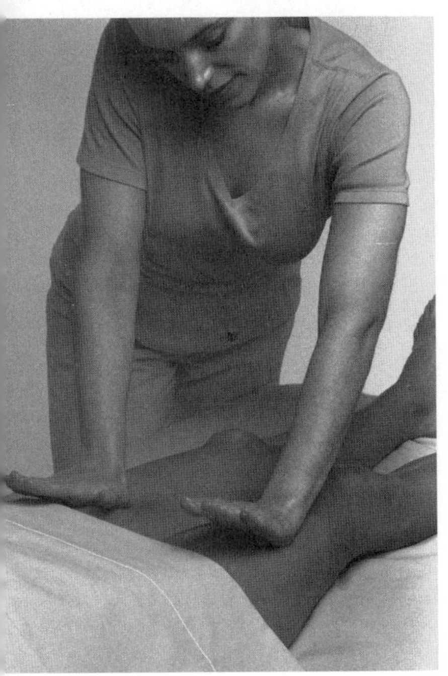

Fig 7-16

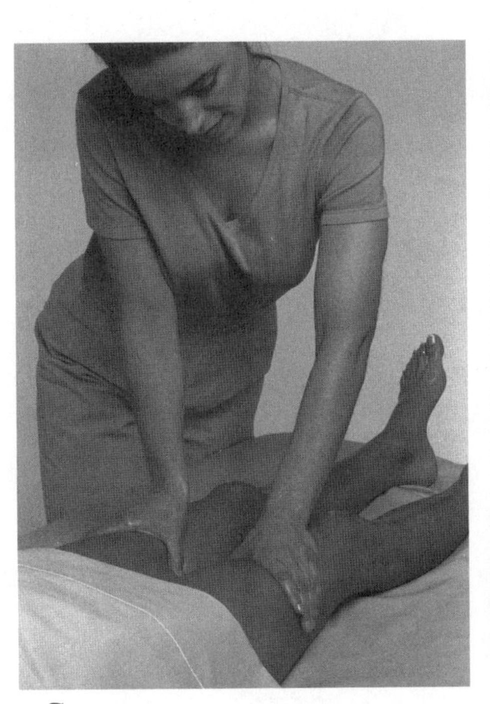

Fig 7-17

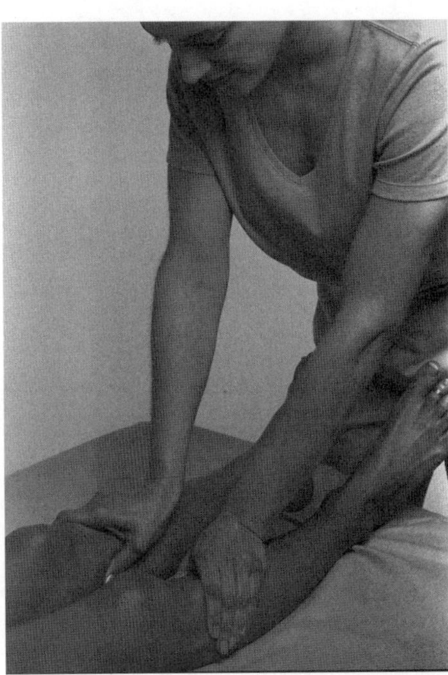

Fig 7-18

25. For 1 minute cover the legs with a cold towel (Fig. 7-19). Grasp the towel rubbing the skin from ankle to groin, using long strokes on each leg for 30 seconds (Fig. 7-20).

Then use a dry towel to rub the legs. Use long strokes from bottom to top for 15 seconds. Do it twice. Now, pull the sheet down covering the legs. Total time: 2 minutes.

26. Roll the sheet off the shoulders down to the hips, and place Narayan oil on the abdomen, chest, and breasts

Stand to the left side of your client. Press your thumbs into the lower abdomen 2 inches below the navel and 2 inches to either side (Fig. 7-21). Push down with a slow motion and deep pressure for 2 seconds and release. Do this 10 times.

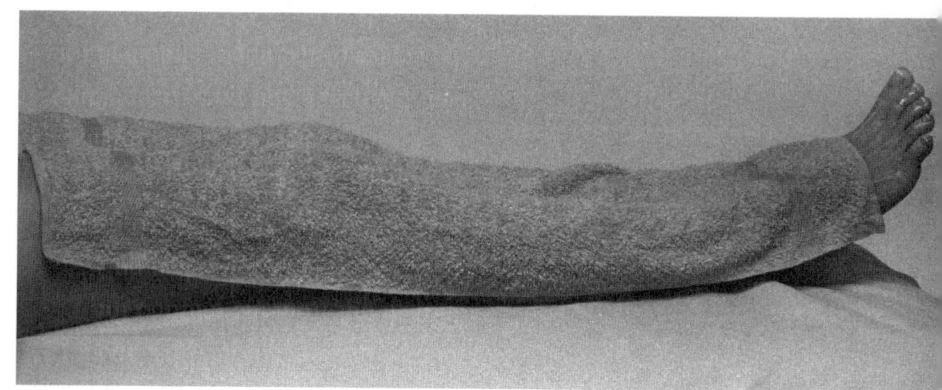

Fig 7-19

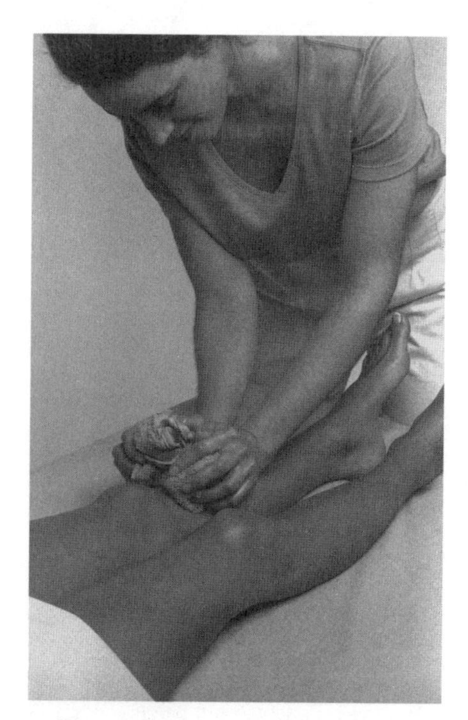

Fig 7-20

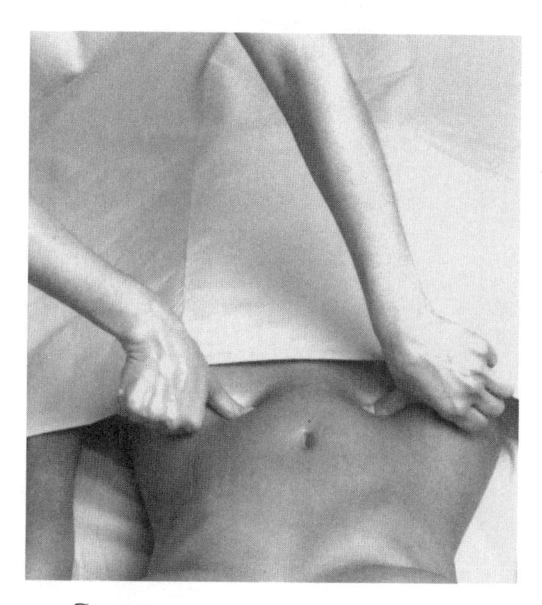

Fig 7-21

27. Move your thumbs to either side of the lower ribs. Now press with both thumbs underneath the ribs, about an inch out from the midline for 2 seconds (Fig. 7-22). Then pull your thumbs back. Repeat 10 times.

28. Place the heel of your left hand near the navel, and press deeply into the center of the upper abdomen for 5 seconds (Fig. 7-23).

29. Make the **collar mudra** with both hands on either side of the navel. Now press deeply into the abdominal tissue with both hands at the same time for 5 seconds (Fig. 7-24). Move your hands a few inches away from the navel and press again. Then slide a couple of inches farther away from the navel and press down one more time. Total time: 15 seconds.

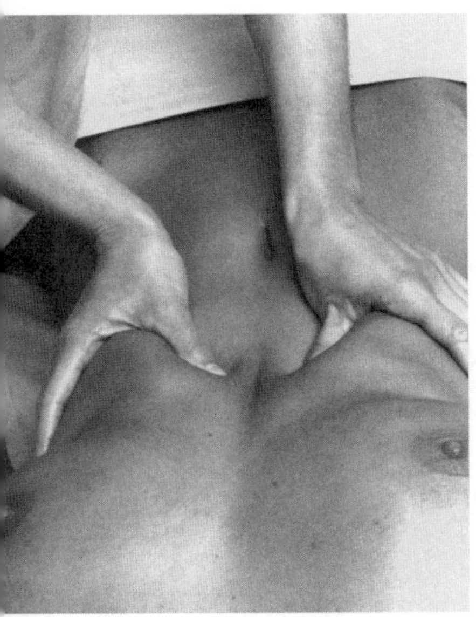

Fig 7-22

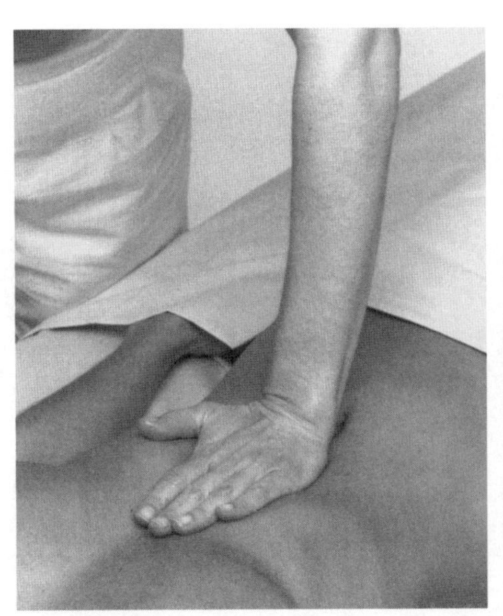

Fig 7-23

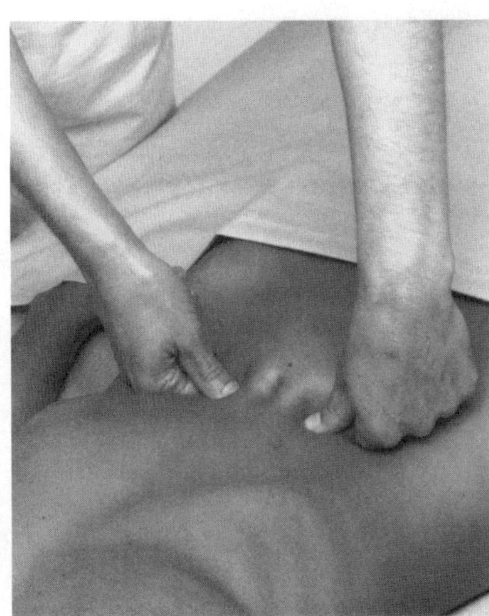

Fig 7-24

30. Now place both fists side-by-side to the left of the navel. Press down for 3 seconds in slow motion, then pull back. Do it 10 times (Fig. 7-25). Move to the right side and repeat 10 times. Total time: 1 minute.

31. Using an open palm, press firmly into the abdomen in 4 spots for 5 seconds in each place (Fig. 7-26). The first is at 12 noon; the second is at 3 o'clock; the third is at 6 o'clock; and the fourth is at 9 o'clock. Total time: 20 seconds.

32. Using your fingers, massage the lower ribs. Begin near the sternum, stroking toward the sides of the body, sliding 3 or 4 inches away. Then mov back, sliding 2 or 3 inches toward the sternum again, using successively longer strokes (Fig. 7-27). Repeat enough times to reach the side of the body. Total time: approximately 2 minutes.

33. Massage the sternum with the fingertips of your left hand. Place your right hand on top of the left, anc use long strokes from bottom to top about 5 times (Fig. 7-28). Time: approximately 15 seconds.

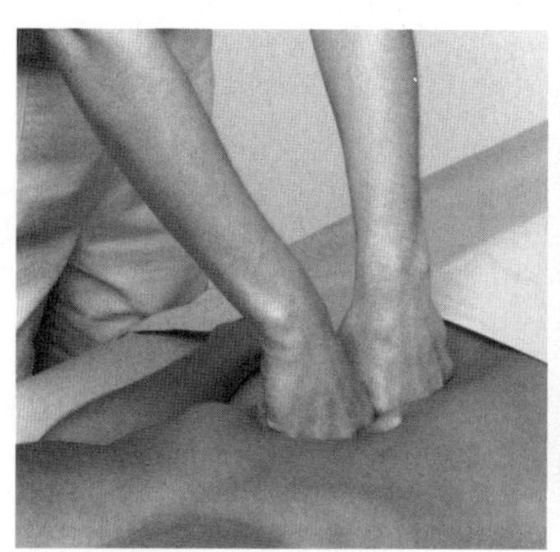

Fig 7-25

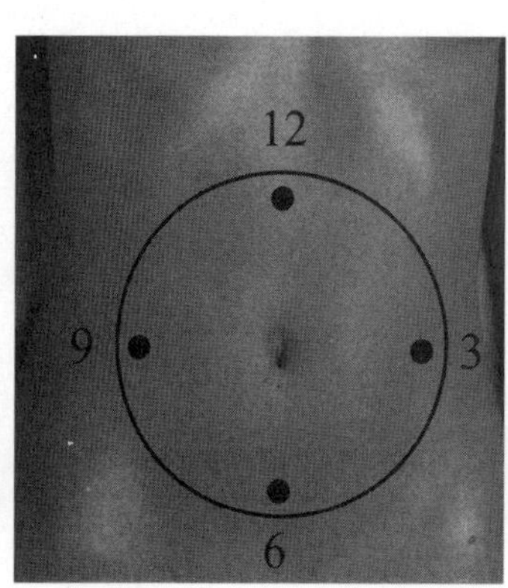

Fig 7-26

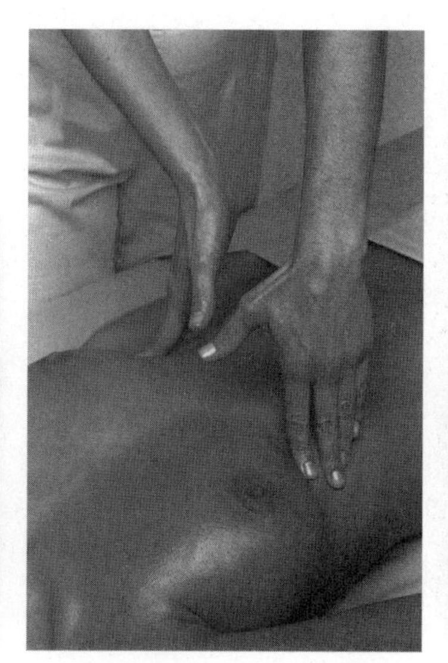

Fig 7-27

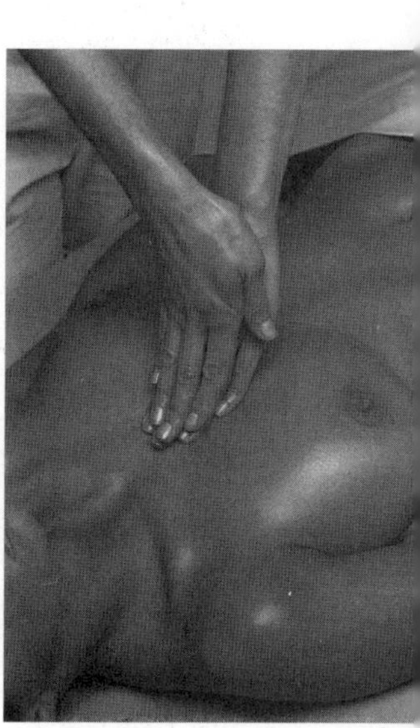

Fig 7-28

34. Make your hands into fists. Slide your knuckles along the lower ribs from the sternum to the sides of the body, following the lower margin of the ribcage. Repeat these long strokes for a total of 20 seconds (Fig. 7-29). Massage on both sides at the same time. Total time: 40 seconds.

35. Chest massage. Stand to the client's left side, with your palms down and your fingers of the left hand pointing towards the client's head. Place these fingers on the right lower ribs, about 3 inches below the nipple and 2 inches to the side. Place your right hand below the right collar bone and next to the sternum, fingers pointing towards your left hand (Fig. 7-30). (If you are treating a woman, the lower [left] hand goes underneath the breast.)

Slide both hands towards each other, then slide away, repeating the movement 4 times massaging the ribs and muscles of the chest wall. Then rotate the hands counterclockwise a few inches and begin again. Cover the entire circumference of the breast. Use the same strokes on a man. Total time: 30 seconds.

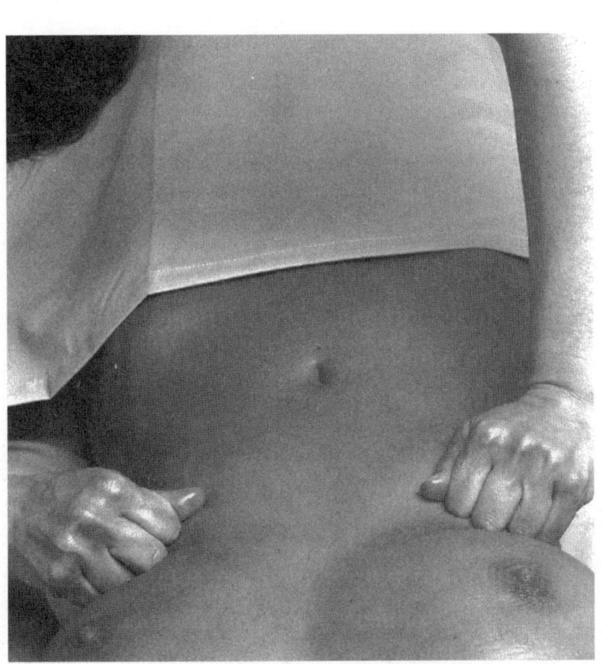

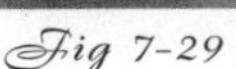

Fig 7-29

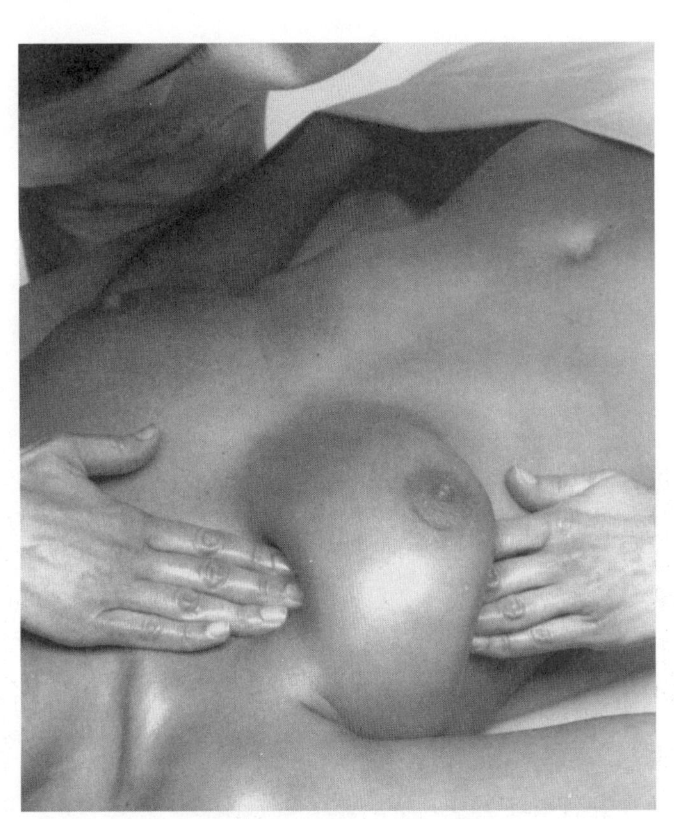

Fig 7-30

36. Stand at the head of the client. Massage the sternum by stroking from the upper section down towards the stomach in 4-inch segments. Do this by sliding down 4 inches, then slide back to the top; stroke down again 5 inches, then slide back to the top; slide toward the stomach 6 inches, then slide back to the top; slide down the sternum again 7 inches; then pull all the way back to the top; stroke down to the end of the sternum, sliding back to the top.
Total time: 15 seconds.

37. Stand to the client's left side. Make fists of both hands. Press your left fist into the abdomen below the navel, and press your right fist into the abdomen above the navel (Fig. 7-31). Both hands press in together 2 or 3 times, for 3 seconds each time.

38. Cover the chest and abdomen with a fresh cold towel.

a. Press down on the pubic bone for 4 seconds, with your fingers on the right side and your thumbs on the left side (Fig. 7-32).

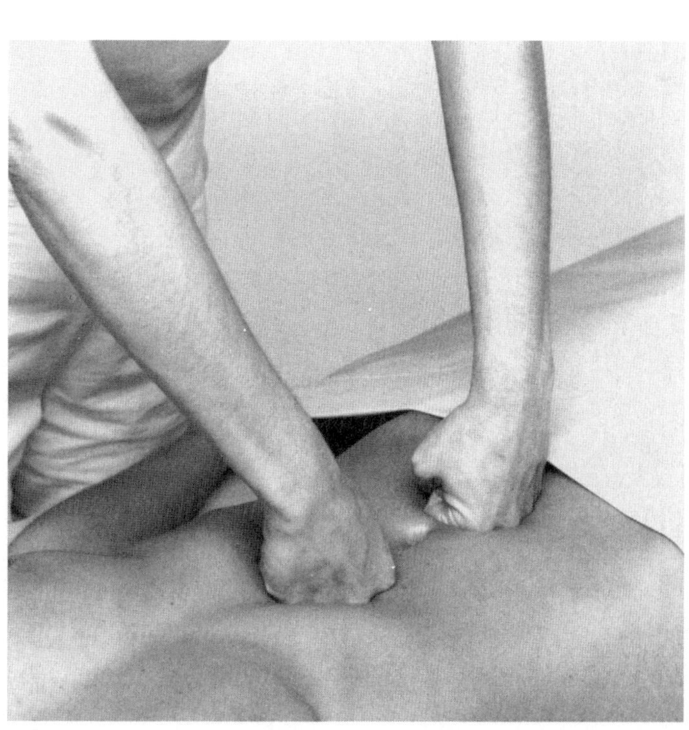

Fig 7-31

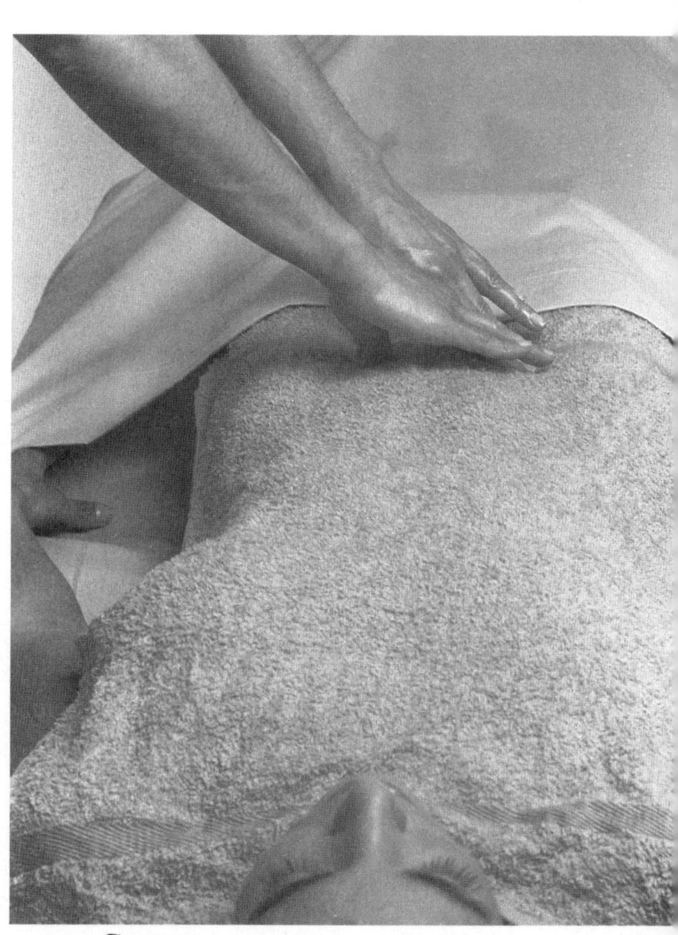

Fig 7-32

b. Place one palm on the towel above the navel and the other below. Press your palms down into the abdomen once (Fig. 7-33). Now, keep the left hand where it is, move the right hand to the chest, and press down once (Fig. 7-34). Use light pressure on top of the towel for a total of 5 seconds.

39. Have your client sit up, legs over the side of the table. Stand to one side placing Narayan oil on the arm, from the shoulder to the wrist. Then place a cold towel around your client's neck. The client's palm is facing down. Now, strongly massage the arm from the shoulder down to the elbow, using long strokes. Use your thumbs side-by-side on the forearm, with fingers behind, sliding from the elbow down to the wrist. Repeat the movements 3 or 4 times, covering the entire arm. Have the client switch to palm up, then you repeat. Spend 1 minute on each arm.

40. Use a cold towel to rub the arms from the shoulder down to the hand, with an up-and-down motion. Spend 15 seconds on each arm. Then rub each arm with a dry towel from armpit to fingertips 2 times.
Total time: 45 seconds.

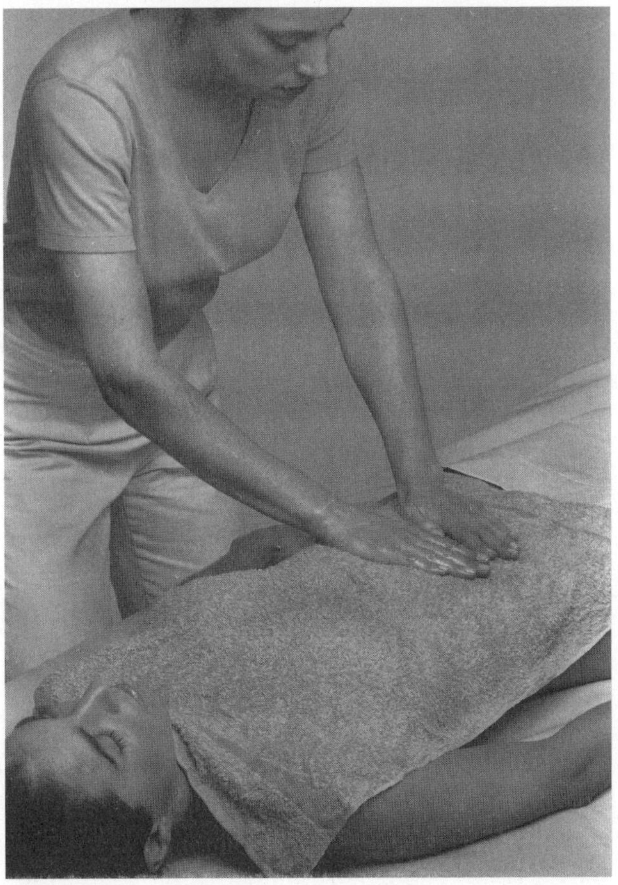

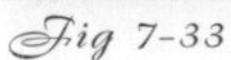
Fig 7-33

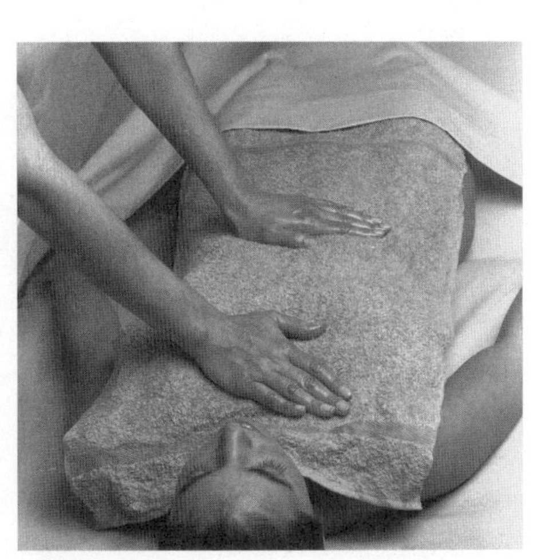

Fig 7-34

41. Slap the client's back with your open palms in a fast rhythm from the shoulders to the base of the spine. Do this 3 times on each side of the spine. It takes about 20 seconds for each side.

42. Take the towel off the neck. Then stand behind your client. Use knife-edge hands to do a karate chop on the shoulder muscles for 15 seconds on each side.

43. The client lies on the stomach. Using your palms, make long up-and-down strokes along both sides of the back muscles, from the lower back to the shoulders. You can alternate sliding one hand up as you slide the other down. Total time: 30 seconds.

44. The client lies on the back. Stand to the left side. Use fingertips to percuss up and down the shoulder, chest, and abdomen area, first on one side of the body, then the other for 20 seconds per side (Fig. 7-35).

You can also use the palms to slap the skin on the same areas. Use a soft touch on a woman's breasts.

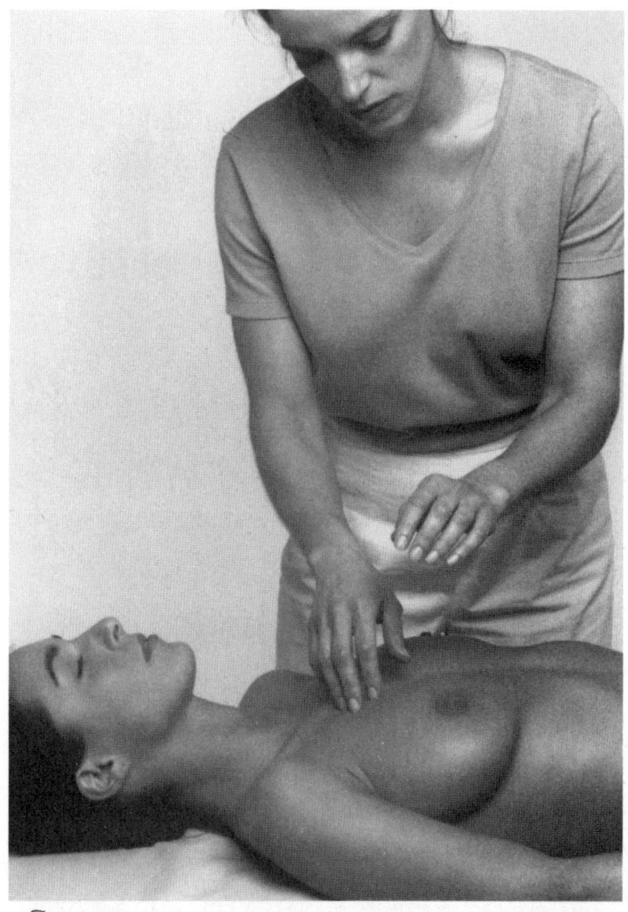

Fig 7-35

45. The client lies on the back. Cover the client with the sheet. Spread a small amount of Narayan oil over the client's right and left hands (Fig. 7-36), then wrap a cold towel around each hand. Have the client lift both arms up to 90 degrees and lower them 5 times (Fig. 7-37). Remove the towels from the hands. Total time: 2 minutes.

46. Begin at the left foot, rubbing Narayan oil over the entire foot. Hold the heel of the left foot with your left hand. Wrap your right hand around the foot, fingers on the sole and thumb on top (Fig. 7-38). Slide the right hand up the foot five times, pressing the fingers into the arch as the thumb strokes the top of the foot. Massage the entire sole.

Then do the same massage steps on the right foot. Take 1 1/2 minutes for each foot.

47. Place a towel over each foot. Have your client lift both legs 1 foot off the table, then down 3 times. Then have her do 3 more double-leg lifts to 90 degrees (Fig. 7-39). Total time: 1 minute.

48. Ask the client to lie face down. Place a warm heating pad on the back and cover with a sheet for 10 minutes.

If the client doesn't have time for this step, a hot shower or bath at home will replace it. Also, exercise will help to re-establish normal blood circulation.

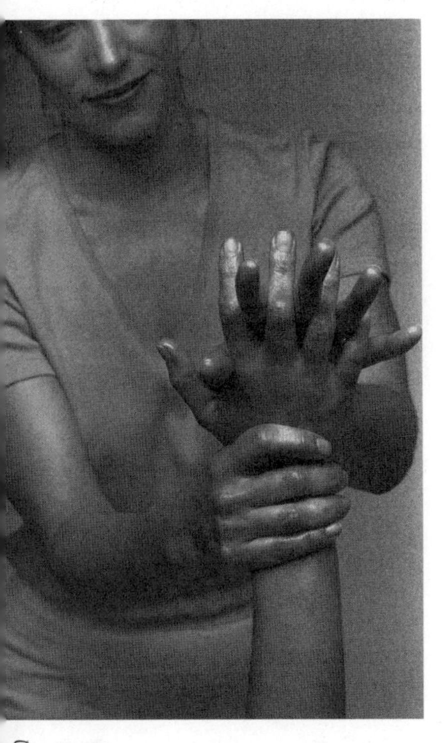
Fig 7-36

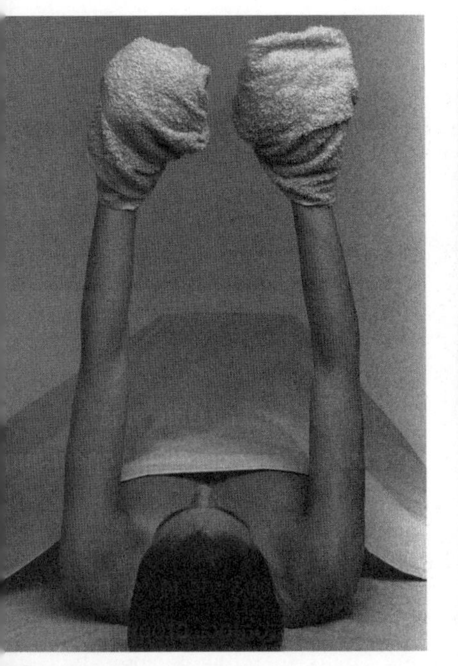
Fig 7-37

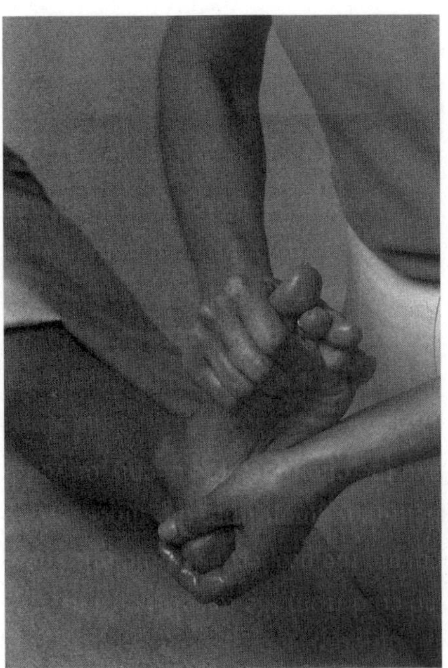
Fig 7-38

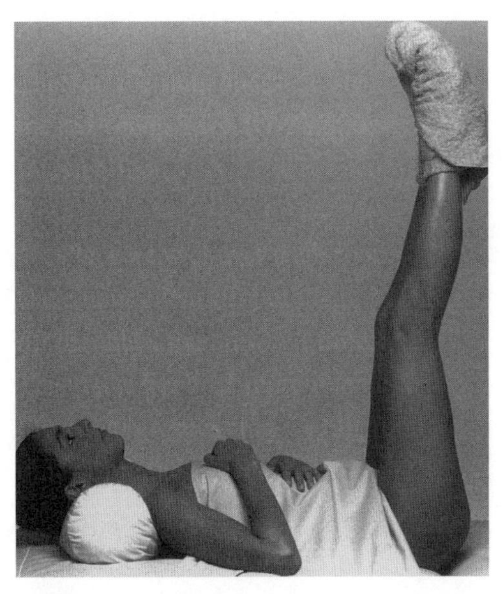
Fig 7-39

Comment

After the treatment, give specific instructions to your clients. They can drink warm yogi tea or vegetable juices such as celery, carrot, or spinach. They can eat soothing, nourishing foods, like warm mung beans and rice. Suggest that they listen to music that helps them to relax. At the same time, they are to do **long deep breathing**.

The Narayan treatment can be very intense. Apply yourself. Concentrate on th client; pray for the client's healing and well-being; and the client shall be transformed.

Some of my patients have had kundalini experiences: rushes of energy througl the spine; swells of energy and feelings inside the abdomen, lower pelvis, sex-organ region, rectum area, heart center, or chest.

I have had to guide a small number of patients after the treatment. They can b full of questions, doubts, and fears, all associated with the treatment. You have to reassure your clients, inspire them with stories and insights, and return then to their own calm inner selves.

Benefits of Narayan Oil Treatment Narayan oil combines eucalyptus, mint, and clove oils to produce its beneficial effects[11].

As an analgesic, Narayan oil has the ability to kill pain and relieve the discomforts of muscle spasms, joint stiffness, muscle soreness from exercise, and inflammations caused by injury or strain.

If the client has a cold, congestion, or a mucous condition, this treatment help open the sinuses and lungs, providing relief.

The Narayan Treatment helps rejuvenate and stimulate the immune system, to better resist germs, viruses, and disease. The treatment can also warm an area of the body for up to 8 hours afterwards. Several clients reported warmth and tingling in the lower back for hours after treatment. Because the oil is partially absorbed by the skin and enters the circulatory system, I believe it travels where the body wants it to go. Therefore the oil may stay in the lower back, abdominal region, or neck muscles; it varies with each person.

Finally, there is strong aromatherapy with this treatment. The fragrance which pervades the room is very healing. Aromatic oils stimulate the mind and sense The scent of Narayan oil intoxicates, helping mentally transport your client to far away places where exotic experiences await.

Chapter Notes

Foreword

Guru Ram Das (1534-1581), the fourth Sikh Guru, was a saint of humility, love, and devotion. He founded the Golden Temple, the center of the Sikh faith and a center of universal healing in Amritsar, India. Renowned as a healer, Guru Ram Das led a life of selfless service.

Introduction

1. **Khalsa**: Pure. Many North Americans who have adopted the Sikh faith have changed their family name to Khalsa. Contact the author to locate Khalsa chiropractors trained in these healing techniques.

2. **Yogi tea** is a blend of cinnamon, ginger root, cardamon seeds, cloves, black peppercorns, and black tea, served with a small amount of milk to neutralize the heat-generating nature of the herbs. When the tea is brewed fresh, covered and cooked on a low boil for 20 to 30 minutes it is delicious. See Yogi Bhajan's: *The Golden Temple Vegetarian Cookbook* (Hawthorn Books, New York, 1978). It can also be purchased in many health food stores in boxed teabags.

3. **Sadhana** is a self-disciplined daily spiritual practice, often beginning before dawn. For those in the Khalsa Chiropractic Association it consists of **kundalini yoga** and meditation.

Chapter 1: The Profession of the Hands on Healer

1. Yogi Bhajan, Khalsa Chiropractic Association meetings, Santa Barbara CA, 3 March 1990.

2. Swami Prabhavananda and Christopher Isherwood. *How to Know God: The Yoga Aphorisms of Patanjali*, Part I, number 35. Vedanta Press, Hollywood, 1953.

3. See: James Allen. *As A Man Thinketh*. Sun Books edition, Santa Fe, New Mexico, 1983. [Original edition 1904.]

4. Shad Helmstetter. *Winning from Within*. Nightingale-Conant Corporation, Chicago, 1982. Audiotape.

5. Also see: Napoleon Hill. *The Law of Success*. Success Unlimited, Chicago, 1969. Distributed by Nightingale-Conant Corporation.

6. Carl S. Cleveland, Sr. Chiropractic Principles and Practice Outline. Cleveland Chiropractic College, Los Angeles. Unpublished manuscript.

7. David Chapman-Smith. The Powerful and Mysterious Placebo. *The Chiropractic Report* 9(5), September 1995.

8. J. V. Basmajian and R. Nyberg. *Rational Manual Therapies*, Williams and Wilkins, Baltimore, 1993.

9. Yogi Bhajan. Khalsa Chiropractic Association meetings. Espanola NM, September 1992.

10. Larry Dossey. *Healing Words: The Power of Prayer and the Practice of Medicine*. Harper SanFrancisco, 1993.

11. *Healing Words*.

"Over time I decided that not to employ prayer with my patients was the equivalent of deliberately witholding a potent drug or surgical procedure.... I simply could not ignore the evidence for prayer's effectiveness without feeling like a traitor to the scientific tradition."

12. For information about kundalini yoga and classes in your area contact the International Kundalini Yoga Teachers Association, Route 2, Box 4 Shady Lane, Espanola NM 87532. Telephone 505-753-0423.

For music recordings, videotapes, books and other products contact Golden Temple Enterprises, Box 13 Shady Lane, Espanola NM 87532. Telephone 505-753-0563.

For yogic herbs, massage and body oils, books, and other products contact Ancient Healing Ways, Route 2, Box 259 Espanola NM 87532. Telephones 505-747-2860 and 1-800-359-2940.

Chapter 2: The Power of Touch—the Healer's Practice

1. Yogi Bhajan. Khalsa Chiropractic Association meetings, 14 August 1986.

2. Ashley Montagu. *Touching: The Human Significance of the Skin*. Harper and Row, third edition, 1986.

3. Gordon Inkeles, *The New Sensual Massage*. Bantam Books, 1992.

4. Yogi Bhajan. Khalsa Chiropractic Association meetings, 11 April 1983.

5. Joseph Heller and William A. Henkin. *Bodywise*. Wingbow Press, 1991.

6. **Scrofula**: swelling of the lymph nodes of the neck.

Chapter 3: Stress Release Treatments

1. Gurutej Singh Khalsa and Gordon Briggs. *StressAway, the Way to Relax: The Complete Forty Day Program*. Gage, Toronto, 1979.

2. Laura Norman. *Feet First: A Guide to Foot Reflexology*. Simon and Schuster, 1988. The foot maps in the book plus the testimonials from her students and clients will open new vistas for you.

3. Nicola Hall. *Reflexology for Women*. HarperCollins/Thorsons, 1994. Another book about treating the feet that focuses on women's problems.

4. A variety of recorded drum music is available from Backroads Music, 418 Tamal Place, Corte Madera CA 94925. Telephone 1-800-767-4748.

5. Yogi Bhajan. *The Teachings of Yogi Bhajan*, number 18. Arcline Publications/Kundalini Research Institute, Box 1550, Pomona, California 91796, 1977.

6. Hazrat Inayat Khan. Cited in Joachim-Ernst Berendt. *The Third Ear: On Listening to the World*. (Das Dritte Ohr.) Translated by Element Books, 1988. Henry Holt edition, 1992.

Chapter 4: Quicktouch Treatments

1. **Navel chakra**: The nerves and center of consciousness around the navel.

2. Yogi Bhajan. Khalsa Chiropractic Association meetings, 1October 1988.

3. John Diamond. *Behavioral Kinesiology: How to Activate Your Thymus and Increase Your Life Energy*. Harper and Row, 1979.

4. Gordon Inkeles, *The New Sensual Massage*. Bantam Books, 1992.

5. Yogi Bhajan. Khalsa Chiropractic Association meetings, 1 March 1991.

6. Yogi Bhajan. Khalsa Chiropractic Association meetings, 11 October 1991.

7. Yogi Bhajan. Khalsa Chiropractic Association meetings, 1 March 1991.

8. Swami Prabhavananda and Christopher Isherwood. *How to Know God: The Yoga Aphorisms of Patanjali*, Part III, number 30. Vedanta Press, Hollywood, 1953.

9. Giovanni Maciocia. *The Foundations of Chinese Medicine: A Comprehensive Text for Acupuncturists and Herbalists*. Churchill Livingstone, 1989.

10. Miriam Lee. *Insights of a Senior Acupuncturist*. Blue Publications, 1992.

11. Yogi Bhajan. Khalsa Chiropractic Association meetings, Santa Barbara CA, 2 March 1990.

12. Yogi Bhajan. Khalsa Chiropractic Association meetings, 29 February 1992.

13. Yogi Bhajan. Khalsa Chiropractic Association meetings, 29 February 1992.

Yogi Bhajan discussed the sugar and salt points: "You sometimes call them potassium (sugar) and sodium (salt) points. They always get upside down. And when those points are uptight, the neck goes off, and the lower back goes out, and the person's mind goes off."

14. Harriet Bienfield and Efrem Korngold. *Between Heaven and Earth: a Guide to Chinese Medicine*. Simon and Schuster, 1991.

Chapter 5: Treatments for Emotional Balance

1. Yogi Bhajan. Khalsa Chiropractic Association meetings, Santa Barbara CA, March 1990.

2. *The Messenger*. The Cost of Mental Illnesses to American Society: The Human and Economic Toll. May 1994. Mental Health Association, San Diego County, CA.

3. Gail Sheehy. *The New Passages: Mapping Your Life Across Time.* Random House/Ballantine, 1995.

4. *The New Passages*.

5. Iona Marsaa Teeguarden. *The Joy of Feeling: Bodymind Acupressure*. Japan Publications, 1987.

6. Yogi Bhajan. Khalsa Chiropractic Association meetings, Santa Barbara CA, March 1990.

Chapter 6: Treatments to Strengthen the Body and Immune System

1. Sources of information on the mind-body connection:

Thorwald Dethlefsen and Rudiger Dahlke. *The Healing Power of Illness*. Element Books, 1990.

Ken Dychtwald. *Bodymind*. Putnam/J.P. Tarcher, second edition, 1986.

Louise L. Hay. *Heal Your Body*. Hay House, Box 6204, Carson CA 90749. Revised edition 1988.

Leon Hammer. *Dragon Rises, Red Bird Flies: Psychology, Energy, and Chinese Medicine*. Station Hill Press, Barrytown NY, 1990.

Narayan S. Khalsa. *Illnesses and Ailments: Their Psychological Meaning.* 708 Mohawk Drive, Boulder CO 80303. 1990. Written by a psychologist, this book has caught many by surprise for its observations of the emotions that cause physical disease.

Ashley Montagu. *Touching: The Human Significance of the Skin.*
Harper and Row, third edition, 1986. This classic is about the power of touch to help us grow, mature, and be content.

Miki Shima. *The Medical I Ching: Oracle of the Healer Within.*
Blue Poppy Press, Boulder CO, 1992.

An interpreation of the *I Ching* from a medical perspective, this book can help a practitioner cultivate insight, expand intuition, and understand the core reasons for ill health. This book enhances the ability to diagnose and prognose, especially unusual symptoms or hard-to-diagnose illness.

2. Yogi Bhajan. Khalsa Chiropractic Association meetings, 17 October 1985.

3. Yogi Bhajan. Khalsa Chiropractic Association meetings, October 1987.

4. Yogi Bhajan. Khalsa Chiropractic Association meetings, 18 October 1985

5. Sewa Kaur, Massage Therapist, commenting after this treatment.

Chapter 7: Ishnaan, the Science of Hydrotherapy

1. Yogi Bhajan. Khalsa Chiropractic Association meetings, 29 February 1992.

2. *Journal of the American Medical Association*, 30 March 1940.

3. Sebastian Kniepp. *My Water Cure*. 1891. Blackwood, Edinburgh. 30th printing. Translated from the German. [Out of print.]

Father Kniepp chronicled the results of long experience with clients from all over Europe, Asia, and America who visited him in his Austrian mountain resort at Grafenberg. Father Kniepp provided water baths, water-walking regimens, back showers, cold-water sheet wraps and many other water remedies for more than 35 years. At the end of his book there is an A to Z compendium of the illnesses, diseases, and maladies which he treated. He printed 33 different editions of his book, all of which sold out.

Here's a partial list of conditions which he treated: asthma, bedwetting, bladder complaints, decomposition of the blood, digestive complaints, inflammation of the brain, mucous congestion, headache, cholera, cholic, consumption, muscle cramps, diarrhea, ringing in the ears, cataracts, fevers, gout, hemorrhoids, colds, insanity, kidney problems, low back pain, migraines, melancholy, nervous exhaustion, rheumatism, sciatica, insomnia, stomach acidity, and many other conditions.

4. Yogi Bhajan. Lecture transcription, page 89. 28 February 1992.

5. **Frog Pose**: A "frog" is a kundalini yoga exercise. Squat down until the buttocks touch the heels with knees spread apart and the arms between the knees. The hands are on the floor. Straighten the legs while keeping the hands or fingertips touching the floor (or as close as you can). Return to the squatting position where the heels are off the floor. Inhale through the nose when you push up and exhale as you squat down. "Frogs" are the repetitions of this exercise, usually in a series of 26, 54, or 108.

6. Yogi Bhajan. Khalsa Women's Training Camp, 21 July 1976.

7. **Sex nerve**: This colloquial term refers to the nerves that are found on the inside of the thighs that connect to the groin and sexual organs. They correspond to the liver meridian in Chinese medicine.

8. Yogi Bhajan. Khalsa Women's Training Camp, 21 July 1976.

9. Dian D. Buchman. *The Complete Book of Water Therapy*. Dutton, New York, 1979. This book encompasses most hydrotherapy healing techniques. It is the single best hydrotherapy reference that I have found. With luck, this book may still be in print. The author comes from a family with connections to all the early, great exponents of American hydrotherapy. They include Simon Baruch, MD, who brought hydrotherapy to the US, and the great health reformer Dr. J.H. Kellog, author of *Uses of Water in Health and Disease*. Thanks to Ms. Buchman's book for help in several sections of Chapter 7.

10. The brand name of the insulated glove I prefer is "Maya Pioneer Bluette." There are many other brands on the market.

11. The oils used to make Narayan oil are natural and complete, with no synthetic aromas or other chemicals added. They are essential oils pressed from the herb or spice, so they are a concentrated form of the real thing. Each of the essential oils that make up Narayan oil (mint, clove, and eucalyptus) has benefits.

a. Mint oil is soothing, cooling, clarifying, and expanding. Therefore it helps relieve mental and emotional tension. Mint is also used for colds, flu, fevers, gas, and mild digestive disturbances.

   Mint is a nervine, an herb that strengthens the nervous system. Nervines move blood and energy through the superficial channels of the body. They are used to correct nervous system excesses or deficiencies. They have a strong action on the mind and are useful in promoting mental health and clarity. Nervines also aid in the treatment of psychological imbalances and mental diseases. Most nervines relieve muscle spasms, thereby relieving cramps and muscle soreness from exercise.

b. Clove oil is a stimulant and aromatic for the lungs and stomach. It promotes peristalsis and is good for helping pranic energy descend. Clove oil dispels chill, disinfects the lymphatic system, and is a powerful pain killer--used since ancient times to relieve toothache. Clove oil also has the ability to relieve nausea, intestinal gas, pain, and distension. It stops hiccoughs and vomiting.

c. Eucalyptus oil is a warming oil with stimulating properties. It helps decongest the chest and sinuses. It restores circulation, relieves pain and blood congestion. It:
   - promotes sweating.
   - relieves muscle tension and joint stiffness.
   - can bring down fevers due to external factors, such as from colds and flu.
   - promotes the eruption and resolution of inflammatory skin conditions.
   - helps disperse surface water.
   - relieves headaches due to cold and congestion.

Together these three herbal oils help fortify the skin and superficial channels against disease.

Narayan oil may be obtained from Ancient Healing Ways, Route 2, Box 259, Espanola NM 87532. Telephones 505-747-2860 and 1-800-359-2940

Glossary

Acupressure point. A point of energy concentration on the skin associated with high electrical conductivity. In acupressure you use finger pressure to press the point or points to alleviate muscular tension. (See pressure point.)

Acupuncture. A traditional form of Chinese medicine. Needles are inserted into the body at key points to release energy blockages and balance the life force.

Apana, apanic energy. A form of life force or *prana* concerned with elimination.

Chakra. A center of life force in the body, for giving and receiving energy. Chakras are the centers of interchange between physical and psychic energy. Chakras are also the etheric counterparts to certain organs, nerve plexuses, and endocrine glands.

Channel. (See nadi.)

Collar mudra. (See p. xvii.)

Cone mudra. (See p. xvii.)

Constitutional restrictions. Physical restraints including tight muscles, poor posture, gait imbalances, poor breathing habits, etc. Tight muscles are especially noticeable in the upper back around the shoulder blades. Also, birth defects, defects from serious injuries, or paralysis from polio are all part of a client's constitution. Most bodywork helps clients ease these restrictions.

Diaphragm. A muscle that separates the abdominal cavity from the thorax. The diaphragm does most of the work in breathing. It mobilizes life energy like no other muscle. It is the prime mover, ahead of the heart, in charging the body-mind with *prana*. The diaphragm area can become blocked in emotional or mental disturbances. A wise practitioner diagnoses the state of the diaphragm and the abdomen to treat the deeper cause of health imbalances.

Ida. The *nadi* (channel) that carries energy on the left side of the body. Associated with the left nostril, the so-called moon nostril. The *ida* cools the body. When the left nostril is more open than the right nostril the right brain hemisphere is activated.

Jacket mudra. (See p. xvii.)

Knife-edge mudra. (See p. xvii.)

Kundalini energy. An aspect of universal supreme consciousness. Kundalini comes from the Sanskrit word *kundal* meaning coil, an energy that is stored and released from the base of the spine. When portions of kundalini energy are released mystic experiences unfold. Kundalini energy is compared with a coiled serpent or the coil of hair of the beloved. These analogies refer to the way the energy moves in spirals. Kundalini is the nerve of the soul; the inner potential of every human; infinite possibilities; pure awareness.

Kundalini yoga. A way to bring the body, mind, and soul into harmony using kundalini energy working through the chakras. Kundalini yoga utilizes exercise, breathwork, relaxation, and meditation.

Long deep breathing. Comfortable and conscious breathing that brings more pranic energy into the physical body. It activates the most important internal muscle in the body--the diaphragm. Long deep breathing is the single most powerful corrective measure to counterflow *prana*. (See *prana*.)

Meridian. A vital life energy pathway in the body that traverses the superficial tissues and penetrates to the deeper organs. A meridian is a series of connected acupressure points.

A working analogy is a comparison with microwave relay stations. These stations pick up an electromagnetic signal when someone dials a telephone number and boosts it so that no matter how far away a person is from the caller the signal will be increased and the person's telephone will ring.

In oriental medicine the main meridians take their names from the organ which they ultimately join. For example, the stomach meridian travels inside the torso going to the stomach, completely permeating it. The meridian roots into the organ completely. The meridians of oriental medicine are equivalent to pranic *nadis*.

Mudra. In hands-on healing a mudra is a hand position of the practitioner that stimulates energy movement at acupressure points. See also Figs. H-1 to H-4, p. xvii.

Nadi (channel). From Sanskrit *nad* meaning movement. Subtle carrier of electromagnetic force in the body. In this book *nadis* are linked by pranic energy to the chakras. (See *ida* and *pingala*.)

Pingala. The channel (*nadi*) that carries energy on the right side of the body. It is sometimes associated with the right nostril, the so-called sun nostril. The *pingala* warms the body. When the right nostril is open more than the left nostril it activates the left-brain hemisphere.

Prana or pranic energy. The subtle energy of life. *Prana* is the force that links our physical, mental, and spiritual energy; the unseen force that moves everything from the smallest subatomic particle to the wind that blows the leaves on a tree. It is the air we breathe that carries pranic energy in yogic philosophy. (See also *apana*.)

Counterflow *prana* is life energy travelling in the wrong direction. It is an imbalance between *prana* and *apana* creating many health problems (headaches, indigestion, constipation, heartburn, night sweats, tight shoulder muscles, etc.)

Pranayam. Breathing exercises in yoga that control *prana*. These exercises activate the diaphragm, energizing and relaxing the body. *Pranayam* also cleanses the subtle pathways inside the body, calming the mind.

Pressure points. Places along meridians on the body with high electrical conductivity. The place on and a few millimeters beneath the skin where disease starts. A disturbance in the smooth flow of *prana* at the skin level produces a little knot. It can be felt with the fingertips. (See acupressure point.)

Venus kriya. A form of meditation or exercise with two people working together, also called partner meditation.

Index

U

V

WXYZ

About Yogi Bhajan

Yogi Bhajan, Ph.D., Master of Kundalini and White Tantric Yoga is from the Punjab, in an area that is now Pakistan. He is the son of a medical doctor. Besides mastering yoga as a youth, he studied other traditional healing arts of India—diet, herbal treatment, yoga therapy, massage, and skeletal adjusting.

He began teaching in the US in 1969 and soon after founded the Healthy, Happy, Holy Organization (3HO) in order to offer classes in wholistic lifestyle including: Kundalini Yoga, meditation, and vegetarian diet. He is a teacher's teacher, and throughout the world today there are 3HO centers where Yogi Bhajan's students share these wholistic lifestyle teachings.

The concept of healing permeates all of his teachings.

Since 1982 Yogi Bhajan has taught at annual conferences sponsored by the Khalsa Chiropractic Association. He has cajoled, coaxed, and encouraged healers from many disciplines to be their best. They include acupuncturists, body workers, chiropractors, curanderos, masseuses, medical doctors, physical therapists, psychiatrists, psychologists, nurses, and the general public. At these conferences he has demonstrated a wide variety of healing techniques. These meetings are held in New Mexico in August each year.

To find out about Yogi Bhajan's current teaching schedule, write to:
Sikh Dharma Secretariat
P.O. Box 351149
Los Angeles, CA 90035
or call (310) 552-3416

About the Author

Waheguru S. Khalsa, D.C. was born in Newport News, Virginia and attended the University of Maine. Finding that he had an interest in alternatives to Western medicine, he enrolled at Cleveland Chiropractic College in Los Angeles, California. He graduated in 1975 and received his license to practice in the same year.

He has advanced training in oriental medicine which includes using herbs to enhance his patients' well-being. He has studied with Yogi Bhajan since 1972.

For 21 years he has maintained a practice in Los Angeles combining the techniques in this book with chiropractic adjustments, diet and nutritional counseling, and kundalini yoga. He works closely with massage therapists in his office, recommending massage for many of his patients. His infectious laughter has kept many patients awake who otherwise would be sound asleep inside his peaceful treatment rooms.

Waheguru enjoys golf. Swimming and body surfing in the Pacific Ocean also give him pleasure. He leads Breathing Trance Seminars that combine kundalini yoga, music, and breathing.

He is married to Hari Kirn Kaur Khalsa, who teaches Celestial Communication, a meditation form that uses music with arm and hand movement.

Waheguru is a founding member of the Khalsa Chiropractic Association, and he was its president from 1992 to 1995.

ORDER FORM

Telephone orders: Call (310)274-8291.
Have your Visa or Mastercard ready.

Fax orders: (310)274-8298

Contact publisher for seminars & videos on material in this book and more. Email: waguru@mindspring.com

5, Beverly Hills, CA 90211

Call for book price and shipping.

Please send _________ copy(ies) of *The Miracle of Healing Hands.*

I understand that I may return the book(s) for a full refund—for any reason, no questions asked.

Company name: ____

Name: ____

Address: ____

City: ______________________________ State: __________ Zip: ______________

Payment: ☐ Check ☐ Visa ☐ Mastercard

Card number: ______________________________

Name on card: ______________________________

Exp. date: ______________________________

Signature ______________________________

Call
(310) 274-8291
and order now.

Do you need help growing your practice?
Find out how to get an unending parade of profitable clients.
We can help you. Call us today for a free report.